914

Landscapes an
Western Europe

Kenneth Maclean *Perth Academy*

Norman Thomson *Moray House College of Education, Edinburgh*

Oxford University Press 1988

i

Preface

Inevitably, a textbook like *Landscapes and People of Western Europe* is an essay in compromise. It represents a balance between the requirements of examination boards, the authors' outlook and approach, the contemporary geography of Western Europe and the limitations of format and extent.

Throughout the book a thematic framework has been amplified by a variety of detailed case studies ranging in scale from the individual farm or factory through sample cities to particular regions. The content includes the main physical and human subdivisions of geography – landforms, climate, biography, agriculture, resources, industry and leisure with a concluding chapter on problem issues. Space, unfortunately has not permitted a separate chapter on communications but relevant themes are integrated elsewhere.

The topics covered should meet the requirements of the GCSE, SEB O and Standard Grade syllabuses in terms of content and key ideas. Most of the material has been classroom tested with a range of academic abilities. There is variation in the size of work units. Assignments also differ in length and degree of difficulty allowing coursework assessment of knowledge, understanding, investigation and evaluation. Atlas work is stressed to ensure that pupils acquire a basic locational knowledge of Western Europe. Where appropriate pupils are encouraged to develop and debate their own values and attitudes to environmental issues.

Emphasis has been placed upon the interaction of place and people, both past and present, as the key to understanding the rich and varied landscapes of Western Europe. Models, when used, must always be subordinate to reality and, as in the examples of the Dutch and West German urgan models, firmly rooted in their national context. Maximum use is therefore made of colour photographs (ground, aerial and satellite), extracts from newspapers, magazines and novels, block diagrams and transects. A key feature is the inclusion of ten topographic map excerpts (Norwegian, West German, French and Dutch) in most cases accompanied by relevant photographs. With this variety of stimulus the authors hope to illustrate the late Professor C. A. Fisher's reminder that geography 'is not the study of abstract space; it is the study of places, real, earthy, inhabited and alive'.

Finally, in writing this book we have been influenced by a Western Europe which is highly urbanised and where it is particularly relevant to consider urban profiles and issues. Equally, in selecting topics, it is a Western Europe where manufacturing industry is undergoing radical change and decision making is in the hands of multinationals such as Ford. It is an area where leisure and tourist industries are growth sectors of employment and where conservation issues involving landscape and minority groups such as the Sami are under debate. There is an increasingly important Mediterranean dimension particularly with the addition of the new agricultural landscapes of Spain, Portugal and Greece to the European Community (EC) with consequent political and economic ramifications for its Common Agricultural and Regional Policies.

K. Maclean
N. Thomson

Contents

Oxford University Press, Walton Street, Oxford OX2 6DP

Oxford New York Toronto
Delhi Bombay Calcutta Madras Karachi
Petaling Jaya Singapore Hong Kong Tokyo
Nairobi Dar es Salaam Cape Town
Melbourne Auckland

and associated companies in
Berlin Ibadan

Oxford is a trademark of Oxford University Press

© Oxford University Press 1988

ISBN 0 19 913317 4

Typesetting by Pentacor Ltd., High Wycombe, Bucks
Printed in Hong Kong

Acknowledgements

Aerocamera/Bart Hofmeester bv: 128; Aerofilms: 20, 37; Bryan and Cherry Alexander: 59 top, 92; ANP Foto: 47 right, 130, 131; Aspect: 10, 41, 58 centre right, 83, 135, 162; ASV: 111; Bibliothèque Royale, Brussels: 7; Biofoto: 18, 99; John Brennan: 36, 104; John Cleare/Mountain Camera: 25; Catalan Villas: 138 top and bottom right, 139 top left; Cover: 58 bottom right, 66; Daily Telegraph Colour Library: 1, 10 centre, 51 right, 72; Danish Dairy Board: 85; Moira Darling: 86 bottom right; Alison Duncan: 64; Robert Estall: 47 centre, 50; Marilyn Farr: 63; FIBO: 46 top; Sally and Richard Greenhill: 5 bottom centre; Susan Griggs: 40 top, 58 top left, 79 bottom, 155 top; Robert Harding: 30 bottom, 33, 34 bottom, 40 bottom, 58 bottom left, 61, 143, 152, 156 top right; John Hillelson: 15 right, 28, 29, 98, 153, 161; Hutchison Library: 5 top and bottom left and top right, 59 bottom left and right, 107 top; IDG: 79 top left and right, 80, 82, 124, 127; Image Bank: 5 centre left; Impact: 134; Frank Lane: 19; LKAB: 93; Kenneth Maclean: 38, 58 top right, 81, 132; Lloyd Martin: 141 bottom; John Massey Stewart: 132 right; Mobil North Sea Ltd: 102; Grazia Neri/Mairani: 30 top, 144; Network: 133; Norwave: 100 right; Philips: 114; Popperfoto: 9; Pressehuset: 100 left; Dorothy Price: 87; Rapho: 34 top, 41 bottom, 129; Rautaruukki Oy: 122; Joachim Schumacher: 107 bottom; Brian Shearn: 157; John Sims: 10 bottom, 69; Spectrum: 15 bottom left, 24, 58 centre left, 77; Frank Spooner: 51 left; STORA: 95, 96; Swiss National Tourist Office: 15 top left; Jeffrey Tabberner: 150; Norman Thomson: 58 top right, 137, 138 centre right, 141 top; Visnews: 75 bottom; Volkswagen: 118, 119; Westermann: 45; ZEFA: 27, 89, 151.

The authors would like to thank the following for their help:

ASV, Sunndalsora; Mr de Boer, Ex Undis; Catalan Villas; Ford Motor Company; G. L. McCorkindale; Map Shop, Upton-upon-Severn; Drs. H. Meijer, IDG, Utrecht; National Library of Scotland Map Room; Her T. Nes, Nes Farm; Philips, Eindhoven; Port Automne de Marseille; Dorothy Price; Duncan Pringle; Rotterdam-Europoort Port Authority; STORA; D. Tyson, and Volkswagenwerk, Wolfsburg. In addition, the embassies of the individual countries all gave assistance, as did the offices of the European Community.

Cover illustration: Geisler Peaks, St Magdalena, in the Dolomite Mountains of Italy (Spectrum Colour Library)

Fig. 1.1 Satellite photograph of part of Europe and North Africa

Chapter 1 Introduction

This book is about the landscape of Western Europe and how people have helped to shape the landscape. By way of introduction, we shall ask some apparently simple questions about Western Europe and its landscape. There are, however, no clear answers acceptable to everyone.

What is Europe?

It is usual to say that Europe is a continent. But is it? Surely a continent is a distinctive land mass, more or less separate from other land masses? Fig. 1.1 shows that, in world terms, Europe is a relatively small triangular wedge of land which broadens to the east forming part of the huge land mass of Eurasia.

We call Europe a continent because of the persistence of a myth held by the early geographers of Ancient Greece (Fig. 1.2). They thought that the world was divided into three parts – Europe, Africa and Asia. Based on imperfect information from Greek traders they believed that the Caspian Sea was part of an encircling ocean and only a narrow isthmus tied Europe and Asia together.

Such ideas continued to be shown on maps for hundreds of years. Fig. 1.3 is an example of a medieval 'T in O' map with Jerusalem at the centre. This was a medieval Christian world view.

Assignments

1 (*Fig. 1.1*) **a)** Trace the outline of the land and name as many land and water features as possible. **b)** Outline the area you consider to be Europe.

2 (*General*) **a)** Do you agree with the view that a continent has to be 'a distinctive land mass'? **b)** Do you think Greece is a West European, an East European or a Middle East country?

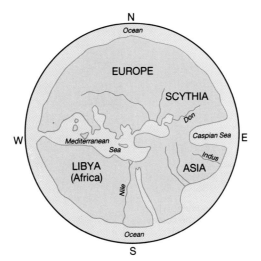

Fig. 1.2 How the Greeks saw the world in about 500 BC

What makes Europe different?

If Europe is not a distinct physical continent, are there certain features of human geography which makes it distinct from the rest of Eurasia? The answer is 'yes' and it has been recognised by map makers since the 17th century. The Ural mountains are normally shown as a boundary between physical Europe and Asia (although, we are more likely to accept the western boundary of the Soviet Union as the eastern limit of political Europe).

Various human (or cultural) features, which have developed over many years, make Europe different.

a The people of Europe (i) are mainly Christian (ii) belong mainly to the Caucasian race and (iii) mainly speak one of the related Indo-European languages.

b Europeans enjoy high living standards, are well fed, healthy and literate in global terms and are part of what the Brandt Report called 'The North' (see Fig. 1.6).

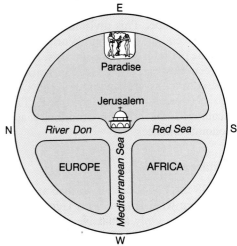

Fig. 1.3 A medieval map with Jerusalem at the centre

c The Industrial Revolution first took place in Europe in the mid 18th century. The harnessing of steam power was the start of numerous innovations such as the railway and the motor car, which have transformed the world's landscapes.

d From the Age of Discovery in the late 15th century onwards, European countries such as Portugal, Spain, Britain, France and the Netherlands were to create a world economy with a movement of people, goods and capital on a vast scale.

e This was to create colonial empires, which lasted until the 20th century. By this means the natural resources and peoples of most of the territory of the 'South' were exploited for the benefit of the Europeans.

Because of the Industrial Revolution and colonialism, the relatively small area of Europe was to have more influence, both good and bad, on the rest of the globe than any other area. European ideas and outlook have spread to every other continent.

Why is Europe divided into West and East?

Fig. 1.4 shows the division of the continent into the capitalist countries of Western Europe and the communist countries of Eastern Europe. This division dates from 1945, the end of the Second World War.

In the period from 1945 onwards, rivalry between West and East Europe increased as these countries were caught up in the 'Cold War' between the USA and the USSR. This encouraged the creation of military and economic alliances.

Military alliances

In 1948 the USSR cut off all road and rail links from what is now West Germany to West Berlin. Only a massive airlift of essential foods and coal kept the people and the city alive.

The military and political tension at the time of the Berlin Blockade was one of the factors which led to the setting up of NATO (the North Atlantic Treaty Organisation) in 1949. It includes among its members Canada and the USA as well as those shown in Fig. 1.4.

When West Germany joined NATO in 1955 the countries of Eastern Europe and the USSR formed the *Warsaw Pact*. From the Soviet viewpoint re-armament by West Germany was seen as a threat. Memories were fresh of the 20 million people killed in the USSR in what is called 'the Great Patriotic War' (1941–45). As seen from the USSR the geography of NATO meant that the Soviet Union was hemmed in by the armed forces of the capitalist countries.

Economic alliances

In Eastern Europe economic links were forged when COMECON was established. By means of the 'Council for Mutual Economic Assistance' the economies of the Soviet satellite countries were closely tied to the USSR.

In the west a massive economic recovery plan was started in 1947 through the American aided Marshall Plan.

Fig. 1.4 The East/West division of Europe

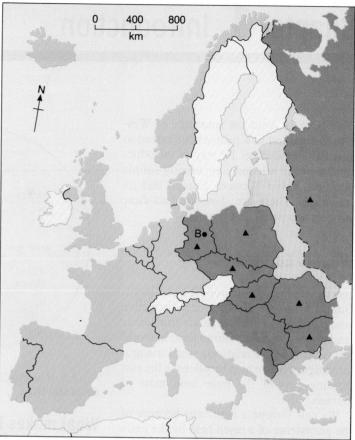

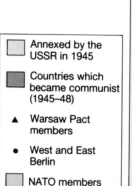

- ☐ Annexed by the USSR in 1945
- ■ Countries which became communist (1945–48)
- ▲ Warsaw Pact members
- ● West and East Berlin
- ☐ NATO members

From the countries of Western Europe itself, there was a gradual move towards economic integration. There were thought to be two advantages: (i) war would be less likely between traditionally rival countries such as France and Germany; (ii) a strong West European economy could emerge.

Over the past 40 years various organisations have developed.

BENELUX This was formed as a result of a trade agreement in 1948 to reduce tariffs between Belgium, the Netherlands and Luxembourg.

ECSC Set up in 1952, the European Coal and Steel Community consisted of Benelux, France, Italy and West Germany. Initially it was concerned with coal and steel production but now it deals with the problems of the rapid decline in these industries.

EC This is by far the most important of these *supranational* organisations and, at first, involved the six countries of the ECSC. The European Community was formed in 1957 after the Treaty of Rome. In various stages (see Fig. 1.5), it was enlarged from the original six members to 12 by 1986. Today, with a population of 320 million it is a major economic power which is run by four main institutions: the European Parliament, the Council of Ministers, the Commission, and the Court of Justice.

When the EC was established it had various aims which included:

a The establishment of a huge 'Common Market' for the farming and factory goods of the member states. The abolition of barriers to trade between the states and the setting up of a common external tariff.

b The freedom of movement of people and capital within the Community.

c The formation of a type of 'United States of Western Europe' with a general sharing of resources and wealth. Poorer regions were to receive aid.

There is no denying the importance of

the EC for its members. Decisions taken in Brussels and Luxembourg have affected the landscapes of the member countries, as will be seen in later chapters of the book.

But the road to a fully integrated Europe is not easy and many issues have to be resolved.

a There is strong disagreement over the 70 per cent of the EC budget spent on agriculture (page 74).

b It is argued that EC policies have increased rather than decreased the gap between rich and poor areas (page 75).

c The gap between rich and poor has increased with the entry of Greece, Spain and Portugal.

d Many believe that too much money is spent on the 'Brussels bureaucracy'.

e Some argue that member states are just in it for what they can get.

EFTA the European Free Trade Association was formed in 1960 and its member states are shown on Fig. 1.5 (Iceland joined in 1970). Unlike the EC, it was a much looser organisation with non-political aims and concerned with free trade. As a result politically neutral countries such as Switzerland felt able to participate.

Do Europeans feel 'European'?

If a 'United States of Europe' ever came about, would people feel that they were 'European'? Would they not think that they were French or Spanish, for example? One difficulty is that people have certain beliefs and prejudices about other nationals. While there can be a funny side to stereotyping, any form of prejudice should be condemned. It comes from a mixture of ignorance and a feeling of superiority which is also extended to the Third World.

Perhaps there is a lesson to be learned from the 'South'. Fig. 1.6 reminds us that while the 'North' is in the lead technologically and economically, it was not always so. And who knows where the dominant culture will be in 500 years time?

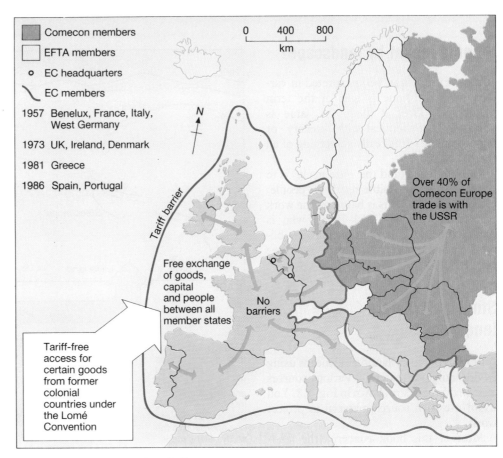

Fig. 1.5 Economic groupings in Europe

Assignments

1 (*Atlas and Fig. 1.4*) List the following countries: **a)** Communist and Warsaw Pact members **b)** Communist/non Warsaw Pact members **c)** NATO members **d)** Neutral countries.

2 (*Text*) **a)** What do the letters NATO stand for? **b)** Explain why it was founded.

3 (*Fig 1.5 and atlas*) **a)** What do the letters EC represent? **b)** Draw a map of the EC members, grouping them according to their date of entry. **c)** List the aims of the EC and explain why it was founded.

Fig. 1.6 The developed 'North' and developing 'South'

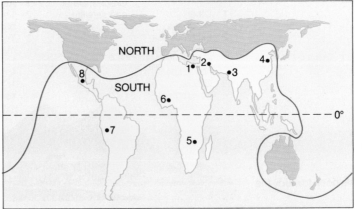

Centres of ancient civilization

1 Nile Valley
2 Mesopotamia e.g. Babylon
3 Indus Valley
4 Hwang Ho
5 Zimbabwe
6 Yoruba
7 Incas
8 Aztecs

⎫ The dividing line between the developed 'North' and developing 'South'

What is meant by landscape?

Just as 'Europe' can be interpreted in various ways the same is true of the term 'landscape'. Does it mean the same as 'nature'? Is it identical with 'scenery' or 'environment'? It is really something of all these, and more?

One approach (and there are many) is to think of it as the visible result of 'people, place and work'. This is based on the work of Patrick Geddes (1854–1933), who is regarded as an important sociologist, botanist, geographer and town planner (see Fig. 1.7).

Studying Western European landscapes

A topic as broad as 'landscape' means using a wide range of material. Various sources used in this book are shown in Fig. 1.8. You could use such source material in project work.

Most of this book concerns the landscapes of Western Europe (France, West Germany, Benelux, Switzerland, Austria, Greece, Italy, Spain, Portugal, Denmark, Finland, Norway, Sweden and Iceland). Reference is made, on occasion, to Europe as a whole.

Landscapes, near and far, are the subject matter of geography. Remember that geography 'is not the study of abstract space; it is the study of places, real, earthy, inhabited and alive' (Professor C. A. Fisher).

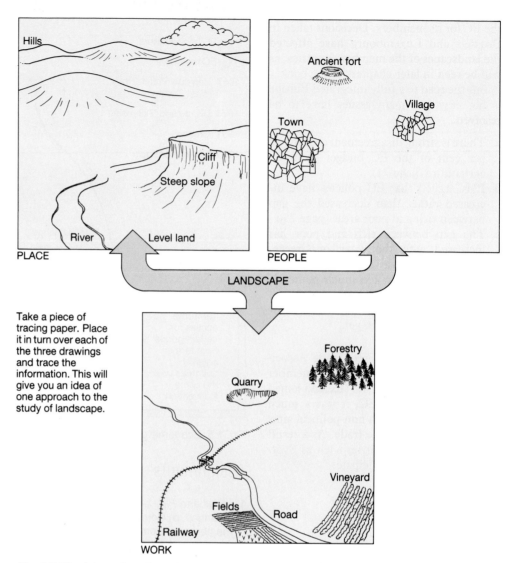

Take a piece of tracing paper. Place it in turn over each of the three drawings and trace the information. This will give you an idea of one approach to the study of landscape.

Fig. 1.7 The interaction of people, place and work to form 'landscape'

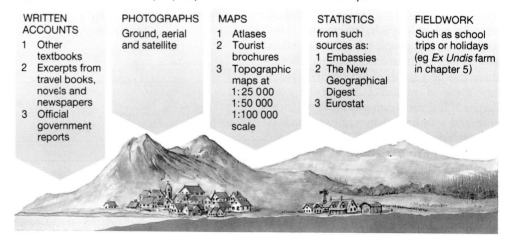

Fig. 1.8 Sources used in this book to study the landscape

WRITTEN ACCOUNTS	PHOTOGRAPHS	MAPS	STATISTICS	FIELDWORK
1 Other textbooks 2 Excerpts from travel books, novels and newspapers 3 Official government reports	Ground, aerial and satellite	1 Atlases 2 Tourist brochures 3 Topographic maps at 1:25 000 1:50 000 1:100 000 scale	from such sources as: 1 Embassies 2 The New Geographical Digest 3 Eurostat	Such as school trips or holidays (eg *Ex Undis* farm in chapter 5)

Chapter 2 People of Western Europe

A mixture of people

People can be labelled and classified according to one or more of the following features: race (that is, physical characteristics), religion, and language. There is now a rich and an increasingly great variety of people in Western Europe (Fig. 2.1). These pictures show some young West Europeans.

Most Europeans have traditionally been classified as belonging to the Caucasoid group (which includes such non-Europeans as Iranians and north Indians). Within Europe, the classification broke down into the 'Nordic' 'Alpine', and 'Mediterranean' people. The distinction between these groups was based on the shape of the skull and the colour of skin, hair, and eyes. In addition, as a result of migration from former West European colonies, there are also the two other major racial groups: Mongoloid and Negroid.

How useful is it to talk about such racial groupings? Think about these points.

a From the physical point of view all of us have far more in common, compared with minor differences in skin colour and facial features.

b Perhaps the only technical racial term which is worth bothering about is the Human Race.

c So-called 'scientific theories' held by Europeans about racial 'purity' and 'superiority' led to the extermination of over 5 million Jewish people during the Second World War. And Jewish people are a distinctive religious group!

Religious beliefs

A rich mixture of religious beliefs may be found in Europe. Christianity spread from

Fig. 2.1 Multi-language sign in Switzerland

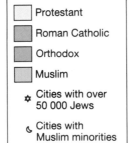

- ▢ Protestant
- ▢ Roman Catholic
- ▢ Orthodox
- ▢ Muslim
- ✡ Cities with over 50 000 Jews
- ☪ Cities with Muslim minorities

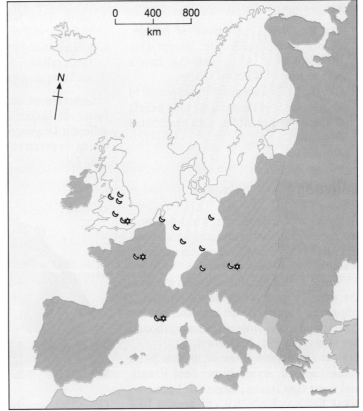

Fig. 2.2 Religious beliefs in Europe and its borderlands

its humble beginnings in Palestine to Europe, but at an early date split into various churches.

One early division took place in 1054 between Eastern and Western Christianity. Today the Eastern Orthodox Church is mainly represented in Greece. Elsewhere its strength has been sapped by government pressure in the Communist block countries (see Fig. 2.2).

The Western or Roman Catholic Church dominated throughout Western Europe until the Protestant Reformation in the 1500s. Today the Roman Catholic Church has its greatest strength in Southern Europe, Poland, and Ireland. The various Protestant Churches are generally strongest in Northern Europe.

In the past, Christianity was taken to the rest of the world; as a result of migration other world faiths have come to Western Europe. Muslim mosques, Sikh gurdwaras and Hindu temples are now part of what are increasingly multi-cultural cities of Western Europe. As a result two issues are at stake:

a Can the 'White Christians' of Britain, France, Netherlands etc. accept that there are other valid beliefs that have a part to play in Western Europe?
b Can the 'New Europeans' be expected to give up some of their deeply held beliefs if these do not fit in with traditional customs?

Language

In the case of Ireland religious differences were the reason for the division of the island in 1922 into a mainly Protestant north and a mainly Roman Catholic south. Over much of Western Europe, however, language is the main factor responsible for separating countries. Many political boundaries often correspond to a change of language, though not always (as Fig. 2.3 shows).

Over 75 per cent of the six million Swiss speak German, about 20 per cent French and 4 per cent Italian. Less than 1 per cent speak Romansch which is a distinctive Italian dialect of Latin origin spoken only in rural areas of south east Switzerland. All four languages are officially recognised in this politically neutral state with a reputation for harmony among its different people.

Such harmony is not always widespread. Within several countries problems exist as a result of language differences. For example:

a Belgium is a divided state with some 6 million Dutch-speaking Flemings in the prosperous north and 4 million French-speaking Walloons in the economically less secure south (see pages 157–158).
b Over a quarter of Spain's 38 million inhabitants have a first language other than Castillian Spanish. Since the death of the former dictator General Franco, the new 1978 constitution has promised increased rights for the various regions and peoples, such as the Catalan speakers of north-east Spain. It does not, however, suit a violent, terrorist minority among the Basque people of the north. Their home language – Euskara – is a very old one and appears not to be related to any other. The terrorist movement called ETA aims to create a separate Basque-speaking socialist republic.

Government attitudes are an important factor in encouraging harmony between different language-speaking groups and in trying to preserve minority languages (see Fig. 2.4).

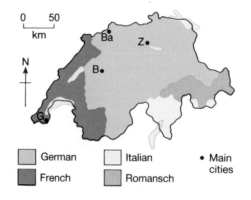

Fig. 2.3 Languages of Switzerland

1 Sami
2 Walloons
3 Frisians
4 South Tyroleans
5 Corsicans
6 Catalans
7 Galicians
8 Basques
9 Bretons
10 Alsatians
11 Welsh
12 Northern Irish
13 Scots

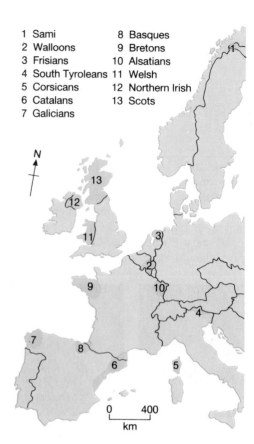

Fig. 2.4 Some minority language and dialect groups of Western Europe

After centuries of trying to eliminate minority languages and dialects the French Government launched a plan in 1985 to rescue these tongues. In 1930 over 50 per cent of the people of Brittany spoke Breton, but the number has declined drastically. The language is to be encouraged in schools, more trained teachers employed to teach it and bilingual road signs made legal. In addition the distinctive Langue D'oc dialect of southern France is also to be encouraged through schooling, exhibitions and festivals.

Not for the first time in its long history, Western Europe is a multi-cultural society. Many people find it difficult to accept this and see minority groups as a threat to traditions and jobs. Perhaps the answer is to keep reminding ourselves that all of us, in world terms, are minority groups?

Population of Western Europe

Fig. 2.5 The Black Death killed thousands in medieval Europe

Nowadays television brings pictures of Third World famine, drought, disease, and war into our homes. It is difficult for Europeans, well-fed and prosperous in world terms, to appreciate fully such suffering. But the people of Europe have long been affected by such disasters (Figs. 2.5 and 2.6).

a As a result of the Black Death (1347–53) between a quarter and a third of Europe's population was wiped out. The plague was carried by fleas and affected both rats and people so it easily broke out and spread on ships and in the overcrowded towns of medieval Europe.
b The Thirty Years War (1618–48) severely affected Germany. It was accompanied by further plague outbreaks and poverty.
c Millions of people died during the Russian Revolution and the First and Second World Wars, particularly in the USSR and Germany.

In spite of setbacks the overall trend has been one of population growth. The rate of growth has, however, varied from place to place and at different times. As the graph

(Fig. 2.6) shows there was a rapid upturn in population from 1750 onwards. Various reasons are put forward to explain this.

a Countries such as Britain then, later, Belgium, France and Germany underwent their Industrial Revolutions. People crowded into rapidly growing industrial towns and cities. By the 1870s the death-rate was falling fast because public health improvements (sewage disposal and clean drinking water) were eliminating diseases such as cholera and typhoid, and a rising standard of living meant that people were better fed, clothed and housed.
b Other mainly agricultural countries, however, such as Ireland, Norway and Sweden also experienced rapid population growth. Along with the other countries of North-west Europe, they had undergone an agricultural revolution. This meant a greater livestock output, higher crop yields, and the adoption of new crops such as the potato. As a result, people improved their diet, and so became more resistant to disease.

By 1914 Europe's population had reached some 450 million. It would have been higher but for 50 million who migrated to North and South America, Siberia, South Africa, Australia and New Zealand.

The USA, especially, was the main destination, attracting some 33 million between 1820 and 1950. Such large-scale international migration is the result of either 'push' factors and/or 'pull' factors. Undoubtedly the USA had a great deal of appeal, but the push factors were probably stronger. Shortages of land, political and religious intolerance, and sheer poverty were some of the key push factors.

Fig. 2.6 Population growth in Europe (including Eastern Europe and European USSR)

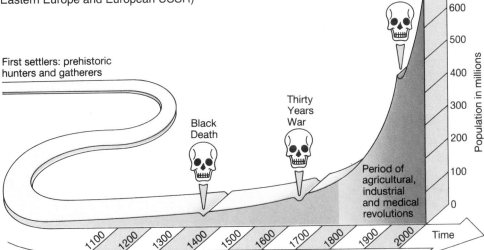

First settlers: prehistoric hunters and gatherers

Black Death

Thirty Years War

World Wars

Period of agricultural, industrial and medical revolutions

Population in millions

600
500
400
300
200
100
0

1100 1200 1300 1400 1500 1600 1700 1800 1900 2000 Time

Western Europe's population: the world setting

After looking at Europe as a whole let's switch to Western Europe itself.

Western Europe's population increased by over three times between 1750 and 1980. By the early 1980s Western Europe had a population of some 350 million. This accounts for over 8.5 per cent of the world's population, but this is a figure which is declining. Western Europe has the slowest rate of population growth, not just in the world, but within the so-called developed countries of the North. While it is estimated that the population of the world will double within 41 years, that of Western Europe may take over 918 years!

There are, however, marked variations between the different countries of Western Europe. Countries such as Ireland, Spain and Portugal have relatively high rates of natural increase; some have a very low or zero rate of increase, while the population of West Germany is declining.

Assignments

1 (*Account and Fig. 2.6*) What factors explain the rapid growth in Europe's population since 1750?

2 (*Revision/research*) Explain the following terms: birth-rate, death-rate, natural increase/decrease, infant mortality.

3 (*Statistics/mapwork*) Look at the statistics on page 165 on birth rate, death rate and infant mortality rate. Try to group the figures for each of these indices into three categories. On a series of base maps, shade in the countries according to your categories. Describe the contrasts which you notice and try to explain your results. Do your results relate to other factors such as GNP. per capita, population per doctor, etc?

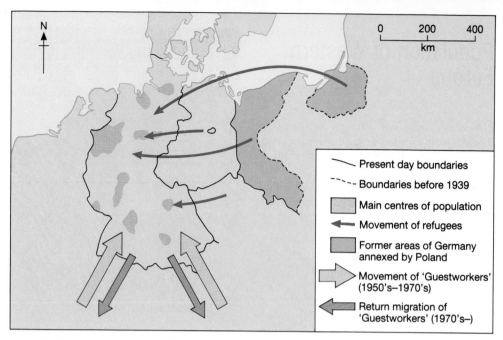

Fig. 2.7 Migration to and from West Germany since 1945

Population changes in West Germany

Today West Germany is one of the richest countries in the world. Yet in 1945, after six years of war, its economy was severely damaged. 60 per cent of its towns and cities were in ruins, while its people were close to starvation. Its rapid recovery has been called the West German 'economic miracle', and the process involved four major types of population change.

1 Post-war refugees

After the end of the Second World War millions of German refugees came flooding into West Germany. Some came from countries such as Czechoslovakia, Hungary and Rumania which had long been the home of quite substantial German minorities. Others came from areas (Fig. 2.7) which before 1939 had been part of Germany and are now part of Poland and the USSR. Finally, a third group were Germans who came from Soviet occupied East Berlin and East Germany (Fig. 2.7).

Fig. 2.8 Population trends in West Germany, 1845–1983

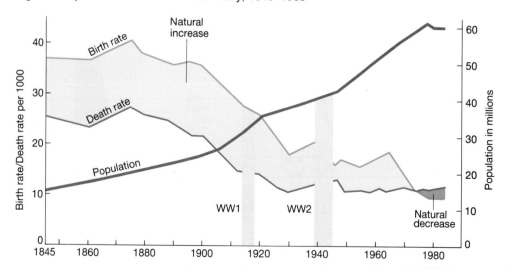

As a result West Germany's population increased by almost a third from 42 million in 1945 to 55 million in 1960. Such a flow of refugees created problems for the West German authorities but they provided a skilled workforce able to help West Germany re-build her post-war economy.

2 Changing birth-rates/death-rates

Another key feature of West Germany's population geography is the changing balance between birth- and death-rates. Fig 2.8 shows that West Germany broadly follows the pattern of population change in the developed world. Overall, birth-rates and death-rates declined and eventually converged by 1971. As the gap narrowed, the rate of natural increase contracted. Indeed, since 1972 the birth-rate has been less than the death-rate. In spite of an inflow in the early 1970s of migrant workers West Germany's population had started to decline.

Several reasons are put forward to explain the fall in the birth-rate, which has affected both southern (mainly Roman Catholic) Germany as much as the (mainly Protestant) north. Apart from the first, they are all connected with the 'economic miracle'.

a As a result of the war, fewer children were born in the period 1944–47. By the late 1960s there were, therefore, fewer potential parents.
b West Germans wish to enjoy modern home comforts (such as colour TVs and dishwashers), as well as holidays abroad.
c Although small flats in the city centre are relatively cheap, larger 'family' housing is expensive.
d Having children is postponed as more German wives go out to work. (The proportion of working married women is, however, lower than in Britain.)

With fewer than 10 births per 1000 people every year, one estimate suggests that by the late 1990s the population will have fallen by some 3 million.

Fig. 2.9 European immigrants arriving in New York at the turn of the century

Young Turks in West Germany: some views

A It's a horrible situation for them here. They can't speak the language so they drop out of school. They drop out of school so they can't find work. They can't find work so they have nothing to do. Then many of them turn to crime or drugs. (*Hubertus Stroeber, West Berlin Social Worker*)

B I hate Germany. When I go to the employment office, I can see that they have jobs because they give them to Germans. But when I come to the window they tell me, 'sorry, we have nothing'. (*Eyup Cit, aged 20*).

C I have German friends, sure, but I know that when I'm not there they make fun of Turks and tell dirty jokes about us. With Turks I am among my own kind. (*Nureltin Ozdekin, aged 18.*)

D I know Berlin but it will never be home to me. People turn their heads away when you ask a question, just because you don't look like them and they know you're a foreigner. But when I go back to Turkey, I feel I just don't belong. (*Huseyin Topcu, aged 16.*)

From *Newsweek*, 1 March 1982

3 'Guestworkers'

In the 1950s and 1960s, West Germany (along with France, Sweden, Denmark, Benelux and Switzerland) attracted over 10 million migrant workers. The majority of them came from Turkey, Yugoslavia, Greece, and Italy. 'Pulled' by the high wages and availability of jobs, and 'pushed' by rural poverty and lack of opportunity, these guestworkers played a very important role in West Germany's economic miracle. They were willing to do the low paid, boring and dirty jobs disdained by the West Germans.

By the 1980s the economic situation had changed. As a result of the recession unemployment had risen. In theory the guestworkers should have returned home, but the reality was different. For one thing many guestworkers preferred to face unemployment in West Germany than return home. Secondly, although worker recruitment had declined drastically, many of the men had been joined by their wives and children (Fig. 9.26).

Today the guestworkers are found mainly in the overcrowded inner city zones, and number over 4.5 million. They are part of the West German population but they are not always accepted. This is especially true in the case of the Turks who are the largest group. There are many problems which have to be overcome and it is among the younger, second generation Turks that the issues are most keenly felt (see page 9). For West Germany (as with Britain and France) perhaps the major population issue is the creation of a genuinely tolerant multi-cultural country where people will be judged for what they are rather than their ethnic origins.

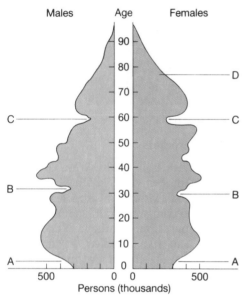

Fig. 2.10 Population structure in West Germany (1980)

4 Population structure

Age and sex pyramids are of value in two main ways. Firstly, they summarise the main trends in a country's birth-rate and death-rate, as well as identifying migration flows. These in turn reflect a country's history. The indentations B and C in Fig. 2.10 are the result of the two World Wars and help to explain the irregular shape of the West German pyramid.

Secondly, they are of value in planning for social provision. The long term effect of an ageing population poses a problem. Already 15 per cent of the population is over 65. It is estimated that by the year 2030 there will be one retired person for every person in a job. As it is more expensive to maintain the elderly than the young this will strain the social services.

Assignments

1 (*Account/Fig. 2.7 and atlas*) Copy Fig. 2.7. Complete the map by naming: West Germany, East Germany, Czechoslovakia, Poland, Berlin. Number 1 to 9 the main population centres. Match, in a key, the numbers with the following: Hamburg, Rhine-Ruhr, Saarland, Nuremburg, Munich, Stuttgart, Bremen, Hanover/Brunswick, Rhine-Main.

2 (*Account/general*) Explain why there were so many refugees returning to Germany in the period after 1945.

3 (*Fig. 2.10*) Copy and complete this table.

Date	Birth-rate	Death-rate	Date of increase/decrease
1845			
1900			
1950			
1980			

4 (*Account/general*) Try to explain:
  a) the overall fall in death-rates;
  b) the general fall in birth-rates.

5 (*Account*) a) Briefly explain the term guestworkers, mentioning their countries of origin. b) Suggest 'push' and 'pull' factors which have encouraged guestworkers to migrate.

6 (*Excerpts*) What appear to be the main difficulties facing young Turks if they remain in West Germany; and if they return to Turkey?

7 (*Research/discussion*) Guestworkers and their children are seen as a major problem for countries such as West Germany. Suggest some possible solutions.

8 (*Discussion*) Many migrant workers have returned to their home countries. What factors would encourage them to return rather than stay?

9 (*Fig. 2.10/account*) To explain the shape of the age/sex pyramid match the letters A–D with the following: gap in births due to the First World War; gap in births due to family planning; gap in births due to the Second World War; excess females over males.

Fig. 2.11 Lyon, France, a high density area

Fig. 2.12 Southern Norway, a medium density area

Fig. 2.13 The Spanish Meseta, a low density area

Population distribution and density

Figs. 2.11–2.14 show the variation in the distribution of population in Europe. A map showing where people live (or don't live) is perhaps the most important single map of any area. This is because such a map summarises all aspects of the geography of an area. Explaining the uneven patterns, with some areas showing high population densities and others low population densities, involves a very wide range of physical and human factors.

Assignments

1 (*Fig. 2.14 and atlas*) Copy and complete the following paragraphs. The answers are found at the end but not in the correct order. The numbers in the text are shown on the map.

The distribution of population in Europe is very _____. There are areas of _____, medium and _____ population density.

The main areas of high population density are numbered 1 to 18. Some of these are centres of industry and _____ with big cities which grew up after the industrial _____ using local resources of _____ and _____. These include, for example, (1) _____, (2) _____, (3) the industrial areas of Northern England and the Midlands, (4) the giant _____ industrial area of West Germany, (5) the _____ coalfield, and Lorraine and the Saar.

Other areas of high population density have arisen around major ports, capitals and industrial centres (using _____ power, oil and gas), often surrounded by rich _____ farmed areas. In Northern Europe these include (6) _____, (7) _____, (8) the _____ (Randstad conurbation), and Hamburg-Bremen. In Southern Europe the main centres include (9) _____ and (10) _____ in Spain; (11) _____ in Portugal (12) _____ and (13) _____ in southern France; the fertile Plain of _____ in northern Italy with (14) _____ and (15) _____; (16) _____ and (17) _____ in southern Italy, and (18) the _____ area in mainland Greece.

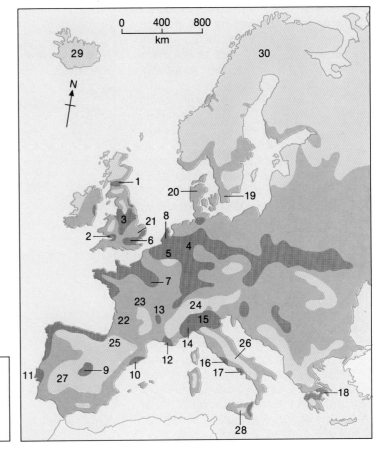

Fig. 2.14 Distribution of population in Europe

Population density
- [ ] Low
- [ ] Medium
- [ ] High

Areas of medium population density are found in other fertile regions of lowland Europe. Much of (19) southern _____ and (20) _____ as well as (21) _____ _____ and (22) _____ (Aquitaine) fall into this category. Such areas show an increase in population. New factories and _____ have moved out from the large conurbations and many people prefer to live in the small and _____ sized towns in such areas.

Areas of low population density are often thought of as _____ regions. They include the _____ areas of southern Europe such as (23) the _____, (24) the _____, (25) the _____, and (26) the _____. In (27) the _____ of Spain and (28) the interior uplands of _____ conditions can be very _____. Isolation, a cold climate and a _____ growing season are problems in (29) _____ and (30) northern _____.

Select from: high; coal; South Wales; London; Madrid; Marseilles; Turin; Naples; Denmark; S.W. France; 'negative'; Alps; Meseta; short; low; revolution; Central Scotland; Franco-Belgian; intensively; Western Netherlands; Lisbon; Lombardy; Rome; Sweden; East Anglia; medium; Massif Central; Apennines; arid; Scandinavia; Iceland; Sicily; Pyrenees; upland; offices; Athens; Milan; Lyons; Barcelona; Paris: hydro; uneven; Ruhr; commerce; iron.

3 (*Statistics/general*) Look at the statistics (page 165) on population density. Try to group these figures into three categories. On a base map, shade in the countries according to your categories. Comment on your results. How valuable is this method of showing population density, compared to Fig. 2.14?

Migrants from Greece

It has already been shown that Greece is one of the source countries for the migrant workers of Western Europe. In this section, a small village in Greece will be studied to see if it is possible to identify reasons for migration of population.

Ambeli is a mountain village in Central Greece. Figs. 2.15–2.17 show the main features of the site as well as of the use of the land. Farming is the main occupation, although it is made difficult by the steep slopes and the small scattered fields. Most people prefer cultivating the land for food to collecting resin from the pine trees, even though it is less profitable.

There are few other jobs in the village, although three families own cafés, and two own small shops. The village is very isolated, and is only accessible by mule track. There are few young people in Ambeli (Fig. 2.18), for several reasons. Attending grammar school after the age of 12 means staying away from home. National service takes young men away for another spell. Many young people leave the village when they marry. Others migrate, some forever, in search of work. As a result, the birth-rate in the village is declining, and the population is ageing.

Young men from Ambeli working abroad

West Germany	11
Belgium	6
Canada	6
Australia	1
South Africa	1
In the Merchant Navy	7

Emigration, even to the USA, began over 80 years ago, but until the 1960s it was temporary. Money saved was sent home to buy a house or more land. Since 1960 the emigration has in most cases been permanent. Migrants still return for holidays and send money home to support their families but have no intention of returning to live in Ambeli. Before 1970 emigrants hoped for a better life outside the village, but now they

Fig. 2.15 The mountain setting of the village of Ambeli

Labels on image: Cold north winds bring snow in winter · Limestone mountains · Average slopes in forest: 40° · Pine forest · The height of the village is 600 metres above sea level · Church · Barns · Cultivated land · Tiled roof · Stone walls · Village land ranges in height from 250–750 metres · Ambeli is a cluster of 31 houses, all within 3 minutes walk of the spring which supplies water. It is surrounded by orchards, gardens and vineyards. There is no electricity supply.

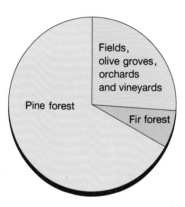

Fig. 2.16 Use of village land (total area 1260 hectares)

Labels: Fields, olive groves, orchards and vineyards · Pine forest · Fir forest

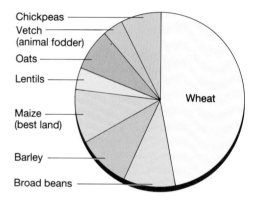

Fig. 2.17 Use of typical farm in Ambeli area, showing main crops (excluding tree crops and vines)

Labels: Chickpeas · Vetch (animal fodder) · Oats · Lentils · Maize (best land) · Barley · Broad beans · Wheat

leave because they dislike the harshness of village life.

The village elders have to accept this emigration, though it will lead to the eventual end of the village. (In 1949 Ambeli was actually abandoned for a year during the civil war. Some of the villagers fought for the communists; others supported the Royalists).

There are many villages in Greece similar to Ambeli, and which suffer from depopulation for much the same reasons. The total population of the country is increasing quite quickly, however, and the urban

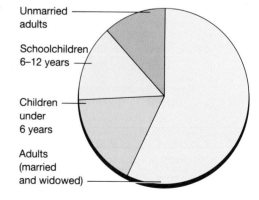

Fig. 2.18 Ambeli's population structure

Labels: Unmarried adults · Schoolchildren 6–12 years · Children under 6 years · Adults (married and widowed)

population is increasing at a faster rate. Fig. 2.19 shows the main towns in Greece. While three out of every ten workers still work on the land, the towns attract people away from the countryside in large numbers. As a result the population of the larger towns has increased very rapidly, for example Athens-Piraeus increased from 2.5 million to over 3.0 million in a decade.

The towns, however, cannot cope with all the people looking for work, and many people have gone to other countries instead. Such emigration is not new, and has not always been for economic reasons (Fig. 2.20).

There are, therefore, large numbers of Greeks abroad. Almost 700 000 Greeks have emigrated to the USA since the 19th century, while in the mid-1970s there were 400 000 Greeks in West Germany. There

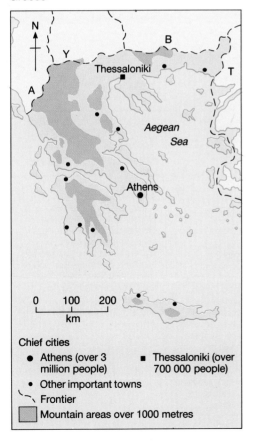

Fig. 2.19 The main population centres in Greece

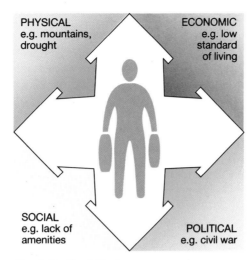

Fig. 2.20 'Push' factors encouraging emigration

are also over 330 000 people descended from 19th century Greek settlers in the USSR.

Political refugees

Just as many people fled from Eastern Europe to the West in the mid 20th century to escape from communist rule (see page 8), others did the reverse. After their defeat in the civil war, over 100 000 Greek Communists emigrated to Eastern Europe in the 1950s.

Migrant workers

Ten years later, there was a great migration of people, especially to the EC and to Australia, but by the late 1970s this had decreased substantially. In the 1980s there was a counter-flow of returning workers and some refugees.

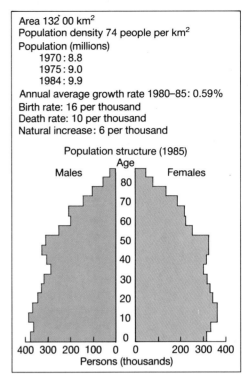

Area 132 00 km²
Population density 74 people per km²
Population (millions)
    1970 : 8.8
    1975 : 9.0
    1984 : 9.9
Annual average growth rate 1980–85: 0.59%
Birth rate: 16 per thousand
Death rate: 10 per thousand
Natural increase: 6 per thousand

Fig. 2.21 Greece: population and structure

Assignments

1 (*Fig. 2.19*) From your atlas, identify the four countries A, Y, B and T.

2 (*Figs. 2.19, 2.21*) What do you notice about the distribution of the major towns in Greece?
What proportion of the total population of Greece is found in the Athens urban area?

3 Studying all the material on both pages, make as detailed a list as possible of the factors which have encouraged emigration from Greece.

4 (*Fig. 2.21*) Only Ireland (1.2 per cent) had a higher rate of population growth than Greece between 1975–82. Suggest reasons for this high growth rate in Greece.

5 (*Figs. 2.10, 2.21*) Study the population structure of Greece. In what ways is it **a)** similar to that of West Germany **b)** different from that of West Germany? What reasons might explain these differences?

13

Urban landscapes of Western Europe

If there is such a person as a 'typical West European', then that individual lives in a town or city. The figures vary from country to country (see page 165) but in West Germany, Sweden, Benelux, France and Iceland almost four out of every five people are urban dwellers. In Southern Europe the figure is lower but it is rather difficult to compare countries. For example, an urban settlement in Norway has a population greater than 200; in Greece, however, it has to be greater than 20,000!

To an increasing extent even those people who live in rural areas are 'mentally urbanised'. Daily newspapers, radio and TV programmes, the educational system, various shopping services are basically urban in origin.

Old and new townscapes

The landscapes (or 'townscapes') of the towns and cities of Western Europe have a long history dating from the Ancient Greeks. By the 5th century BC there were not only some 600 towns in Greece itself, but Greek trading towns were scattered throughout the Mediterranean. Present-day Marseille is as much a Greek foundation as Athens.

As the Roman Empire grew, towns spread north to France, Germany and southern Britain. Lyon, for example, was an important strategic centre while Cologne grew as a trading town. Although many towns declined with the troubles of the Dark Ages, many more rose up in later Medieval times. Population growth, increased trade and the local power of a lord or the church encouraged the development of towns. Because of the threat of attack towns were usually defended with a wall and castle, and ideally a defensive site was sought. Those towns which were well placed for trade such as Venice, Genoa, Amsterdam, London, and Antwerp saw

their population steadily outstrip the smaller towns.

With the coming of the Industrial Revolution in the 19th century there was a dramatic increase in the population of certain towns and villages. Because of the growth of coal mining, the iron and steel industries, and the expansion in textiles, people were 'pulled' to the rapidly expanding cities of the Ruhr, Lorraine and the Franco-Belgian coalfield, for example.

Rapid population growth also affected the capital cities of Western Europe. London, Paris, Berlin and Brussels were centres of business and government for both their home country and their colonies overseas. Vienna was capital of the large Austro-Hungarian Empire, and by the time of the First World War it had a population of some two million.

With such a long history of urban development the past is always apparent in Western European townscapes (Fig. 2.22). The street layout of central Turin is

SITE
The core of present day cities occupies the original site. Some sites are defensive, eg:

Paris: a river island site.
Bern: an incised meander site.
Stockholm: a lake island site.
Venice: an island site:
Salzburg: a high point site.

Other examples include trade route sites eg.

Koblenz: a confluence point.
Innsbruck: a bridging point.

STREET LAYOUT
In most towns and cities the street layout is narrow and irregular, especially in the central area. In some cases it is laid out in a grid iron pattern eg. Turin.

HOUSING
Housing density generally is high, with more people living in apartments than in the UK. Most people who are better off prefer a city centre residence closer to place of work and entertainment. Very high residential densities are found in the historic core of the Mediterranean cities such as Naples.

URBAN CONSERVATION
From the 1960s there has been increased opposition to the destruction of older houses. Restoration schemes are now common but such houses are often too dear for the working class. Usually, only the middle classes can buy or rent such houses (a process called 'gentrification'). Some cities, eg. Bologna in Italy with its communist local authority, limit the rents of restored houses to prevent gentrification. Such city conservation schemes are tourist attractions.

NEW HOUSING
New high rise apartment blocks built in large estates have developed since 1945 as part of Government policies. This was essential because of the substantial war damage eg. in Koblenz 75% of housing had been destroyed. By the 1970s there had been an increased demand for single dwelling houses in the suburbs and dormitory towns even in areas of land shortage such as the Netherlands.

OFFICES, SHOPS AND TRANSPORT SYSTEMS
Major new offices - HQ's of EC organisations and multi-nationals have been set up in cities such as Brussels, Luxembourg and Strasbourg. Urban motorways have developed eg. major ring roads and expressways; hypermarkets are located on outskirts with huge car parks; metro systems have been built or extended, eg. in Barcelona, Hamburg, Cologne, Milan and Paris.

Fig. 2.22 Past and present in a townscape

basically that of Roman times; the impressive palaces of Vienna are a reminder of 19th century Imperial power, while the 2400-year-old Acropolis looks down (when the pollution haze permits) on the overcrowded streets of Athens.

Post-1945 changes have encouraged townscapes of a similar appearance to emerge throughout Western Europe. Rebuilding after the Second World War, the growth of car ownership, increased affluence, and the need for improved housing have been the cause of this uniformity. The common features of such townscapes are modern office blocks, high-rise flats and urban motorways.

In spite of these changes, the cities of Western Europe are an interesting mixture of the old and the new.

Some townscapes of Western Europe

Fig. 2.23 The medieval centre of Berne, Switzerland

Fig. 2.24 Central Dusseldorf, Germany, showing the tall Thyssen building

Assignments

1 (*Fig. 2.23*)
   a) What are the natural advantages of this site?
   b) What do you notice about the houses and main buildings in this part of the city?
   c) How would you deal with traffic flow in this area?
   d) How do you pick out the steepest slopes around the city core?

2 (*Fig. 2.24*)
   a) Look at the Thyssen building. In what way is it different from the other modern buildings shown?
   b) What uses have been made of the open space in central Düsseldorf?
   c) Is there any evidence of older buildings which survived war damage?

3 (*Fig. 2.25*)
   a) Draw a sketch of this street scene.
   b) Describe your impressions of this part of Naples. Where else might you see such a townscene?

Fig. 2.25 A street in the 'Casbah' of central Naples, Italy

Dutch townscapes

While there are certainly similarities between the cities of Western Europe, especially as a result of developments since 1945, there is no such thing as a 'typical' Western European city. It is possible, however, to show a typical city or model for a particular country. Fig. 2.26 shows such a model for the Netherlands. You must remember, though, that each town and city in that country is unique.

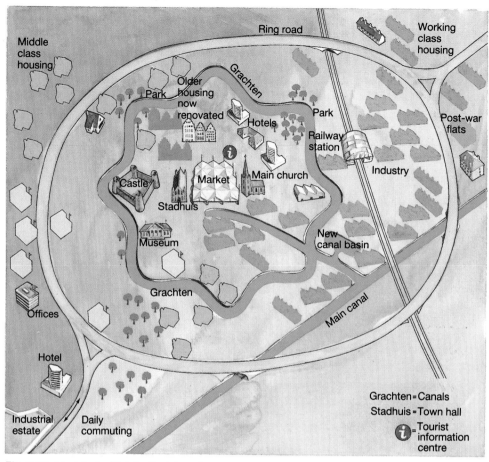

Fig. 2.26 Model of a Dutch city (after G. J. Ashworth)

Assignments

1 Copy the following paragraphs after looking at Fig. 2.26. You should complete the gaps using the words provided and select the correct 'lefts' or 'rights'.

In the model of a Dutch city there is an inner and outer area. These are separated by a canal/railway system, which is sometimes star-shaped. Originally, such canals or _____ were part of the town's defence system which included a _____ and a town wall, both of which may have been removed. The original outer canal may have been filled in and is today occupied by a broad street or a park.

Today the inner area centres on offices/the market, the town hall (or _____) and the main church/station. While the market square is a useful car park for most of the week, on market day shopkeepers set up stalls. This part of the town with its older buildings is popular with _____; there are restaurants and cafes while some older houses have been converted into _____.

The outer city developed mainly from the 19th century onwards with the coming of the railway/motorway. Stations were usually located within/beyond the original core. As a result shops/factories were encouraged to move to sites nearer the railway or the new enlarged canal basin. These sites offered more/less room for expansion. In the same way many offices have moved to the _____ beyond the original core and now occupy purpose-built accommodation.

From the 19th century onwards the _____ classes were able to afford houses in the new suburbs away from the _____ populated core. In the period after the Second World War tall _____ were built by the local authority to re-house mainly _____ class people.

With a rise in living standards many Dutch people have moved to lower density single residence houses. These are either in the suburbs or in _____ villages from which they can _____. Others, however, still prefer a city centre house, possibly in an area of older housing which has been _____.

With the growth in motor transport, _____ roads have been constructed and traffic restrictions imposed on the _____ city. This has further encouraged the movement of offices out to the suburbs, factories (to new industrial _____), and even of modern hotels. Easy access to the excellent Dutch road _____ is an important locational factor.

Missing words: network, inner, dormitory, flats, middle, suburbs, estates, commute, working, tourists, hotels, stadhuis, grachten, castle, ring, renovated, densely.

2 (Fig. 2.26) Draw a cross section through the model of a Dutch city to show the main features of land use.

3 (General) How does the model of a Dutch city compare with British or American models of urban land-use?

Chapter 3 Physical landscapes and people

The satellite image (Fig. 1.1) shows Europe as a triangular-shaped peninsula tapering westwards to the Atlantic from Asia. In terms of continental size (assuming it is a continent) Europe may be small, but it has a very varied physical landscape. Mountains, plateaus, plains and valleys of varied geological age exist relatively close together, and are rarely far from the sea. For Europe is a land of peninsulas and islands, sometimes described as a 'peninsula built up of peninsulas'.

What is meant by the physical landscape? One answer is that it is a group of land forms. It could consist of a series of volcanoes rising above a broad coastal plain fringed by sand dunes, or a series of steep sided valleys eroded by glaciers. But is that a full enough answer for the twentieth century? After the presence of humans over several million years we should remember that people, as well as nature, can alter the physical landscape, whether deliberately or accidentally. In this chapter therefore, account is taken of the role of people in changing the landscape as well as the effect that landscape has on people in Europe.

Landform processes

Fig. 3.1 summarises the two main sets of processes which create landforms.

Internal processes

These operate within the earth's crust and include volcanic eruptions and large-scale earth movements which can result in fold mountains or rift valleys. Today we know that such processes are the result of plate tectonics. At present the landforms of Mediterranean Europe (such as Etna) or Iceland, are being shaped by active plate movement, but in the past all areas have been shaped by such activity.

External processes

Just as soon as internal forces build up the land the processes of weathering, erosion and transportation wear it down by removing outputs of sediments.

Fig. 3.1 The main landform-creating processes

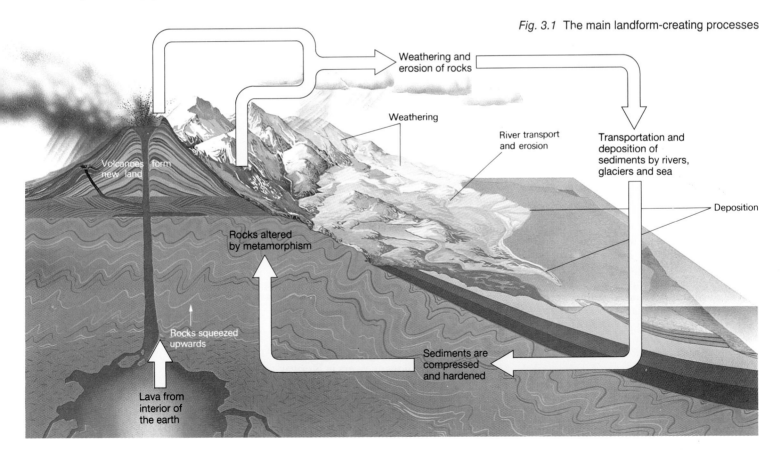

Weathering and erosion of rocks

Weathering

River transport and erosion

Transportation and deposition of sediments by rivers, glaciers and sea

Deposition

Volcanoes form new land

Rocks altered by metamorphism

Rocks squeezed upwards

Sediments are compressed and hardened

Lava from interior of the earth

Structure zones of Western Europe

As a result of these internal and external forces operating over millions of years the varied physical landscapes of Western Europe have developed. In general there are five major structure zones in Western Europe.

The Baltic Shield

Geologists believe that some rocks of granite or gneiss are up to 3000 million years old, and were formed when there was little oxygen on the earth.

Such rocks form part of the Baltic Shield (see Fig. 3.2). Much of it lies under large areas of North, East and Central Europe but it appears at the surface in Finland and much of Sweden. Millions of years ago the area was high, but it has been intensely eroded so that today it forms, for the most part, a low undulating surface mainly below 180 metres in height.

An important feature of the shield landscape is the presence of lakes, thousands of which are particularly scattered over Central Finland. They are the result of ice sheets which blanketed the shield, eroding hollows, excavating and transporting rock debris and exposing fresh rock surfaces, as this extract suggests.

> Later in my travels, I was to see just how dramatically the ice had sculpted the land. In that bleak region, where a scanty soil cover barely disguises the solid bedrock, glacial scars show up livid on hills, and exposed rock surfaces are fluted and grooved with parallel scratches that resemble the paw marks of a bear.
>
> (from *Lapland*, by W. Marsden)

For the past 600 million years this area has been geologically stable. During this time while major earth forces were affecting other parts of Europe, the Baltic Shield has

Fig. 3.2 A Baltic shield landscape in Finland

acted as a buffer zone during major mountain building eras.

The Caledonian mountains

One such mountain-building period, which occurred some 400 to 500 million years ago, is known as the Caledonian. Ancient North America and Ancient Europe were then much closer together (see Fig. 3.3). So close were they that they collided. Sediments lying in the sea between the continents were pushed up into mountains, with the Baltic Shield taking the strain.

The resulting Caledonian mountain range extended in a characteristic northeast to south-west trend. This can be seen in the present mountains of Scandinavia and north and west Britain. Once they were as high as 5000 metres but today after extensive erosion they reach only 2500 metres.

The Scandinavian mountains have been tilted so that the western edge is highest. As a result, westward flowing rivers in Norway are short compared to the long easterly rivers of Sweden which drain to the Baltic Sea. Often the course of the Norwegian rivers follows west-trending faults which

have guided valley development. Such valleys were deepened by glacial erosion and eventually formed the distinctive fjord coast of west Norway (see page 38).

Fig. 3.3 Areas of mountain-building 500–300 million years ago

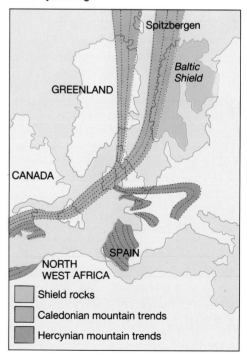

- Shield rocks
- Caledonian mountain trends
- Hercynian mountain trends

The North European Plain

Lying between the mountains and uplands to the north and south is the North European Plain (see Fig. 3.8). This plain stretches eastwards from the North Sea, extends northwards to include Denmark and eventually broadens into the great plains of the USSR. Essentially it is a sedimentary lowland, but it is anything but featureless, rising in places up to 180 metres. Various deposits, from ice, wind, sea and river, give landscapes ranging from flat to hummocky. Hills with steep edges (escarpments) occur in the Paris Basin, where limestone and chalk rocks have been gently folded up (see page 78).

Although there are certain infertile areas this plain has long invited and attracted settlement. As well as extensive areas of rich cultivated land, there is easy access to the sea across the plain and to the mountains to the south. This encouraged trade and the growth of towns and cities. In addition, on the southern margins of the plain coal and minerals encouraged the development of industry.

The Hercynian uplands

South of the North European Plain lies a series of rounded plateau areas which reach a maximum of 1800 metres. These are the eroded remnants of the Hercynian mountains, formed before the separation of North America and Europe. Fig. 3.3 shows the west-east trend of the mountains, especially in Brittany and the Meseta. Later earth movements resulted in marked faults and fractures, breaking up the mountain system into a series of distinctive blocks.

The Rhine rift valley and the impressive steep-sided Rhine gorge (see pages 47 and 48) are two resulting landscape features. Another consequence of the faulting was igneous activity. In Brittany granite was intruded, later to be exposed at the plateau surface; in the Eifel volcanic activity continued as late as prehistoric times. Fig. 3.5 shows some of the features of the Eifel.

Fig. 3.4 Remains of a volcanic cone in the Eifel region with a Maare lake filling the old crater

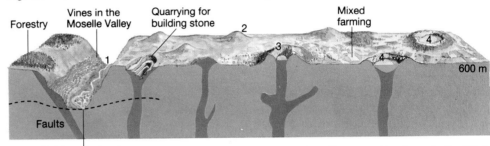

Fig. 3.5 Landforms and land-use in the Eifel

Over 50 volcanic ash cones rise above the plateau which also has the round maare – lakes – filling the craters of gas explosions.

The Alpine fold mountains

Fig. 3.8 shows that the Alpine fold mountain system lies south of the Hercynian Uplands and includes such ranges as the Pyrenees, the Dinaric Alps, the Apennines as well as the Swiss Alps. The Alpine mountains are the uplifted sediments of a former sea bed, pushed up by the African plate against the Hercynian blocks.

During this mountain building period it was rather like a geological storm. At the centre, like enormous waves curving over, rock layers were highly folded and contorted (forming recumbent folds and nappes). Away from the centre the geological waves were gentler. Such gentle waves formed the Jura mountains with its anticlines and synclines (see Fig. 3.6).

Fig. 3.6 Simplified structure section from the Jura mountains to the Swiss Alps

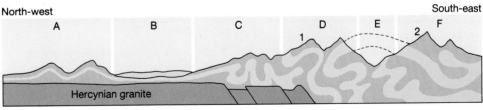

A Jura mountains
B Swiss plateau
C Pre Alps
D High limestone Alps, e.g. Bernese Oberland
E Rhône-Rhine trench
F Pennine Alps
1 Jungfrau
2 Matterhorn

Today the scenery is made up of jagged, snow-capped peaks, separated by narrow U-shaped valleys, thanks to the effects of ice action. Fig. 3.6 shows a simplified subdivision of the Swiss Alps into several ranges. Lying between the limestone peaks of the Bernese Oberland and the crystalline mountains of the Pennine Alps lies the major trench followed by the Rhine and Rhone valleys. Fig. 3.7 shows the importance of the Swiss plateau where there is dense settlement and intensive cultivation and how such valleys help communications.

Geologically speaking, the Alps are young, only 30 million years old. Similar tectonic forces are responsible today for the earthquakes and volcanic eruptions which affect, for example, the south of Italy (see page 28) and Greece. Another area of tectonic instability is Iceland. Located on the mid-Atlantic ridge, eruptions such as Surtsey and Heimaey are just two in a long history of volcanic action as this extract suggests.

'God has not yet finished making Iceland. In the last 500 years one third of all the lava extruded from the guts of the earth to the face of the planet has surfaced in Iceland and, of 200 known volcanoes, thirty are still very much alive. Iceland suffers from a bad case of geological acne.'
(from *Running Blind*, by Desmond Bagley)

Assignments

1 (*Fig. 1.1 and atlas*) Trace an outline sketch map based on the photograph. Name the following: Mediterranean Sea; Baltic Sea; North Atlantic Ocean; Adriatic Sea; Gulf of Bothnia and Bay of Biscay. Name as many peninsulas as you can.

2 (*Account*) Giving examples, explain the statement 'Europe is a peninsula built up of peninsulas'.

3 (*Fig. 3.1 and account*) Copy the diagram. Using two colours shade the arrows to distinguish (i) Internal processes, from (ii) External processes.

4 (*Revision/research*) Write brief notes to

Fig. 3.7 The Rhône emerging from the Alps. The city of Geneva is in the foreground with Lake Geneva on the left

explain the following terms: weathering; erosion; metamorphic; igneous and sedimentary.

5 (*Fig. 3.2, account and atlas*)
   a) In which area of shield rock, other than Finland, might the photo have been taken?
   b) Suggest three differences between the Baltic Shield and the Caledonian Mountains.
   c) Draw an annotated sketch of the physical landscape in the photograph.

6 (*Fig. 3.8, atlas and account*)
   a) Describe the location and extent of the North European Plain.
   b) What are the main differences between the North European Plain and the Baltic Shield?
   c) Suggest some similarities between the North European Plain and the Baltic Shield.

7 (*Figs. 3.4, 3.5, 3.8/atlas and account*)
   a) Name two Hercynian uplands in France, one in Belgium and three in West Germany.
   b) What evidence of past volcanic activity is shown in the photograph of the Eifel?
   c) Copy Fig. 3.5 and complete the key to the physical features 1–4. Select from:

(1) Lake filled craters formed by gas explosions; (ii) Steep sided valley of River Moselle; (iii) Volcanic ash cone; (iv) Volcanic cone with crater.
   d) Briefly describe and explain the various land uses.

8 (*Revision/research*) Write brief notes/draw diagrams to explain: anticline; syncline; recumbent fold; nappe and fault.

9 (*Figs. 3.4, 3.6, 3.8/atlas and account*)
   a) Suggest differences between the Caledonian fold mountains and the Alpine fold mountains.
   b) Copy Fig. 3.6. Using an atlas, add on heights.
   c) What are the physical differences between the Swiss Alps north and south of the Rhine – Rhone trench?

10 (*Fig. 3.8 and atlas*) Make a copy of the map.
   a) Name the mountains, uplands and volcanoes numbered 1 to 15.
   b) Mark on the names of the main rivers and the African, Eurasian and North American plates.
   c) Draw structure/relief sections with labels of uplands, lowlands, sea areas etc. (i) west-east from Norway to Finland; (ii) north-south through Germany to the Alps.

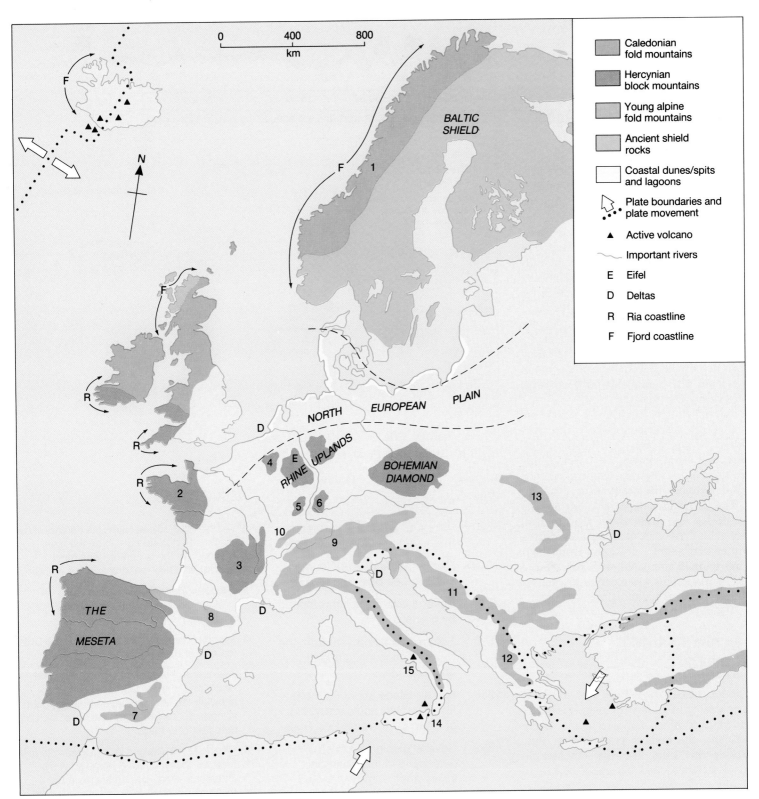

Fig. 3.8 Aspects of the structure, relief and drainage of Europe

Glaciated landscapes: upland areas

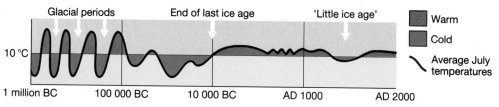

Fig. 3.9 Temperature changes and ice ages in the past million years

Ice Ages and 'Little Ice Ages' in Europe

Over the past two million years there have been 16 Ice Ages. Fig. 3.9 shows some of these and shows that the last Ice Age finished about 10 000 years ago.

Much of Europe was blanketed by ice during the last (Pleistocene) Ice Age. The pre-glacial landscape was dramatically changed by the ice and its meltwater streams. Most of the ice spread from the mountain areas shown on Fig. 3.10.

As the climate became warmer the ice retreated. This does not mean that the ice sheets moved backwards! Rather the front areas of ice melted. In certain of the mountain areas active remnants of the Ice Age survive as valley glaciers.

Such a period of ice retreat which we are at present experiencing is called an *interglacial*. Given the high rainfall of the mountains of Europe, however, it would only require a drop in average temperatures of a few degrees before glaciers again advanced.

This certainly happened during the 'Little Ice Age' from about 1550 to 1850 (see table). Average temperatures during winter were about 1.3°C lower from about 1560 to 1600 compared with the 1880 to 1930 period. This was a period marked by famines, avalanches and glacial advances.

The Mer de Glace as a hazard

The Mer de Glace (see Figs. 3.11 and 3.15) is now some 14 kilometres long. It is one of the glaciers which flows from Mt. Blanc (4807m), the highest peak in the Alps. During the 'Little Ice Age' the Mer de Glace advanced and became a hazard to nearby settlements, as shown on the following table.

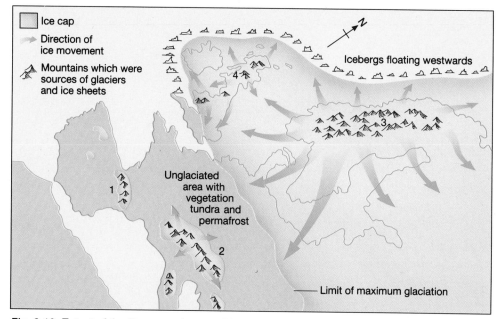

Fig. 3.10 Extent of the European ice cap 20 000 years ago

Advances of the Mer de Glace

Date	Event
1600	Village of Les Bois damaged by the advance of Mer de Glace.
1640's	Glacier advanced and came close to Les Bois and Les Tines.
1714	Several villages still threatened by glaciers.
1835	Seracs (ice pinnacles) from the Mer de Glace threatened to fall on Les Bois.
1850	Mer de Glace about 50 metres from Les Bois and causing blocks of ice to fall towards Les Tines.
1852	Several glaciers form an avalanche in the Chamonix valley after warm winds and heavy rains.

Assignments

1 (*Atlas/Fig. 3.10*) **a)** Name the centres of ice dispersion numbered 1–4 on the map. **b)** Which of these centres was most important? Give reasons for your answer.

2 (*Account/general*) What factors do you think would limit the maximum extent of glaciation?

3 (*Account/table*) What is meant by the Little Ice Age and when did it occur?

4 (*Hazard table/Fig. 3.11*) Pick out the Mer de Glace on the map. Draw a sketch map showing the Mer de Glace threatening the villages of Les Bois and Les Tines. Add on dates on your map.

5 (*Fig. 3.11*) **a)** Make a list of as many tourist facilities that you can distinguish in the Chamonix area. **b)** Explain the route followed by the road approaching the Mt. Blanc tunnel.

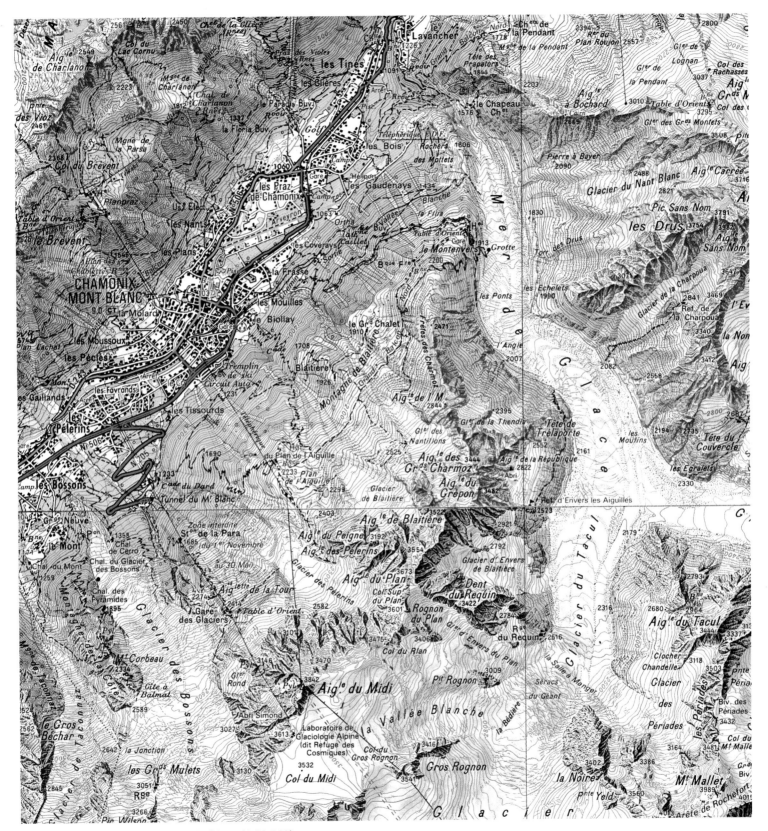

Fig. 3.11 Chamonix and the Mer de Glace (1:50 000)

Cirques and glacier ice

How does a valley glacier actually start? This can be seen in the formation of *cirques* (also called *corries* or *cwms*) which are large bowl-shaped hollows in mountains. It is in such hollows that glacial ice slowly builds up in various stages (Fig. 3.12). 1) High altitude allows heavy snow to build up in mountain hollows. 2) Snow at this stage is fluffy (each snow flake has a delicate lace-like pattern). 3) As it piles up, the air is squeezed out of the snow crystals, and after several years granules of crystallised snow called *névé* or *firn* develop. 4) Over the years, with more weight from fresh snowfalls, compressed glacial ice forms. 5) Eventually the ice moves downslope as a valley glacier and crevasses form on its surface. 6) At the back of the glacier a deep crevasse called a *bergschrund* develops. 7) Frost-shattered rock falls from the cirque backwall to be carried away by the ice. 8) Where the ice is thickest it erodes away the base of the cirque – now often occupied by a deep lake. 9) The ice in the cirque has a rotational movement. As a result erosion at the edge of the corrie is not so powerful so 10) a rock lip forms at the cirque entrance.

When two cirques form back to back the sharp edge between them is called an *arête*. If three or more cirques form back to back the result is a *pyramid peak*. The best example of such a peak is the Matterhorn (see Fig. 3.14).

Assignments

1 Read the account about cirques and glacier ice. Copy Fig 3.12, the model diagram. Write the numbers 1 to 10 in the appropriate place on the diagram. Write out a summary key.

2 (*Fig. 3.13*) This diagram shows the stages in arête/pyramid peak development. Copy the diagrams and show the following either by adding notes and/or a key: arête; pyramid peak; small cirque; direction of glacier; medium cirque; large cirque.

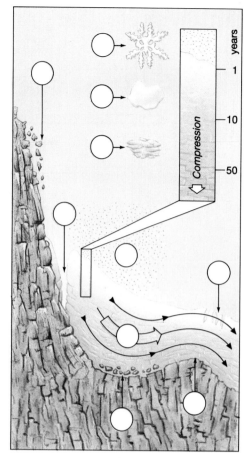

Fig. 3.12 Formation of glacier ice and a cirque

Fig. 3.13 Stages in arête and pyramid peak formation

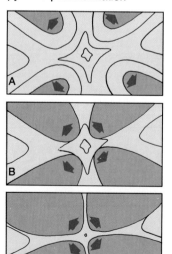

Alpine glaciers

Fig. 3.15 shows the Mer de Glace glacier, already discussed as a hazard. Today, along with its Alpine neighbours, it is just a small remnant of its Pleistocene ancestor. But by studying such glaciers it is possible to appreciate just how they profoundly changed the preglacial landscape.

Glacial movement On average Alpine glaciers move about 30 centimetres a day. But this has obviously varied from year to year, season to season, between different glaciers and even within the same glacier. Various ideas have been put forward to explain just how a huge mass of ice really moves. Depending on the temperature of the ice, movement involves one or more of the following: 1) sometimes the ice behaves like a very thick toothpaste that moulds its shape as it moves downhill. 2) Sometimes large sections of the ice slide past each other along fault lines in the ice. 3) Sometimes a layer of meltwater forms upstream from an obstacle. This allows the glacier to slip downwards over the obstacle and then refreeze.

Fig. 3.14 The Matterhorn, a classic pyramid peak

Fig. 3.15 The Mer de Glace

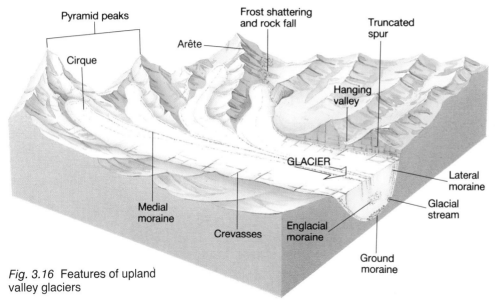

Pyramid peaks

Cirque

Arête

Frost shattering
and rock fall

Truncated
spur

Hanging
valley

GLACIER

Medial
moraine

Crevasses

Englacial
moraine

Lateral
moraine

Glacial
stream

Ground
moraine

Fig. 3.16 Features of upland valley glaciers

Glacial erosion How is it that glacier ice, which is softer than rock, appears to be such a powerful agent of erosion? 1) Glaciers are like a vast conveyor belt. From the valley sides rockfalls and frost shattering can cause a mass of rock fragments to land on the glacier surface. 2) The glacier ice may erode by plucking. If the underlying rock is well jointed pieces of the rock can be incorporated into the ice when meltwater at the base of the glacier freezes on to the rock. 3) By the process of abrasion pieces of rock embedded in the ice can grind away at the solid bedrock of the valley. As a result of this action the rock beneath the glacier may have scratches or striations which vary in size from a few millimetres to a metre deep and up to 100 metres long.

Glacial landforms As a result of glacial erosional processes, distinctive landforms are produced. Vast amounts of material are excavated and transported by ice in the form of *moraine*. Various types of moraine are shown on Fig. 3.16. One type of moraine not shown is *terminal moraine* – a heap of unsorted rocks of all sizes, clays and

sands deposited at the snout, i.e. the lowest part of the glacier.

Among the erosional landforms cirques, arêtes and pyramid peaks have been noted. *Glacial troughs* are the product of erosion as the glacier widens and deepens the pre-glacial valley (by up to 1000 metres in some cases). Such a trough is typically 'U' shaped in cross-section.

Twists and turns of pre-glacial valleys may be straightened. The lower end of pre-glacial spurs may be 'quarried' away to leave *truncated spurs*. Finally, tributary glacial valleys are often left as *hanging valleys* when the main thicker glacier erodes its valley more deeply.

A word of caution 1) Examples exist in the Swiss Alps of V-shaped valleys. Sometimes these contain morainic deposits which proves that ice movement occurred. 2) Powerful meltwater erosion may be very important. In Fig. 3.16 there is a sub-glacial stream. Such streams flowing under pressure at high velocities can erode deep gorges. 3) Material close to the glacier base may, over a long period, have been transferred downwards. Originally it may have landed on the ice as a result of frost shattering.

Examples such as these suggest that not all glaciers act as powerful agents of erosion, nor do they do so at all times.

Assignments

1 (*Account*) Describe the main processes by which ice is believed to erode. Why is frost shattering an important part of the plucking process.

2 (*Fig. 3.15*) Imagine investigators place stakes to measure the flow of the Mer de Glace. Line X–X shows the initial position; the Y–Y after 2 years. Explain the different positions.

3 (*Account and Figs. 3.15, 3.16*) Draw a sketch of Fig. 3.15. Match the following to the numbers: crevasses; cirque; pyramid peak; arête; scree slope; truncated spur; lateral moraine.

Landscapes of the North European Plain

Glacial erosion and deposition occur in both upland and lowland areas. Some of the most extensive features of glacial deposition can be seen in the complicated landscapes of the North European Plain (Figs. 3.18 and 3.20).

The landscapes are complicated because a series of advances and retreats of ice took place from upland Scandinavia. Fig. 3.17 shows their maximum extent, when the ice reached the foothills of Central Germany and covered the whole of the plain. It also shows the extent of the last advance which ran north-south through Jutland. Various landscapes have resulted and have been altered by people over a long period of time.

Landscapes of glacial deposition

These can be seen in the hummocky landscape of east Jutland, the islands of Fyne

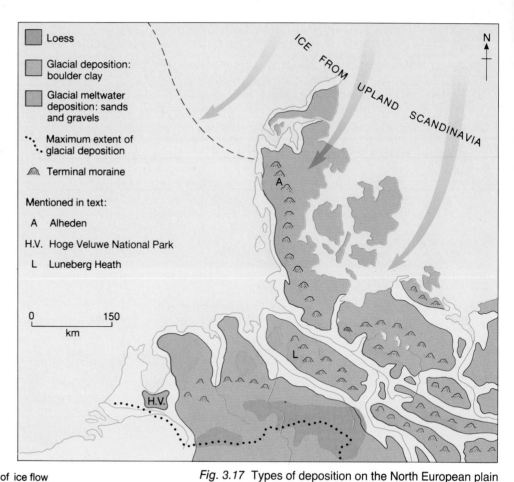

Fig. 3.17 Types of deposition on the North European plain

Fig. 3.18 Formation of a glaciated lowland

Fig. 3.19 The Lüneburg Heath

and Zealand and the plain of Northern Germany (Fig. 3.19). They are the result of melting ice dumping rock waste or till. Such material is unsorted and consists of both large and small rocks, as well as fine clay particles. Most of this material has been spread out from the base of the ice. Sometimes the till has been shaped and moulded by the moving ice into streamlined mounds called *drumlins*. Usually they are clustered together in *swarms*. The highest features in Denmark are the terminal moraines rising to over 150 metres. This material built up at the ends of glaciers and marked a stand-still period in ice movement. The Jutland moraine is quite distinctive; in northern Germany many such moraines have been reduced by later erosion.

Areas of glacial deposition have provided a soil which for the most part is fertile. Farming yields and settlement density are higher in these areas compared to regions of fluvio-glacial origin.

Landscapes of fluvio-glacial deposition

As ice decayed enormous volumes of meltwater were produced, laden with sand and gravel. The meltwater often formed streams inside the ice and created long ridges or *eskers*; *kames*, on the other hand, were formed by material which was poured into crevasses or into ice front deltas (see

Fig. 3.18). Much material was spread far from the ice front by meltwater streams to form extensive plains of sand and gravel. The surface material of Jutland, west of the terminal moraine, was formed this way.

These sand and gravel spreads eventually developed a heath type of vegetation which was mainly used for sheep pasture. Gradually, much of it has been won for forestry and farming, often involving 'pioneer' settlers (see Fig. 3.20). Remaining stretches of heath are often preserved as nature reserves, for example, the Lüneburg Heath (see Fig. 3.19) and national parks, such as the Hoge Veluwe in the Netherlands (see page 132).

Landscapes of wind deposition

This is the most fertile deposit of all and blankets large areas to a depth of twenty metres. These *loess* deposits result from strong winds blowing at the end of the Ice Age and picking up the finest particles from the glacial and fluvio-glacial deposits, depositing them in the foothill zone. From the earliest farmers onwards this area has always supported a greater population density compared with the surrounding areas.

Urstromtäler

Rivers such as the Ems, Elbe and Weser follow, for part of their course, broad, flat-bottomed, marshy valleys called Urstromtäler. These were carved out by meltwater flowing near the ice margin towards the North Sea.

Assignments

1 (*Fig. 3.18/account*) Match the numbers 1 to 6 on the diagram with the following: moraine dammed lake; braided river; sub-glacial stream; surface glacial stream depositing gravel fan; disappearing stream; meltwater river.

2 What is a terminal moraine? Describe and explain the location of the Jutland moraine.

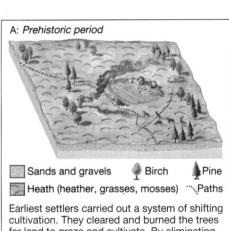

A: *Prehistoric period*

Sands and gravels   Birch   Pine
Heath (heather, grasses, mosses)   ⋯Paths

Earliest settlers carried out a system of shifting cultivation. They cleared and burned the trees for land to graze and cultivate. By eliminating trees heathland came to dominate.

B: *1800 German pioneer farmers*

Village design was German 'street' village

59 German families migrated in 1763

The heathland was seen as an unproductive area used for sheep rearing and turf for roofing. The Danish King invited German war refugees to settle as pioneer farmers. They cleared the heath in autumn; deep ploughed the land, adding lime and manure; and sowed the seed (rye, oats and buckwheat in spring).

C: *Present day*

Improved soil   ⁺⁺⁺⁺Railway
Coniferous plantation

Today little remains of the heath. Farms are now dispersed with larger rectangular fields. Dairying and arable crops (for animal feed) dominate with easy access to markets both national and international.

Fig. 3.20 Changing heathland landscapes in the Alheden district, Denmark

Volcanic landscapes

Mount Etna: recent eruptions

Headlines like this were carried by newspapers in May 1983. Millions of tonnes of lava were flowing from Mount Etna, Europe's largest volcano. A new vent had appeared on 28 March. The lava tongues were over six kilometres long and had engulfed one hotel, three restaurants, twenty five houses and valuable orange groves on the southern slope of Etna.

To prevent further damage to villages lower down an attempt was made to divert the lava flow (see Fig. 3.23). It was planned to excavate a diversion canal. Using mechanical shovels, bulldozers and lorries, over a hundred men worked furiously for a fortnight amidst swirling sulphur clouds. When the explosions broke the lava wall on 15 May a new tongue of lava flowed into the channel. However, because the explosion was not as powerful as planned, only about 20 per cent of the lava was diverted.

Similar experiments will no doubt occur in the future. Etna, rising to over 3322 metres, is one of the most active volcanoes in the world. This is partly explained by its location at the junction between the Eurasian and African plates (see Fig. 3.8). Locally, the Etna area is especially unstable with the volcano straddling the intersection of three major fault zones. (see Fig. 3.21).

Geologically speaking, it is remarkably young and most of it has been built up in the past 100 000 years. The 1983 eruption was the fifth since 1970. It was only one in a long history of eruptions which have built up this composite cone volcano with its alternate layers of ash and lava.

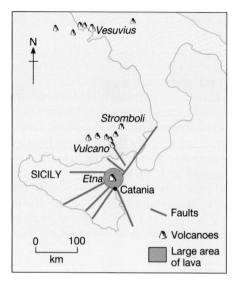

Fig. 3.21 The main volcanoes of Southern Italy

Fig. 3.22 Lava flowing down a newly-dug channel

Fig. 3.23 Eruption of Mount Etna, Italy, 1983

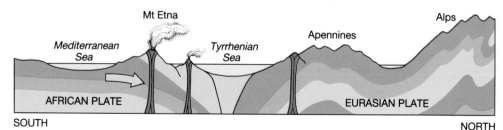

Fig. 3.24 Mount Etna in relation to plate boundaries

28

Evil Etna?

In spite of the damage inflicted by eruptions, over a million people live on the lower slopes of Etna. This gives a very high population density of up to 800 per square kilometre. Various factors explain this.

a Compared with the limestones and crystaline rocks found elsewhere on Sicily, the volcanic rock (once it has weathered) is relatively fertile.

b Springs emerging from the volcanic bedrock have been a factor in the growth of large villages. Nowadays these are expanding as dormitory settlements for the city of Catania.

c As a result of such soil and water resources, a 'regione cultivata' has developed, especially on the south and east flanks of Etna, up to levels as high as 1000 metres high (see Fig. 3.26). Vines, olives, almonds, orange and lemon groves, together with market gardens, create an intensively cultivated landscape. Farms are usually very small, seldom larger than 2 hectares.

The Biagi farm (see Fig. 3.25) is fairly large by local standards. For Signor Biagi there are advantages and disadvantages with the size, layout and environmental setting of his farm. Trees and crops may be withered by the hot blasting effect of the Sirocco blowing from the Sahara in winter and spring.

Another environmental hazard could, of course, be the devastating impact of a lava flow. People like the Biagis live with the potential anger of Etna all their lives. How do they cope with this threat? (Fig. 3.23). One way is to eliminate any sense of uncertainty. 'It's in the hands of God' is a typical attitude. Another way is to eliminate the hazard completely. People tend to adopt an attitude of 'It happens to other people, not us'. In other words, they create a psychological barrier and they shelter behind it.

Tourists are also attracted to Etna. Its snow-covered peak is popular with skiers. New roads, chairlifts and chalets have been built (and some have been destroyed) on

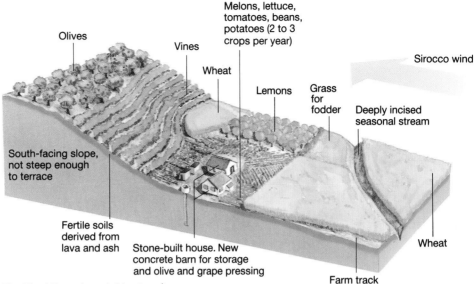

The Biagi Farm (area 1.4 hectares)

Once part of a large estate which has been sub-divided, this farm supports a family of four, although two other children have left home to find work (in a local tourist hotel and a sulphur mine). Mainly a subsistence farm, the only cash crop is lemons and, occasionally, some surplus wine and olive oil.

The fields are cultivated by mule-drawn plough and hoe and the wheat is harvested by scythe.

The livestock consists of one mule and three sheep (grazed in a lemon grove to keep down grass) as well as some chickens.

Fig. 3.25 The Biagi Farm on the southern slopes of Mount Etna

Fig. 3.26 The proposed area of the Etna National Park

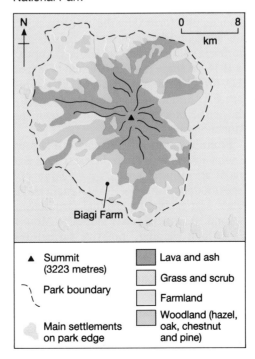

- ▲ Summit (3223 metres)
- Park boundary
- Main settlements on park edge
- Lava and ash
- Grass and scrub
- Farmland
- Woodland (hazel, oak, chestnut and pine)

this mountain. Such economic developments, along with the clearance of woodland (see Fig. 3.26), have created problems for the Italian conservation association. They have proposed that Etna be declared a National Park.

Fig. 3.27 Lava-flow overwhelming a vineyard

29

Fig. 3.28 Mount Vesuvius, Italy

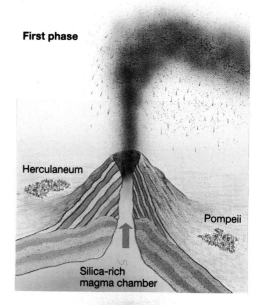

First phase

Herculaneum

Pompeii

Silica-rich
magma chamber

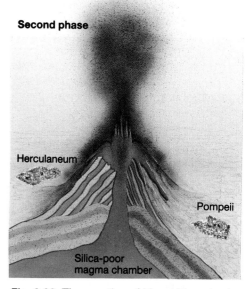

Second phase

Herculaneum

Pompeii

Silica-poor
magma chamber

Fig. 3.29 The eruption of Mount Vesuvius in AD 79

Fig. 3.30 A victim from Pompeii

Vesuvius AD 79: a past eruption

The oldest record of an eruption of Vesuvius described the popular Roman resorts of Pompeii and Herculaneum on the afternoon of 24 August AD 79. There were two phases in the eruption.

a (See Fig. 3.29). For the first 11 hours Vesuvius hurled a vast column of pumice some 20 kilometres into the atmosphere. This type of eruption is known as the 'Plinian' type. Pliny the Younger was a Roman historian who described the event. The town of Pompeii was covered by pumice and ash up to a depth of 2.7 metres. Within four hours roofs were collapsing under the enormous weight, killing people in the houses below.

b Just before midnight, the pumice column collapsed and the first of six fiery avalanches of gases, pumice and rocks flowed down the mountainside (see Fig. 3.29). Such glowing avalanches are called *nuées ardentes* (fiery clouds) and they descended on Herculaneum and Pompeii. With temperatures ranging from 100°C to 400°C, these dense ash clouds overwhelmed the terrified residents. Many at Pompeii had been trapped in the houses by the earlier pumice fall and were suffocated by the glowing avalanche.

Today the extensive excavations at Pompeii, with plaster casts of the victims taken from moulds formed by the ash (Fig. 3.30) are a major tourist attraction. So is the dormant volcano itself, which last erupted in 1944. Its shape is quite different to that of AD 79. The summit rises to 1281 metres (see Fig. 3.31), and is partly encircled by the crescent-shaped caldera known as Monte Somma.

From its summit the extensive Plain of Campania can be seen to the east. This is a major agricultural lowland with large villages around the base of the mountain and a dense scattering of individual farmhouses beyond. As on the lower slopes of Mount Etna, high yielding, intensive agriculture has been encouraged by the mild Mediterranean winters, a long growing season and the volcanic soil. To ensure maximum use of space, fruit trees (apricots, cherries and apples), vegetables and vines are usually grown in a two or three tier system. Italians describe this as *coltura promiscua*.

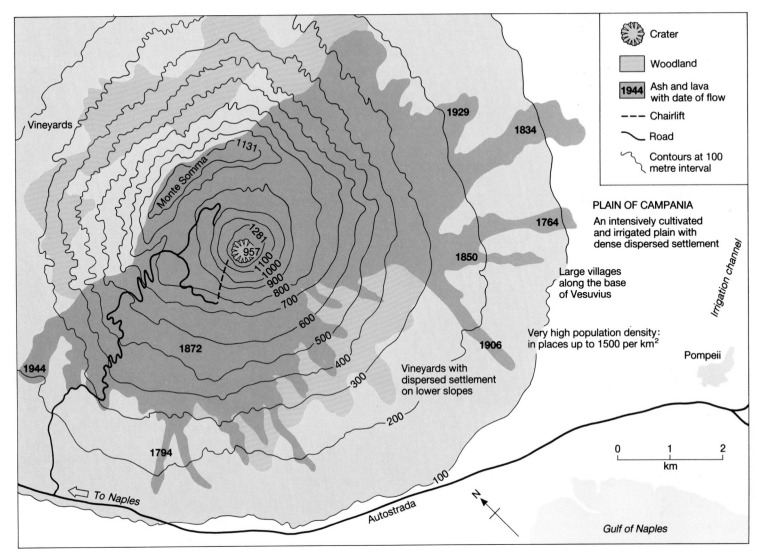

Fig. 3.31 Lava flows and land-use on Mount Vesuvius

Legend (map):
- Crater
- Woodland
- 1944 Ash and lava with date of flow
- --- Chairlift
- Road
- Contours at 100 metre interval

PLAIN OF CAMPANIA
An intensively cultivated and irrigated plain with dense dispersed settlement

Large villages along the base of Vesuvius

Very high population density: in places up to 1500 per km²

Vineyards with dispersed settlement on lower slopes

Vineyards

Monte Somma

To Naples

Autostrada

Gulf of Naples

Pompeii

Irrigation channel

Assignments

1 (*Atlas/account*) Describe the location of Etna and explain why it is a particularly active volcano.

2 (*Account/Fig. 3.23*) Why was it necessary to divert the lava flow, how was it attempted, and how successful was the attempt?

3 (*Account*) Explain as fully as possible why there is such a high population density on lower Mount Etna.

4 (*Account*) What arguments would you put forward to support the establishment of a Mt. Etna National Park? What sort of opposition would you expect?

5 (*Account/research*) Imagine that you had been present at the eruption of Vesuvius in AD 79. Write a newspaper account, with headlines and sketches, of the 24 hour period.

6 (*Fig. 3.31, and account*) Draw an annotated cross-section from the Monte Somma caldera through the summit south eastwards. Add notes on physical features, vegetation, land use and settlement. Use appropriate symbols.

7 (*Account*) In what ways do people adjust to the hazards of living on the lower slopes of Etna?

8 (*Account*) The diagram below shows a concentric model of land use on a volcano in the Mediterranean area. How far does this model represent actual land use on volcanoes such as Mount Etna and Vesuvius?

A Volcanic ash and lava
B Forest zone
C Cultivated area – vines, fruits, vegetables etc.

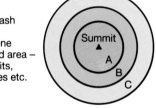

31

Fig. 3.32 Part of the Cévennes National Park (1:100 000)

32

The Cévennes National Park

Fig. 3.32 is a map showing part of the Cévennes National Park. This is located in the south of the Massif Central part of the Hercynian zone (see page 19). Averaging 1000 metres in height, the Massif Central is a highly faulted series of plateaux which dip towards the north and west. As a result of its complicated geological history it has a rich variety of landforms. (Fig. 3.33).

a The 'puy' landscapes are the result of past volcanic activity encouraged by structural upheavals.
b Extensive granite uplands form, for example, the high, steep south-east facing scarp face of the Cévennes (Fig. 3.36) with its highest peak Mt. Lozère.
c Limestone country called Les Causses is found in the south-east. It has a distinctive landscape of cliffs, depressions, caves and steep sided gorges such as that of the River Tarn (Fig. 3.34).

Covering an area of 840 square kilometres, the Cévennes National Park is one of six French National Parks set up since 1963. Each of these parks has two main zones.

a An inner zone where wildlife, vegetation and scenery is to be preserved.
b An outer zone where planners try to preserve the landscape as far as possible yet still allow limited development, such as new tourist accommodation.

The inner zone of the Cévennes National Park has only 538 inhabitants. Few farms were established on its stony and waterless limestone uplands. On the other hand, the outer zone is well populated with over 4000 inhabitants. During the summer there are some 60 000 visitors, who take part in a wide range of activities.

Assignments

1 (*Fig. 3.33 and text*) Describe the location of the Cévennes National Park.

Fig. 3.33 Rock types, relief and drainage in the Massif Central

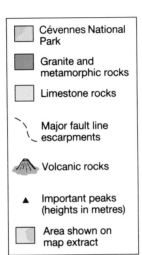

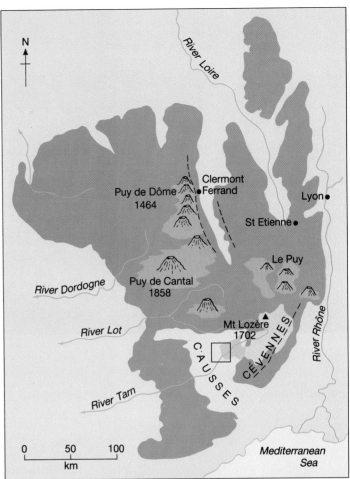

2 (*Fig. 3.33, 3.36 text*) What are the two main types of scenery found in the Cévennes National Park?

3 (*Fig. 3.32*)
  a) Name the two main rivers shown on the map.
  b) Describe the slope and height of the valleys of these two rivers.
  c) What is the average height of the plateau?
  d) There are many depressions on the plateau surface shown on the map by blue dots? How large are these depressions?
  e) Comment on the amount of surface drainage on the plateau.
  f) Make a list of the different recreations which can be carried out in this area.

4 (*Text*) Draw a model diagram to show the two planning zones typical of a French National Park.

Fig. 3.34 The gorge of the River Tarn

Fig. 3.35 (*left*) The Aven Armand limestone caves

Fig. 3.36 (*below*) The Cévennes: valley of the Buegas

The map extract of the Causses (Fig. 3.32) shows many features of a Karst landscape, named after a limestone area in Yugoslavia. The limestone of the Causses is a hard permeable rock. It is permeable because it contains many cracks or joints which allow water to pass freely through it. Such limestone is also affected by chemical weathering, caused by rain water which is a mild carbonic acid. This turns the insoluble limestone (mainly calcium carbonate) into a soluble form of calcium bicarbonate which can be removed by water. As a result of such chemical weathering, various distinctive landforms have developed (see Figs. 3.35, 3.36 and 3.37).

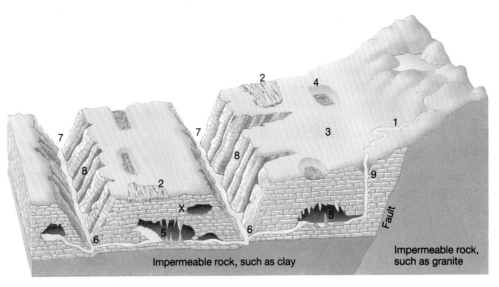

Fig. 3.37 Karst landforms

Karst landforms

1 Surface features In the Causses, where the limestone is exposed, the surface of the rock becomes criss-crossed with grykes. These are limestone joints enlarged by solution. The blocks of limestone between the grykes are called clints. (In the Causses these features are known as *lapies*). A wide area of clints and grykes is called a limestone pavement, while limestone outcropping on the sides of hills and gorges (above the River Tarn for example) forms scars.

2 Closed depressions The plateau surfaces are pitted by numerous hollows, some up to 500 metres in diameter. Such depressions are known locally as *sotches* and are formed by the underground enlargement of the joints by chemical action. The surface material gradually subsides into the underlying limestone cracks. As a result these depressions are often covered by the residue of the limestone solution, a red coloured clay soil called *terra rossa*. This clay is impermeable and can support patches of arable land and pasture which has long been grazed by sheep kept mainly for their milk from which Roquefort cheese is made.

3 Underground features Much of the water in Karst areas flows underground along joints and in cave passages. Seasonal streams may flow over the impermeable covering in the depressions and gradually disappear into the limestone. Sometimes streams or rivers may disappear more dramatically into deep swallow holes. The River Jonte, for example, flows intermittently underground west of Meyrueis until it re-appears at Les Douzes (see Fig. 3.32).

As the water flows underground, often for many kilometres, the original joints are enlarged both by chemical action and the erosion power of the water. Eventually caves – some very large – form underground. The shape of such caves depends on their depth below the water table because water flows at high pressure. At higher levels, above the usual water table, the cave has an oval cross section (X on Fig. 3.37). It only contains water when the rainfall is very heavy and the water table rises.

One of the most famous caves is the Aven Armand (see Fig. 3.35). Lying 195 metres below the surface, it contains dripstone features including Europe's tallest stalagmite, 29 metres high. As water drips from the ceiling, calcium carbonate forms either the chunkier stalagmites on the floor or the thinner stalactites attached to the ceiling. Occasionally they join to form a limestone column. Ridges of calcium carbonate called gours may form as carbonate is precipitated from turbulent underground streams.

4 Resurgences When an underground stream reaches impermeable rock, it re-appears as a spring or resurgence. The River Tarn's flow in the stretch shown on Fig. 3.34 is maintained by a series of resurgences; for example, near Le Detroit. In one recorded eight-hour period the water level of the Tarn rose in its gorge by almost 20 metres.

Assignments

1 Why should a potholer check on the weather forecast before descending into the cave system in the Causses?

2 After reading the text, copy Fig. 3.37. Draw up a full key by matching the numbers on the diagram with the items listed below: limestone pavement with clints and grykes; depressions (sotches) floored with terra rossa soil; stream flowing over impermeable rock; swallow hole; limestone plateau; caves with stalagmites, stalactites, rock pillars deep gorges; resurgence where underground streams reappear.

Coastal contrasts

Western Europe, with its ragged outline, has many different types of coastline. Over a long period of time these have been shaped by erosion and deposition due to wind, waves, currents and tides which all affect the different rocks of the land behind the coast.

Any attempt to classify coastlines is difficult. Three groups can, however, be picked out: submerged coastlines; fjord coastlines; and coastlines of deposition.

Submerged coastlines

Fig. 3.38 and Fig. 3.42 show the St. Brieuc estuary in Brittany. In common with Bantry Bay in South-west Ireland, Milford Haven in South-west Wales, the mouths of rivers such as the Dart and Exe in South-west England, and also the estuaries of North-west Spain, it is an example of a *ria* coastline. The word ria is, in fact, a Spanish term, for example, Ria de Vigo, and describes the lower course of a coastal valley that has been submerged as a result of a rise in sea level. Most of the rias of Western Europe were formed when sea level rose after the Ice Ages. As Fig. 3.39 suggests ria is typically V-shaped in cross-section; it deepens toward the sea; the upper reaches are often silted as the flow of its tributaries is checked. The steeper lower slopes often support woodland which gives way to fields above. Old hard crystalline rocks such as granite usually underlie the rounded hills and low plateaus which separate rias.

Rias have long provided well-sheltered natural harbours. Much of Spain's fishing fleet (the largest in the EC) is based in the north west while many French boats operate from Brittany. The fishing ports of Roscoff and St. Malo support cross-channel ferries; Brest and Ferrol are old established naval bases, while Bantry Bay and Milford Haven are oil tanker terminals.

Ria coastlines are popular with tourists; small fishing ports now function as holiday centres, and the tributary branches of the rias are busy with leisure boats.

A unique tidal power station has been built upstream from the mouth of the Rance in Brittany. Reversible turbines in the barrage take full advantage of (i) the enormous difference between high and low tide levels (ii) the resulting 20 kilometres per hour speed of the tidal flow. The electricity generated is fed into the French national grid.

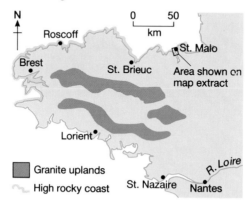

Fig. 3.38 The coastline of Brittany, France

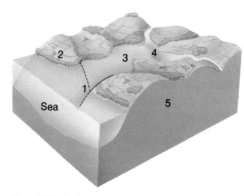

Fig. 3.39 A ria coastline

Fjord coastlines

Fjords are perhaps the most spectacular form of coastal landscape. Long, deep, narrow inlets of the sea, bounded by steep mountains they are found in North-west Iceland, North-west Scotland and, most impressively, in Norway. Sogne Fjord (see Figs. 3.43 and 3.44) is one awe inspiring

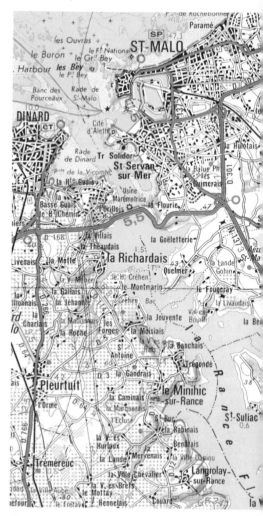

Fig. 3.40 The Rance estuary (1:100 000)

Fig. 3.41 The Rance tidal power station

Fig. 3.42 The St Brieuc estuary, France. Draw an annotated sketch to show: the meandering nature of the river, the steep wooded hillsides at the mouth, a cliff and wave-cut platform, the plateau surface, a small fishing village, strip fields and any port features.

Fig. 3.43 Sogne Fjord, Norway

Fjord descriptions

Below us the mountains of the mainland hefted the sea aside into narrow strips with rippling ice worn shoulders . . . . their snow patches gleaming white in the sunlight. Away to port the sea was littered with skerries; islands of rocks, white and bald from a million years of glacial polishing.

Three quarters of Norway is barren, uninhabitable. Surely this included the land below us? Yet here and there the gleam of a white painted house proved the contrary. Man was here, clinging precariously to the scree skirts, building on barren rock and harvesting the sea. . . .

Directly below us the islands seemed to float in patches of livid green as though rimmed by mineral discoloration. Elsewhere the water had the flat, black look of great depth. Flat, with no corrugation for we were over the Inner Lead, that maritime highway that runs 1600 km almost uninterrupted from North Cape to the Naze, a salt water river protected by islands banks. Boats like toys arrowed the mirror stillness, ploughing the water thoroughfare that has created the sea's toughest sons.

. . . . Sogne Fjord is one of the most awe inspiring waterways in the world . . . . its subsidiary fjords carving far to the north and south; it is said to be as deep as the mountains that engulf it are high.

Balestrand, half way up the fjord, is where the subsidiary fjords begin to radiate out. Up past Balestrand runs the Fjaerlands Fjord, a narrow slash of water the colour of which changes from black to icy green and then to the frozen milk colour of glacier water as it cuts right to the very fringe of Jostedalsbre.

At first the steep mountain slopes are clothed in firs but gradually the tree line descends and round a bend you come face to face with the glacier that made this waterway, its frozen fangs lipping ice green over the black shadowed bulk of the mountain.

(from *Harvest of Journeys* by Hammond Innes)

example (see the Hammond Innes description).

Unlike rias, fjords have been eroded by glaciers so they differ in various ways:

a In cross section, fjords have the classical U-shaped valley. Steep, often vertical, slopes rise to high plateaux known as vidda – bleak treeless areas. Above these there may be peaks which can support small ice caps such as the Jostedalsbre (see extract).

b Overall, fjords are much deeper. Sogne Fjord averages 800 metres for most of its length. (Check its maximum depth on Fig. 3.44).

c Fjords have floors which are deeper in their middle and shallower near the mouth. The shallow entrance floor is called a threshold.

d Sometimes tributary valleys are left 'hanging' above the main fjord channel.

Off-shore, marking the seaward end of the fjord, lie the *skerries*. These are rocky islands which help to provide shelter for the relatively calm stretch of water between them and the fjord entrance. This water, known as the 'inner lead', permits safer passages for all types of vessels from the Viking longships of the past, to the fishing boats of the present.

The deep water of the fjords has been a locational factor encouraging the construction of oil rigs and production platforms, as well as ore-processing plants. But space is limited so that towns such as Sunndalsora, with its alumium smelter, have been built on the deltas at the head of its fjords (see page 111). Such deltas also support fjord-side farms whose fields and fruit trees add to the very high scenic quality of the fjord landscape.

Assignments

1 (*Fig. 3.42*) Describe this coastline and the surrounding land. In what way does the coastline remind you of a river?

2 (*Fig. 3.39*) Copy this block diagram. Match the numbers with these labels: area of old

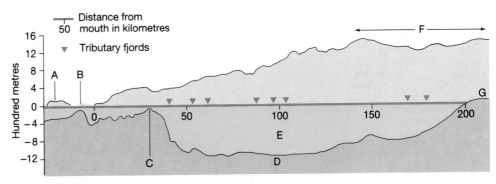

Fig. 3.44 Long profile through Sogne Fjord

hard rock; V-shaped cross section deepening to the sea; steep, often wooded lower slopes; silted tributary; winding drowned river valley.

3 (*Atlas, Figs. 3.38 and 3.40*) Describe the location of the Rance estuary. Draw a sketch map to show: the Rance estuary, Dinard, St. Malo, the main roads, the Tidal Power scheme, off-shore islands, ferry routes (to where?).

4 (*Account and Fig. 3.41*) What are the advantages of the Rance for tidal power?

5 (*Extract*) Pick out phrases which tell you that glacial ice helped to form fjords.

6 (*Atlas and Fig. 3.44*) Give the location, length, height and depth of Sogne Fjord. Copy the long profile and match the letters with these labels: plateau (vidda); threshold; skerryguard; delta at fjord head; very steep sides; inner lead; deeply eroded glacial trough.

7 Fjord/ria contrast: Draw up a table to compare ria/fjord coastlines using the headings: location; cross section; long profiles; formation; use to people.

For discussion/research

1 Why does a fjord have a threshold?
  a) Did the ice meet warmer coastal water and begin to melt at this point?
  b) Is it a morainic deposit marking the limit of ice?
  c) Was it because ice, having eroded a very deep trough in a restricted valley, could not erode so effectively when it spread out at the fjord mouth?

2 Is a fjord a submerged or emerged coastline?
  a) Surely it is a submerged coastline? Sea level rose at the end of the ice age and submerged the glaciated valley, creating a fjord.
  b) But land rose in Scandinavia at a faster rate than the rise in sea level, so surely fjord areas have emerged from the sea? Fjords are not coastal features in origin; they are just glaciated valleys which reach the coast and have been occupied by the sea.

Coastlines of deposition

Fjords and rias are backed by upland areas. Coastlines of deposition are mainly found in extensive lowland areas such as the Great European plain. Several types can be distinguished: *sand dunes*, *deltas* and *spit/lagoon* formation, although there is overlap between these categories.

1 Sand dunes

Since the end of the Ice Age, wind and wave action caused a building up of sand along various coastal stretches to produce a long line of dunes. These are best seen along the west coast of Denmark, the Dutch and Belgian coasts and in south west France. These dunes can rise to over 60 metres high in the Netherlands while they have been blown inland by westerly winds for up to 9 kilometres in the Landes of South-west

Fig. 3.45 (*right*)
Sand dunes near
Bordeaux, France

Fig. 3.46 (*below*) The
Skagen Nature Reserve
on the Danish coast.
A variety of dune
types including barchans
and transverse dunes
is found here

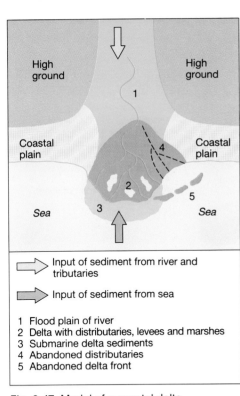

Fig. 3.47 Model of a coastal delta

Key:
- ⬇ Input of sediment from river and tributaries
- ⬆ Input of sediment from sea

1 Flood plain of river
2 Delta with distributaries, levees and marshes
3 Submarine delta sediments
4 Abandoned distributaries
5 Abandoned delta front

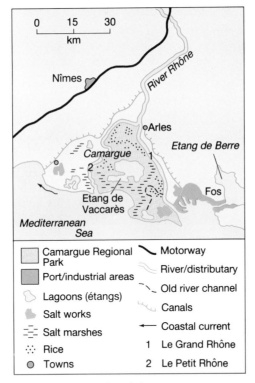

Fig. 3.48 The Rhône delta

Key:
- Camargue Regional Park
- Port/industrial areas
- Lagoons (étangs)
- Salt works
- Salt marshes
- Rice
- Towns
- Motorway
- River/distributary
- Old river channel
- Canals
- Coastal current
- 1 Le Grand Rhône
- 2 Le Petit Rhône

Fig. 3.49 Landscapes of the Camargue: (*upper*) browsing flamingoes, (*lower*) rice cultivation

France (Fig. 3.45). Recently, many sand dune areas have been stabilised by plants such as marram grass and coniferous trees (Fig. 3.46).

2 Deltas

Deltas are found at the mouths of large West European rivers such as the Po, the Ebro, the Rhine, and the Rhône. Most of the information on this page refers to the Rhone delta, while Fig. 3.47 is a model showing the main physical features of a delta.

A description of the Camargue

To the newcomer the Camargue does indeed appear to be an inhospitable wasteland, a desolation of enormous skies and limitless horizons, a flat and arid nothingness, a land long abandoned by life and left to linger and die all summer long under a pitiless sun suspended in the washed out steel-blue dome above. But . . . there is water here, and no land is dead where water is: there are large lakes and small lakes and lakes that are no lakes at all but marshes sometimes no more than fetlock deep to a horse, others deep enough to drown a house. There are colours here, the ever changing blues and greys of the wind rippled waters, the faded yellows of the beds of marshes that line the etangs, the near blackness of smooth crowned cypresses, the dark green of wind-break pines, the startlingly bright green of occasional lush grazing pastures, strikingly vivid against the brown and harsh aridity of the tough sparse vegetation and salt flats, hard baked under the sun that occupy so much the larger part of the land area. And, above all, there is life here: birds in great number, very occasional small groups of black cattle and, even more rarely, white horses: there are farms, too, and ranches, but these are set so far back from roads or so well concealed by windbreaks that the traveller rarely sees them.

(from *Caravan to Vaccares* by Alistair Maclean)

Assignment

Study Figs. 3.47 and 3.48, and then copy out the following paragraphs, filling in the gaps with the words provided.

A coastal delta is a continuation of a river's _____ plain out into the sea. They have a _____ lying near _____ surface. Due to continual _____ the river divides into channels called _____. These often sub-divide, sometimes reunite and change course, leaving old abandoned channels. Salt _____ and lagoons are common features.

The size and shape of a delta depends on many factors. These include how much _____ is brought down by the river and the ability of the _____ to carry material away. The Rhone delta has a _____ shape whose shoreline alters as the main distributary arms advance 20 to 50 metres annually. Coastal currents, moving in a _____ direction have formed sandspits and bars behind which large lagoons such as the Ètang de _____ have developed.

Missing words: Vaccarés, sediment, sea, distributaries, triangular, westerly, marshes, flood, level, deposition, low.

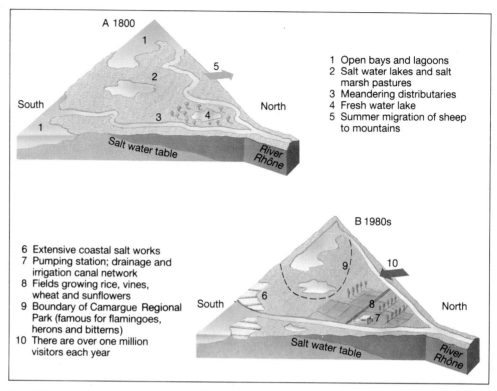

A 1800

South

North

1 Open bays and lagoons
2 Salt water lakes and salt marsh pastures
3 Meandering distributaries
4 Fresh water lake
5 Summer migration of sheep to mountains

Salt water table

River Rhône

B 1980s

6 Extensive coastal salt works
7 Pumping station; drainage and irrigation canal network
8 Fields growing rice, vines, wheat and sunflowers
9 Boundary of Camargue Regional Park (famous for flamingoes, herons and bitterns)
10 There are over one million visitors each year

South

North

Salt water table

River Rhône

Fig. 3.50 The changing man-land relationships in the Camargue (see pages 64 and 65)

Deltas are usually important for one or more reasons:

a In spite of the silting problems, major ports, such as, Rotterdam-Europoort, and the new industrial complex of Fos have developed on deltas with ease of access to inland areas.
b Intensive agriculture can take advantage of the usually fertile soil, e.g. Po delta.
c Less accessible parts of deltas may act as a refuge zone for wildlife, such as Guadalquivir.

A clash of interest can occur between the various land uses. The Rhône delta (the Camargue) shows this. In the early nineteenth century this wetland environment supported reed-cutting, fowling and fishing around the lakes and lagoons. On the salt marshes farmers and gypsies reared sheep, the famous Camargue bulls, and semi-wild white horses. As a result of irrigation and drainage schemes earlier this century, the landscape has changed (see Fig. 3.50).

Three land uses have been in conflict.

a In the south-east there has been an expansion in the coastal salt industry.
b Thanks to dyking and drainage farming has expanded southwards. Rice is a major crop, as are also wheat, sunflowers and (now less important) vines. Farmers claimed that the salt industry increased the soil salinity.
c An early solution was to create a nature reserve which acted as a buffer zone between the salt industry and the farmers.

In 1972 the Camargue was declared a Regional Park; similar to an English National Park. Around the nature reserve there is an area of privately owned marshes where many of the birds feed. The problem nowadays is whether farmers would prefer to drain such wetlands and make more money from new farmland. Perhaps they should be given conservation grants to retain the marshland ecology?

3 Spits and lagoons

To the west of the Rhône delta, currents and waves have built sand and shingle spits and bars which enclose lagoons (étangs). These type of formations are found elsewhere; on the Baltic coast they are known as a Haff (lagoon) and a Nehrung (spit). (Development of the Languedoc coastline of France is described on page 160.)

Assignments

1 (*Extract on the Camargue*) Pick out the phrases which tell about a) the Mediterranean climate, b) the size and relief of the Camargue.

2 What are the land use conflicts in the Camargue? Is it fair to talk about the 'vanishing Camargue'? (*Text and Fig. 3.50*).

Managing the Dutch physical landscape

'God made the world but the Dutch made Holland' is an old Dutch saying. Over a long period of time the Dutch, applying new technology, have transformed and managed their physical environment by carrying out extraordinary schemes of land reclamation and flood control.

Land reclamation in the Netherlands up to 1800

Fig. 3.51 shows the Netherlands during the Roman period. Pliny, the Roman historian, talked about 'the people dwelling on the islands of the Rhine, who live on mounds they have made.' These marsh dwellers were known to the Romans as Frisians and their mounds were called Terps (see Fig. 3.52). Embankments were built to link these mounds and to protect the small fields round about. In this way the first sea dykes were constructed. Gradually more extensive areas were enclosed, and, from about 800 AD onwards, building sluice gates ensured that surplus water could be discharged more easily at low tide. Areas from which the surplus water has been removed are known as polders, and by creating them the Dutch have altered their landscape.

In their struggle the Dutch have often been hindered by nature. For example, between 1200 and 1300 a series of violent storms and floods caused the sea to cover all the islands at the entrance to Lake Flevo and to create the Zuider Zee (see Fig. 3.51). A second problem was the seasonal flooding of the River Rhine and its distributaries. Although the Romans had constructed the first river dykes and polders, the effect of spring floods could be very damaging. A third reason for land loss concerned the Dutch themselves. By the 17th century the population had grown and the Netherlands was an important trading and industrial power. Peat cutting was required to make

up for the lack of coal resources. However peat excavations flooded and either created new lakes or enlarged existing lakes such as the Haarlemermeer which grew from 2600 hectares in 1530 to 16 000 by 1700. (See Fig. 3.58).

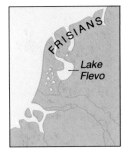 

Fig. 3.51 The Netherlands in (*left*) the first and (*right*) fourteenth centuries AD

In spite of these problems, land reclamation has continued at varying rates over the centuries. The methods of polder reclamation have altered dyke design, drainage techniques and the size of area to be reclaimed.

The earlier dykes were little more than simple dams of sand and clay. Gradually the Dutch learned to strengthen the dykes with seaweed, timber and grasses and to slope the dyke towards the sea. Pumping techniques developed from simple single windmills (originally introduced from the Middle East) to whole series of powerful windmills by the 18th century. As these techniques improved, larger areas could be drained. The Haarlemermeer was not drained until 1852, an operation that took three years pumping by only three steam engines compared to the 160 windmills once suggested. In spite of the flood dangers from the lake waters, the people of Haarlem opposed the project because their sewage was deposited in the lake!

Once drained, the former lake bed was used for arable farming. Today (see Figs. 3.53 and 3.58) the northern part is occupied by Schiphol airport, with its runways 4.5 metres below sea level. The shortage of living space in the Netherlands and the need for careful planning is shown in Fig. 3.53. Has the KLM Jumbo landed on a motorway, or does the Rotterdam-Amsterdam motorway pass under the runway?

Fig. 3.52 Development of the Frisian terps
Fig. 3.53 Jumbo jet on the runway at Schiphol airport

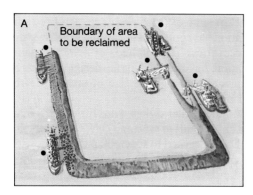

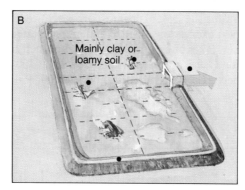

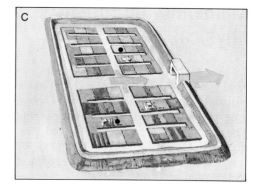

Fig. 3.54 Stages in reclaiming a polder from the Zuider Zee. Sometimes prehistoric remains and wrecked ships are found on the former sea bed

Twentieth century reclamation: the Zuider Zee scheme

Various plans had been suggested over the years to reclaim the Zuider Zee. Matters came to a head with food shortages during the 1914–18 War and a severe flood in 1916. In the 1920s the plan of Cornelius Lely (Minister for Transport and Water Affairs) was broadly adopted. Over the next 50 years the best of Dutch experience and skill has been applied to their biggest drainage and reclamation scheme so far.

A key element was the building of the 30 kilometre long Barrier Dam, completed in 1932 (Fig. 3.55). Behind this dam with its sluice gates the fresh water Ijsselmeer replaced the former salty Zuider Zee. With the sea excluded, work then began on the five proposed major new polders (see Fig. 3.55 for dates). Draining and reclaiming the polders involves various stages. In simplified form they are shown in Fig. 3.54.

Stages in reclaiming a new polder

a After soil surveys of the underwater area, a dredger cuts a central trench – the first stage in dyke construction.
b Floating cranes build up the outer dyke walls of tough boulder clay dredged from Ijsselmeer.

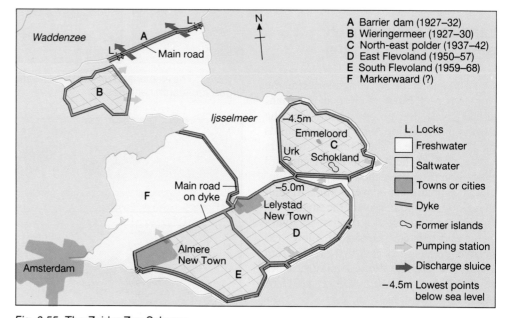

A Barrier dam (1927–32)
B Wieringermeer (1927–30)
C North-east polder (1937–42)
D East Flevoland (1950–57)
E South Flevoland (1959–68)
F Markerwaard (?)

L. Locks
Freshwater
Saltwater
Towns or cities
Dyke
Former islands
Pumping station
Discharge sluice
−4.5m Lowest points below sea level

Fig. 3.55 The Zuider Zee Scheme

c Sand is pumped using dredgers and barges to form the 'core' of the dyke.
d Reed mats are laid on the outer wall.
e The mats are pegged down and then covered with a layer of basalt blocks shipped from the volcanic uplands of West Germany.
f A road is built along the top of the dyke and the top slopes are seeded with grass.
g Over many months water is pumped out using the diesel or electric pumps whose superior power has allowed such large areas to be reclaimed.
h The smaller canals and ditches are dug out, using trenching machines with very wide caterpillar tracks (the main canals

were dredged while the polder was still submerged).
i Reeds are sown from aircraft. They help to dry out the soil and keep down weeds.
j When the soil is sufficiently dry, underground field drains are laid. These discharge rain water into the network of ditches, small and large canals which eventually lead the water into the Ijsselmeer and the sea.
k The Regional Development Authority grows crops such as rapeseed and cereals for five years, in order to break in the land. Farm buildings and roads are built. Private farmers apply to take over a farm. (See page 80).

Fig. 3.56 Satellite photograph of the Netherlands

The results of such polder reclamation are shown in the satellite photograph (See page 45). It shows various contrasts: between the 20th century 'new' polders and the surrounding 'old' polders; between the most recently reclaimed South Flevoland with its varied land use and the earlier Wieringermeer Polder; and between the silted Waddenzee and the fresh water of the Ijsselmeer. Also shown is the as yet unclaimed Maarkerward which may better serve the Dutch as a source of water for domestic and recreational purposes.

Assignments

1 (*Text*) What is meant by a polder? Describe the difficulties which the Dutch have had to overcome in reclaiming land.

2 (*Text*) Explain what has happened to the size of polders over the years.

3 (*Fig. 3.55 and text*)
   a) Describe the location of the Zuider Zee and how it was formed.
   b) Imagine you were Cornelius Lely. Prepare an outline plan giving the main proposals in your Zuider Zee scheme.

4 (*Fig. 3.54 and text*) Make large copies of the three diagrams. Match each dot on the drawings with the text, and write brief notes on the drawings.

5 (*Figs. 3.55 and 3.56*) Using a piece of tracing paper, draw an outline map to show: (i) Barrier dam; (ii) The 4 new polders; (iii) Amsterdam, Lelystad and Almere; (iv) Ijsselmeer; (v) Silting in the Waddenzee; (vi) The dyke of the Maarkerwaard.

6 Draw graphs to show the following figures. Describe and explain the changes in land use (see page 44). **A** – Wieringermeer, **B** – N.E. Polder, **C** – E. Flevoland, **D** – S. Flevoland

Percentage land use	A	B	C	D
Farmland	87	87	70	50
Residential	1	1	8	18
Woods, nature, reserves and recreation	3	5	16	25
Canals, dykes, and roads	9	7	6	7

Fig. 3.57 A pumping station in the Netherlands

7 What are the arguments for and against the reclamation of the Maarkerwaard?

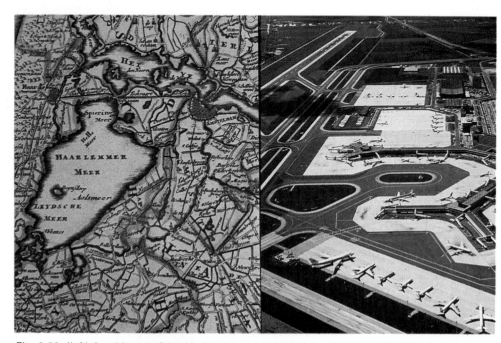

Fig. 3.58 (*left*) An old map of the Harlemermeer, (*right*) an aerial view of Schiphol airport

From the Alps to the North Sea: the Rhine

The importance of the Rhine

The Rhine flows through a variety of physical landscapes. It is therefore a suitable topic to complete this chapter and is presented in the form of maps, diagrams, extracts and assignments.

Assignments

Copy this account and complete it (selecting 'lefts' or 'rights'), using an atlas and Fig. 3.59.

Although the Rhine, which is 1320/2420 km long, is not the longest river in Europe, it is the most important for several reasons.

1 Various countries share the river. These include Italy/Switzerland where it rises; Netherlands/Belgium where its delta meets the North/Baltic sea, and West/East Germany. It is also a boundary for the tiny country of Liechtenstein/Luxembourg, as well as Austria and France/Belgium.

2 It is very important commercially. The valley allows excellent north-south/east-west links from the North European plain through the Caledonian/Hercynian uplands to the Alps. Road, rail, pipeline and river traffic follow the valley. Along with its tributaries such as the Danube/Main, Marne/Moselle, Neckar/Rhône and the network of canals the Rhine

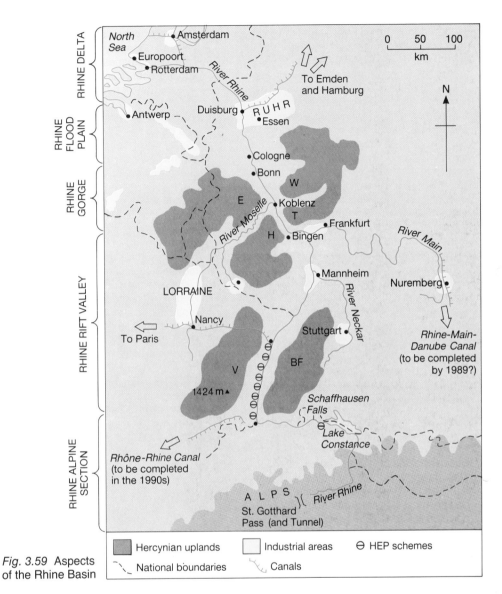

Fig. 3.59 Aspects of the Rhine Basin

Legend:
- Hercynian uplands
- National boundaries
- Industrial areas
- Canals
- HEP schemes

Fig. 3.60 The Schaffhausen Falls

Fig. 3.61 The Rhine gorge

Fig. 3.62 The Rhine flood plain

is the world's busiest waterway. Traffic will become busier when new canal links are completed: a) The New Rhône-Rhine canal (replacing an existing small canal) will link the North Sea with the Mediterranean/Black sea; b) The completed Rhine-Main-Danube canal will link the North Sea with the Black/Baltic sea. These will be able to take the Europa push barges which handle cargoes up to 3000 tonnes. There is a fear, however, that barges from East Europe will provide a lot of competition on the Rhine once the Danube link is completed. Rhine ports have developed. Basle/Zurich, for example is a modern port 800 kilometres from the sea and handles a quarter of Swiss foreign trade, German cities such as Mannheim, Mainz and Duisburg are large industrial ports using finished goods/raw materials such as coal, iron, gravel, sand etc. transported by water.

3 The Rhine is a major source of hydro-power. Power is generated from the Schaffhausen falls in Austria/Switzerland and the 8/12 power stations on the French/German side of the Rhine between Basle and Strasbourg.

4 Historically the Rhine has been disputed as a boundary by France and Germany, but today these countries have to co-operate. Because of the presence of giant power stations and factories, the Rhine has been described as the 'sewer of Europe'. The country most likely to suffer from this pollution is The Netherlands/West Germany. Strict regulations are now in operation, to reduce water pollution.

Landscape zones of the Rhine Valley

From its source to its mouth the Rhine Valley changes in character. Five contrasting stages are usually picked out (see Fig. 3.59). Two of these, the Rhine gorge and the Rhine Rift valley, are shown in more detail on the following pages.

Assignments

1 Match the following five descriptions with the five landscape zones:

a) Once the river crosses the Dutch-German boundary it splits in to several large distributaries – the Lek, the Waal and the Issel. The land is level and river polders (below river level) have been reclaimed, giving fertile farming land.

b) The Rhine starts as two main streams: one which has its source in an Alpine glacier, the other in a mountain lake. Before flowing north to Lake Constance it follows a broad U-shaped valley.

c) North of Bonn the Rhine flows through a broad level plain. Its banks have been straightened and strengthened. In this section it passes through the main industrial region of West Germany – the Ruhr. Barge traffic is particularly busy in this stretch.

d) Lying between the Vosges and the Black Forest, the Rhine valley has a broad flat floor which extends from Basle to Bingen. The valley bottom has been let down between parallel faults. This is one of the major farming zones of West Germany.

e) The river flows from Bingen to Bonn between the steep sides of the Hunsruck and Taunus. Its south facing sides are terraced for vines while the plateau tops are used for forestry, farming and recreation.

The Rhine rift valley

Assignments

1 (Figs. 3.59, 3.63 and 3.64) Copy this account and complete it (selecting 'lefts' or 'rights').

The Rhine Rift Valley was formed when magna/lava heated the earth's crust. This forced up a syncline/dome. Tension was created in the earth's crust/core and rising/falling magna broke through, causing volcanic eruptions.

Because of the stresses the highest/lowest part of the dome sinks down to form the floor of the rift valley. The floor is bounded by blocks called horsts/graben, whose sides are marked by a series of parallel faults. The block in the west is the Vosges/Black Forest. Some 30/10 kilometres to the east lies the Vosges/Black Forest horst.

Over thousands of years the valley floor

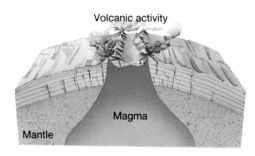

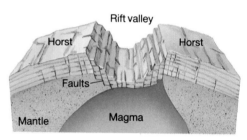

Fig. 3.63 Formation of a rift valley or graben

has been covered by sedimentary/metamorphic rocks. Layers of sand, gravel and alluvium have been laid down by the original straightened/meandering course of the Rhine.

2 The rift valley is one of West Germany's most productive agricultural zones. Suggest two reasons to explain this.

3 Study Fig. 3.65. Explain the distribution of vineyards and orchards. Why do they not extend to the lower area? Suggest three different uses for the forested uplands.

4 (Fig. 3.64 and the extract)
a) What were the main causes of Rhine flooding and when did it occur? b) How did flooding affect the location of settlements? c) Make a tracing of Fig. 3.64 to show the past and present courses of the River Rhine. Discuss the past and present courses, and suggest various measures which could be taken to control flooding.

Avoiding flood in the Rhine rift valley

For centuries the great river, carrying the water of the melting snows from Switzerland, Austria and Liechtenstein, has twisted and turned, sweeping one way and then the other under its own momentum to change its course to such an extent that over the ages it has worn for itself a bed of shingle buried in silt, a plain which is in places nearly 30 km from side to side . . .

Crossing such plain, the turbulent Rhine has always been unpredictable. A violent flood was no uncommon event in former centuries and overnight the river might desert its course for a new one . . . settlements built upon its banks were liable to be swept away and natural pru-dence led the people of the plain to build their towns well to the side of the course. Except for Mannheim – an artificial and relatively modern creation – there is no single town actually set upon the river, all the way from Breisach to . . . near Mainz.

And so for many kilometres the Rhine flows but through nowhere at all. The modern bed is an improved and corrected one with flood banks set well back, but apart from an occasional inn where a ferry crosses from shore to shore the river is flanked only by its fringe of deserted swamps and thickets, with a line of poplars standing upright along the top of each bank.

(from *Small boat to Bavaria* by Roger Pilkington)

The Rhine gorge

For just over an hour our course lay along a somewhat unspectacular river . . . Then through the cold rain we could dimly see ahead of us the barrier of higher land and the narrow cleft cut by the river to separate the Hunsrück from the Taunus hills. There we should enter the famous defile of the Rhine at Bingen.

A geologist might be pardoned for thinking that the Bingen gap was eroded along the line of a fault . . . But the master of a Rhine motor ship will know that . . . a giant . . . worked away most conscientiously with hammer and chisel . . . hewing . . . a furrow from the crest of the hills to the level of the water.

. . . As the Rhine between Eltville and Rüdesheim flows almost due west its right bank is a succession of vineyard villages, whilst the opposite shore is devoted to market gardening, fruit growing and miscellaneous industry. Away to our right we could see the terraces from which came the great vintages of the Schloss Johanisberg.

(from *Small boat through Germany* by Roger Pilkington)

Fig. 3.64 The course of the Rhine has been straightened, with flood banks added to prevent some of the flood disasters of the past

Fig. 3.65 Land use in the Rhine Valley

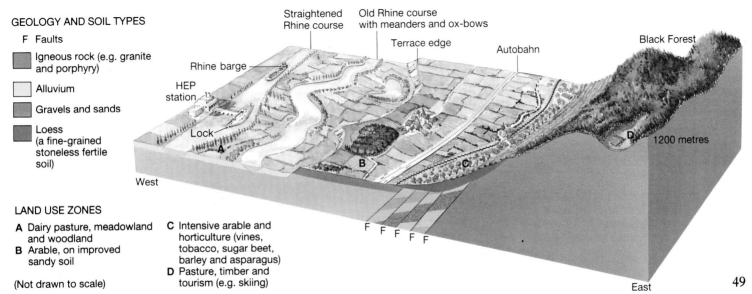

GEOLOGY AND SOIL TYPES

F Faults

Igneous rock (e.g. granite and porphyry)

Alluvium

Gravels and sands

Loess (a fine-grained stoneless fertile soil)

LAND USE ZONES

A Dairy pasture, meadowland and woodland
B Arable, on improved sandy soil

C Intensive arable and horticulture (vines, tobacco, sugar beet, barley and asparagus)
D Pasture, timber and tourism (e.g. skiing)

(Not drawn to scale)

49

Fig. 3.66 Bingen, in the Rhine gorge

Fig. 3.67 The Bingen area (1:50 000)

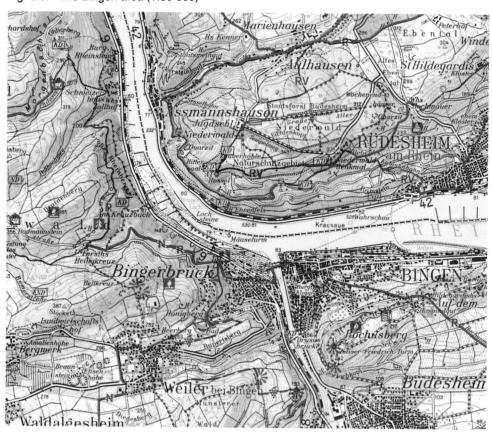

Assignments

1 (*Figs. 3.66 and 3.67, and account*)
   a) Locate Bingen and name the uplands in the background of the photograph.
   b) Suggest which direction the camera was pointed.

2 a) What crop is being grown in the foreground of the photograph?
   b) Suggest three reasons to explain the location of this crop.

3 Give some evidence to suggest that the Rhine valley is a major centre of communications.

4 Describe the site of Bingen. In what way has its site affected the layout of the town?

5 Using map and photographic evidence, suggest the main functions of Bingen.

6 Describe and explain the distribution of woodland in this area.

7 Draw either a simplified section to show the main features of relief and land use in this area, or an annotated sketch to summarize the physical and human landscape of the area.

Chapter 4 The biosphere and people

Climate and weather

Although Europe is a small continent, there are great variations in its climate (Figs. 4.1, 4.2 and 4.3). There are several major reasons for this:

a The range of *latitude*, from 35° to 71° N that is, from Crete to North Cape.

b The range of *altitude*, from below sea level (the polders) to over 4800 m (Mt Blanc).

c The moderating effect of the sea on the land, especially in Northern Norway.

d The effects of *continentality*, that is, distance from the sea, in Central Europe.

Fig. 4.3 is a generalised map of climate types. It should be remembered that there are no definite boundary lines between types; one type merges into another very gradually.

Notice that on the evidence of the climate statistics on page 163, there are great variations within a particular climate type. These variations are mostly the result of latitude, that is, north-south differences, but there are also differences from west to east in the Mediterranean.

Remember that these figures are only *means* for temperature and rainful and that the extremes are not shown. Nor are yearly variations such as the drought of 1975 and 1976. However, if these qualifications are borne in mind, it is possible to compare the climate of one place with another. Vardo's climate (Fig. 4.4) clearly reflects its northerly latitude. Latitude also affects the length of daylight as Fig. 4.5 shows. In general, the length of the growing season decreases as latitude increases. In the south of Europe, providing there is enough water, the growing season lasts all year (see the statistics for Rome and Athens, page 163).

Fig. 4.1 Winter conditions in Paris

Fig. 4.2 A heatwave in Berlin

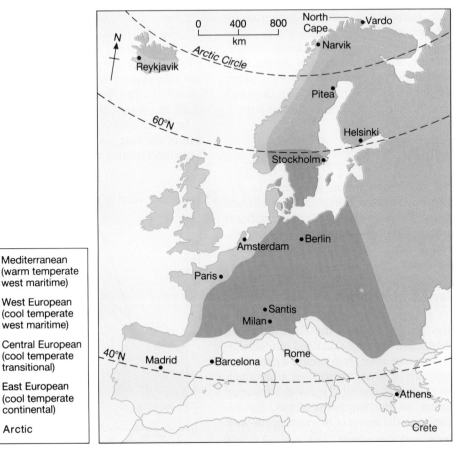

Mediterranean (warm temperate west maritime)

West European (cool temperate west maritime)

Central European (cool temperate transitional)

East European (cool temperate continental)

Arctic

Fig. 4.3 Climate types in Europe

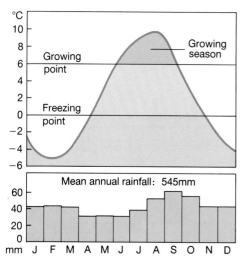

Fig. 4.4 Vardo: an arctic climate

Northern Norway in winter

We passed out of the pine forest, and on through sparse colonies of silver birches, until we reached the bare white waste which was the beginning of the vidda ... The snow flakes came down so thickly now that I could scarcely see the sledge in front, and a biting wind howled across the plateau, whipping the surface into a haze of ice particles. The sharp crystals cut into my face, cracking my lips and almost blinding me ...

(from *Reindeer are Wild Too*
by Joan Newhouse)

Central Spain (The Meseta)

The river beds are wide and bleached and dry. For the most part we are looking down at steppe which is iced in the long winter, and cindery like a furnace floor in the short summer ... Nine months of winter, three months of hell is the proverbial description of Castilian weather ... a dry climate of fine air under a brassy sun, where the cold wind is wicked and penetrating.

(from *The Spanish Temper*
by V. S. Pritchett)

Corfu in summer

Summer gaped upon the island like the mouth of a great oven. Even in the shade of the olive groves it was not cool. The water in the ponds and ditches shrank and the mud at the edges became jigsawed, cracked and curled by the sun ... The sun played a tattoo on your skull, and the baked ground was as hot as a griddle under your sandalled feet.

(from *Birds, Beasts and Relatives*
by G. Durrell)

Temperatures

Fig. 4.6 shows the pattern of temperatures over Europe with selected isotherms for January and July. The annotations on the map reinforce the importance of latitude, altitude, and the influence of the sea. Notice the effect of the North Atlantic Drift on the January 0°C isotherm. The mountain areas of Europe will be considered later.

Rainfall

Fig. 4.7 shows the mean annual rainfall distribution over Europe. Again altitude and distance from the sea are significant factors, although latitude is not so important. The driest areas of Europe are in the south-east.

Types of rainfall

Figs. 4.6 and 4.7 show that there is a strong connection between relief and rainfall. *Relief* (or *orographic*) rain occurs when warm moist air is forced to rise over a mountain range, and is cooled. Heavy precipitation occurs on the windward slopes, for example, on the coasts of Norway, north-west Spain and Yugoslavia. The leeward slopes or deep valleys in the mountains may receive little rainfall and are thus said to be in a *rain shadow* (see Fig. 4.7). Sweden is in the rain shadow created by Norway with the result that Stockholm has only one-third the rainfall of Bergen.

In Berlin most rain falls in the summer half of the year (58 per cent from April to September) during thunderstorms caused by *convectional* heating. Such downpours often break the summer drought in the Mediterranean region and can result in serious flash floods and damaging erosion.

However, most of the rain over Europe is brought by fronts which are caused when contrasting air masses meet and warm moist air is forced to rise over cold air. The areas of low pressure or *depressions* which

Fig. 4.5 Seasonal changes in hours of daylight

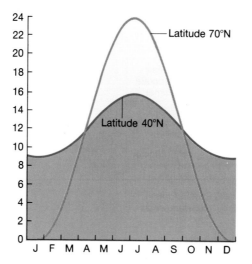

In Europe, as elsewhere, the hours of daylight vary according to the seasons and the latitude. This is shown in the graph on the left. Norway is the country in which the variations are most obvious e.g.

	Midnight sun	Total darkness
Bodo (67°N)	3 June – 7 July	15 December – 29 January
North Cape (71°N)	13 May – 29 July	18 November – 24 February

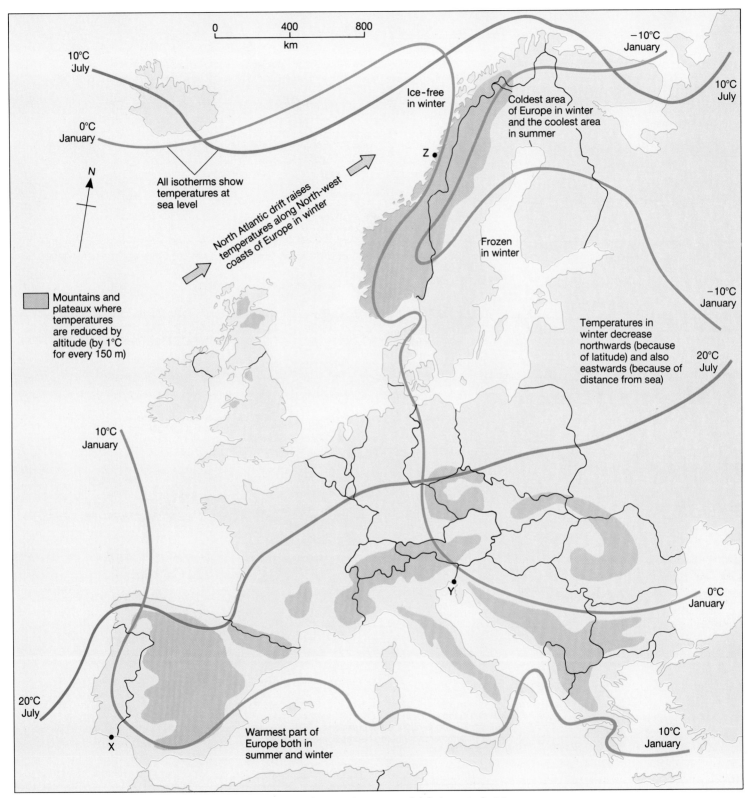

Fig. 4.6 Factors that influence temperatures in Europe and mean January and July temperatures

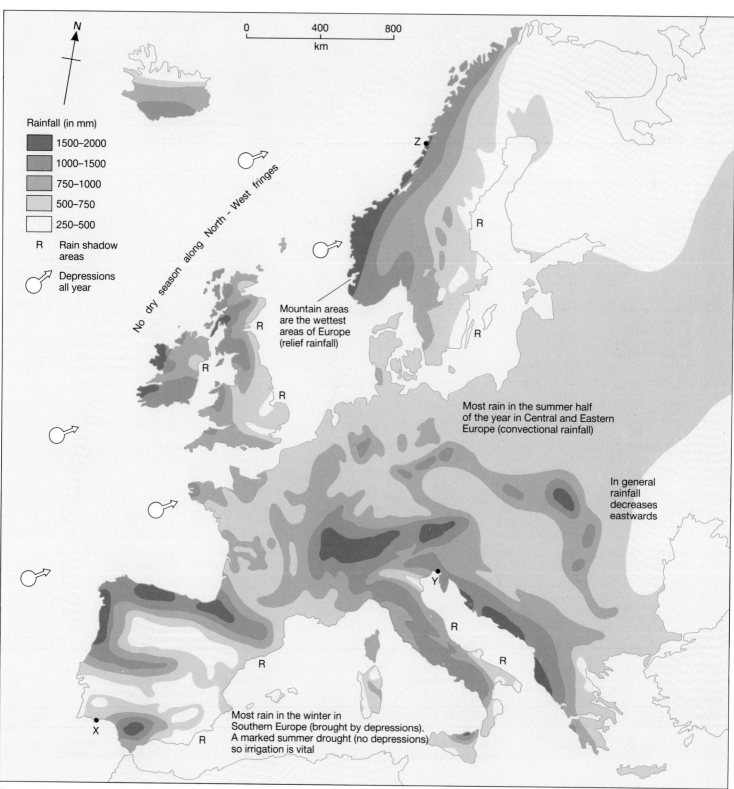

Legend:

Rainfall (in mm)
- 1500–2000
- 1000–1500
- 750–1000
- 500–750
- 250–500

R — Rain shadow areas

⟲→ Depressions all year

N (compass)

0   400   800
km

No dry season along North - West fringes

Mountain areas are the wettest areas of Europe (relief rainfall)

Most rain in the summer half of the year in Central and Eastern Europe (convectional rainfall)

In general rainfall decreases eastwards

Most rain in the winter in Southern Europe (brought by depressions). A marked summer drought (no depressions) so irrigation is vital

Fig. 4.7 Mean annual rainfall distribution in Europe

are thus formed are carried eastwards by the jet stream (a fast-moving air stream about 10 km above the surface moving in a corkscrew fashion in mid-latitudes). These depressions bring *cyclonic* rain to:

a North-West Europe throughout the year (see Fig. 4.8)

b Mediterranean Europe in the winter months

Fig. 4.9 shows the different air masses that affect Europe. For most of Europe, the Polar Maritime and the Tropical Maritime are the most important air masses.

The continental air masses are associated with settled weather (in contrast to the unsettled weather brought by the depressions). This settled weather is related to the existence of a high pressure area. Fig. 4.9 indicates the difference in the characteristics of the two air masses, and the resulting weather.

In general, the weather in North-west Europe is changeable and difficult to predict accurately. The weather elsewhere in Europe, with increasing distance from the Atlantic Ocean, is less liable to sudden change and is easier to forecast.

Heatwave kills 100 in Greece

ATHENS (Reuter) More than 100 people have died from a blistering five-day heatwave in Greece, hospital sources said yesterday.

Temperatures topped 42C (107F), with hundreds of people being admitted to hospital. There were water shortages in Athens and the underground stopped for several hours on Thursday after heat buckled the rails. Agriculture suffered and farmers in northern Greece had to carry water to irrigate their land.

Many Athens shops stayed closed, with fewer cars in the capital's normally congested streets. More than a million people are expected to flee Athens for the countryside at the weekend. The heatwave is expected to last until tomorrow. (*The Independent* 25 July 1987)

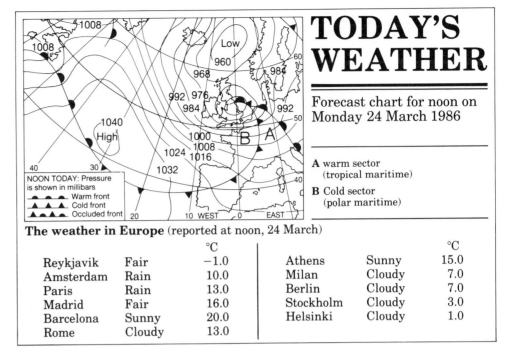

TODAY'S WEATHER

Forecast chart for noon on Monday 24 March 1986

A warm sector (tropical maritime)

B Cold sector (polar maritime)

The weather in Europe (reported at noon, 24 March)

		°C			°C
Reykjavik	Fair	−1.0	Athens	Sunny	15.0
Amsterdam	Rain	10.0	Milan	Cloudy	7.0
Paris	Rain	13.0	Berlin	Cloudy	7.0
Madrid	Fair	16.0	Stockholm	Cloudy	3.0
Barcelona	Sunny	20.0	Helsinki	Cloudy	1.0
Rome	Cloudy	13.0			

Fig. 4.8 Weather conditions associated with a depression

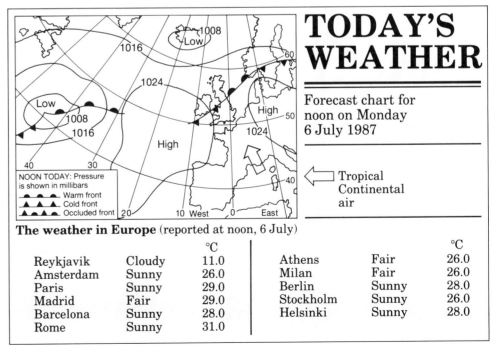

TODAY'S WEATHER

Forecast chart for noon on Monday 6 July 1987

Tropical Continental air

The weather in Europe (reported at noon, 6 July)

		°C			°C
Reykjavik	Cloudy	11.0	Athens	Fair	26.0
Amsterdam	Sunny	26.0	Milan	Fair	26.0
Paris	Sunny	29.0	Berlin	Sunny	28.0
Madrid	Fair	29.0	Stockholm	Sunny	26.0
Barcelona	Sunny	28.0	Helsinki	Sunny	28.0
Rome	Sunny	31.0			

Fig. 4.9 Weather conditions associated with an anti-cyclone

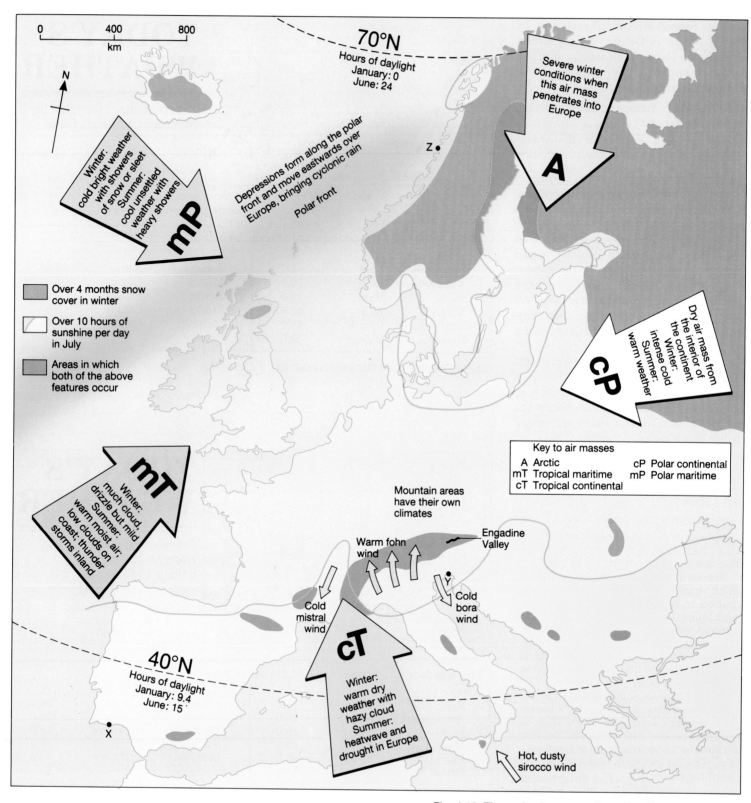

Scale: 0, 400, 800 km

70°N
Hours of daylight
January: 0
June: 24

Severe winter conditions when this air mass penetrates into Europe

A

Z •

mP
Winter: cold bright weather with showers of snow or sleet
Summer: cool unsettled weather with heavy showers

Depressions form along the polar front and move eastwards over Europe, bringing cyclonic rain

Polar front

Over 4 months snow cover in winter

Over 10 hours of sunshine per day in July

Areas in which both of the above features occur

cP
Dry air mass from the interior of the continent
Winter: intense cold
Summer: warm weather

Key to air masses
A Arctic   cP Polar continental
mT Tropical maritime   mP Polar maritime
cT Tropical continental

mT
Winter: much cloud, drizzle but mild
Summer: warm moist air; low clouds on coast: thunder storms inland

Mountain areas have their own climates

Warm fohn wind

Engadine Valley

Y •

Cold bora wind

Cold mistral wind

cT
Winter: warm dry weather with hazy cloud
Summer: heatwave and drought in Europe

40°N
Hours of daylight
January: 9.4
June: 15

X •

Hot, dusty sirocco wind

Fig. 4.10 The main air masses that affect European climates

Mountain climates

It has already been mentioned that mountains are areas of high rainfall and that they create rain shadow effects. More correctly, they are areas of high *precipitation*, much of which is in the form of snow. Fig. 4.10 shows that the Alps for example have more than four months of snow cover.

The statistics for Santis show how high the precipitation can be, and how short the growing season is.

Mountain areas have climates which change with altitude (see Fig. 4.12). They may channel strong local winds (see Fig. 4.10) and *aspect* dictates choice of site for settlement and cultivated land (see Fig. 4.11).

Aspect is particularly significant where valleys are aligned from west to east (examples include the valleys of the Upper Inn, Rhine and Rhône). Where there are deep valleys at right angles to these, wind is often channelled with great force as air moves from area of high pressure to low pressure.

The *mistral* wind is a strong cold wind which can occur between November and April. It is funnelled between the Alps and the Massif Central when air is drawn southwards along the lower Rhone Valley by low pressure over the Mediterranean. Crops have to be protected by shelter belts.

The föhn wind

I became aware of a sudden change in the air . . . now I felt light puffs of wind against my cheek, puffs of astonishing warmth. It was the föhn wind. As I laboured across the slopes, putting all I knew into the speed which meant safety, the puffs of warm air increased to stronger blasts, and they were not warm, they were hot . . . Never have I experienced so sudden a rise in temperature on a mountain, and never have I seen safe snow change to unsafe snow so quickly.
(F. S. Smythe: *An Alpine Journey*)

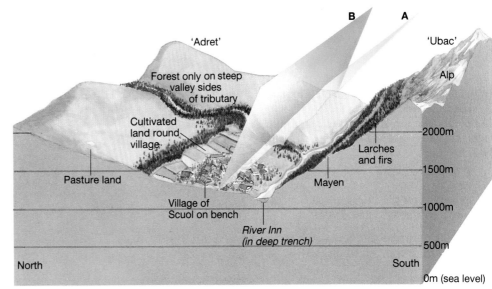

A Angle of midday sun in spring and autumn (43°) B Angle of midday sun in midsummer (66½°)

Fig. 4.11 Aspect in the Engadine, an Alpine valley

The *föhn* wind is a warm wind which causes avalanches and melts snow. Warm air from the south is attracted by low pressure north of the Alps. The air is further heated by compression as it descends into the transverse valleys.

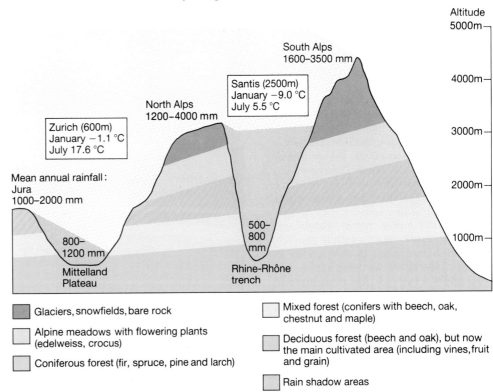

Fig. 4.12 The effect of altitude on climate and vegetation in Switzerland

Weather and people

The föhn and mistral winds both have great impact on the lives of people in the Alps and the lower Rhône Valley. Fig. 4.10 also shows the area affected by the hot *sirocco* wind which can shrivel up crops (see the Biagi farm page 29).

Fig. 4.10 also shows other aspects of the climate and weather which affect people. For example, people in Northern Scandinavia have to adjust to a period of:

a complete darkness and permanent snow cover with frozen lakes and rivers in winter;

b perpetual daylight in mid-summer.

The map also shows the area in the south of Europe which has over 10 hours of sunshine each day in July. This, together with high temperatures (which may be up to 35°C), has both advantages and disadvantages. The photographs on the right suggest how weather can affect people in different ways.

Spring in the Cévennes

'If February does not pay its debts' says a Cévenol proverb, 'March will have to do it.' It is suddenly much colder. Stiffened washing creaks upon the line. The sky is thick grey, the air silent. By ten o'clock tiny spots of white are drifting down. By eleven it is snowing hard. By noon the terraces and slopes are plain white. Everyone huddles indoors. Not a footprint in the street, not a wheelmark. 'When it rains', says another proverb, 'stay at home; when it snows, stay in bed'. . . . The olives are much at risk, and four hours of snow can mean a meagre oil crop for two or three years to come.

(from *A Village in the Cévennes* by H. Willings)

Fig. 4.13 Heatwave and drought in Southern Europe a) A Spanish beach b) Crop irrigation

Fig. 4.14 The effects of heavy snowfalls a) Snow-plough clearing roads b) Alpine ski resort

Fig. 4.15 Drought and flood a) An empty reservoir during the 1975/6 drought in Europe b) A flash flood in south-east Spain

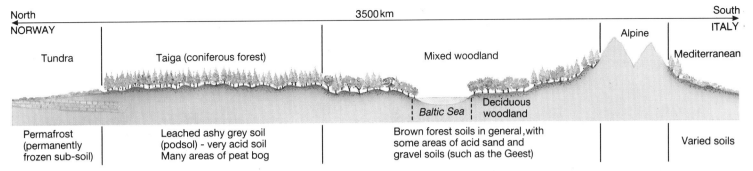

North
NORWAY

3500 km

South
ITALY

Tundra — Taiga (coniferous forest) — Mixed woodland — Alpine — Mediterranean

Baltic Sea — Deciduous woodland

| Permafrost (permanently frozen sub-soil) | Leached ashy grey soil (podsol) - very acid soil. Many areas of peat bog | Brown forest soils in general, with some areas of acid sand and gravel soils (such as the Geest) | Varied soils |

Fig. 4.16 North/south transect of Europe showing natural vegetation and soils

Natural vegetation and soils

Fig. 4.20 on page 60 shows the general distribution of the different types of natural vegetation *before* the impact of farming was apparent. Again it should be remembered that there are no sharp dividing lines between the different types. Instead they merge gradually. The *taiga*, for example, ends with a zone of change where trees become smaller and fewer until the treeless *tundra* is reached.

The transect diagram (Fig. 4.16) shows the sequence of vegetation zones from north to south. This sequence is similar to the zones found on mountain sides in the Alps (see Fig. 4.12).

The transect also shows some information about soils. In the Alpine and Mediterranean zones soils vary: in the Mediterranean area soils may be alluvial (as in the Valencia huerta); volcanic (as in the Vesuvius area); brown forest, or red (terra rossa) in limestone areas. It is in the south of Europe that mis-use of the land has most often resulted in *soil erosion* (see p. 70).

Fig. 4.20 identifies the zones that have been most affected by agriculture. National parks attempt to protect surviving areas of natural vegetation and their associated wildlife. The surviving areas of wetlands, such as the Carmargue, are now under threat from development.

Fig. 4.17 Summer tundra vegetation

Fig. 4.18 Mediterranean scrub

Fig. 4.19 Deciduous woodland

59

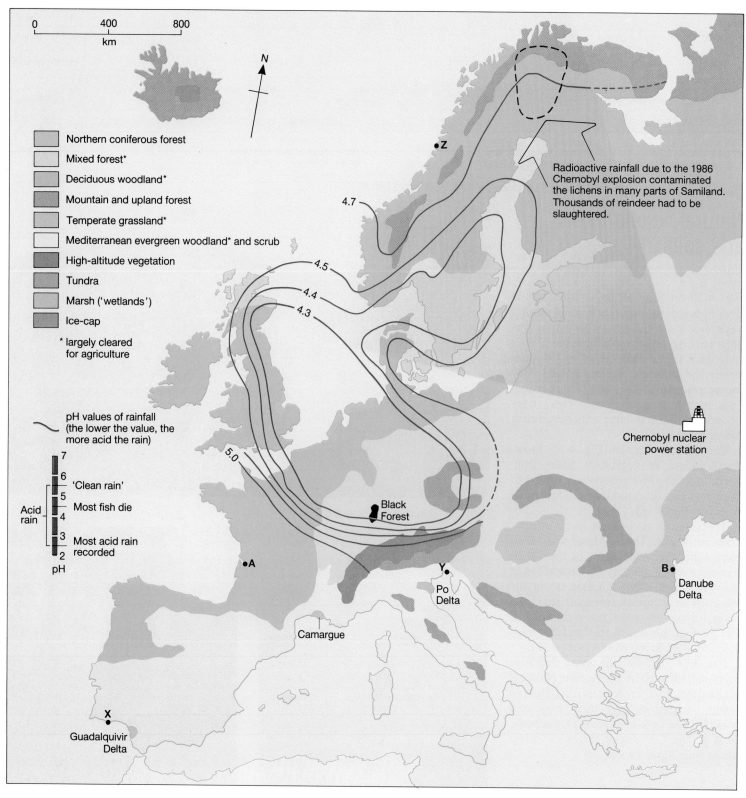

Scale:
0 — 400 — 800 km

N

Legend:
- Northern coniferous forest
- Mixed forest*
- Deciduous woodland*
- Mountain and upland forest
- Temperate grassland*
- Mediterranean evergreen woodland* and scrub
- High-altitude vegetation
- Tundra
- Marsh ('wetlands')
- Ice-cap

* largely cleared for agriculture

pH values of rainfall (the lower the value, the more acid the rain)

Acid rain

pH
7
6 — 'Clean rain'
5 — Most fish die
4
3 — Most acid rain recorded
2

Radioactive rainfall due to the 1986 Chernobyl explosion contaminated the lichens in many parts of Samiland. Thousands of reindeer had to be slaughtered.

Chernobyl nuclear power station

• Z

4.7

4.5

4.4

4.3

5.0

Black Forest

• A

Y •
Po Delta

• B
Danube Delta

Camargue

X •
Guadalquivir Delta

Fig. 4.20 The main natural vegetation zones of Europe

Fig. 4.21 The effects of acid rain on the Black Forest

Acid rain

Fig. 4.21 shows the effects of acid rain on part of the Black Forest, while Fig. 4.20 shows the areas of West Europe most affected by the problem. The forests of Southern Scandinavia are also highly sensitive to the effects of acid rain. Thirty years ago the lowest pH values of rain were over 5. Governments and the European Community are now seeking to control the emissions of toxic chemicals into the atmosphere. Power stations, factories and motor vehicles are all to blame. Oxides from these sources form acids in the atmosphere and eventually fall in rain or dust, often far from their source.

Assignments

1 List the three most important factors which influence climate.

2 Describe the effects of the North Atlantic Drift on the climate of the Norwegian coast.

3 Study the graph of Vardo (Fig. 4.4), and then complete the following paragraph in your notebook:

Vardo is in Northern _____, and has an _____ climate. The lowest temperature is in _____ with a mean temperature of _____°C. The highest temperature is _____°C in _____, late in the summer. _____ months have mean temperatures below freezing point, and only four months have mean temperatures above _____ _____ (6°C). The mean annual rainfall is only _____mm. It is _____ distributed. _____ and _____ are the driest months (36 mm), while _____ is the wettest month with 63 mm. From November to April, precipitation will be in the form of _____. Because Vardo is north of the Arctic Circle, there will be no _____ in December and January, and no _____ in June and July when the midnight sun is the most striking feature of the climate.

4 Draw climate graphs to show the climates of Paris, Berlin, Athens and Helsinki. Draw them in the same way as the graph of Vardo, although the scales will have to take account of higher temperatures and slightly higher rainfall. Data on p. 163.

5 Describe briefly the climate of each of the capital cities. In which city would you prefer to live? Give features of the climate to support your decision.

6 Study the figures for Santis and the information about mountain climates.
   Write a paragraph about the climate of Alpine areas such as Santis, mentioning both advantages and disadvantages.

7 How can the same type of weather have different effects on different people?
   Study the photographs on p. 58 and then write a paragraph on this topic in your notebook.

8 Figs. 4.6, 4.7, 4.10 and 4.20 contain a great deal of information. Three places, X, Y and Z, are marked.
   By studying the four maps, it is possible to say that place Y has:

   a January mean above 0°C but well below 10°C.;

   a July mean well above 20°C;
   between 1000 and 1500mm rainfall per year;
   almost 10 hours of sun per day in July;
   a Mediterranean evergreen vegetation.

   Write out a list of the features of the climate of X and Z in your notebook. Name the type of climate each represents and its natural vegetation.

9 Explain what is meant by orographic rain; convectional rain; cyclonic rain. Which is most important in Europe?

10 Study Fig. 4.10 and an atlas map of the Northern Hemisphere. Describe the effects of an air mass reaching Europe:
   a) in summer, from: (i) the Sahara Desert (ii) the Atlantic Ocean south of 23½°N (iii) the Atlantic Ocean north of 66½°N.
   b) in winter, from: (i) the Arctic Ocean (ii) the Atlantic Ocean south of 23½°N (iii) the centre of Siberia.

11 Study the weather reports for the cities in Fig. 4.8 and the figures below. Comment on the changes in the daily weather.

	Sunday 23.3.86		Tuesday 25.3.86	
Reykjavik	Cloudy	−1°C	Sunny	−4°C
Paris	Sunny	10°C	Rain	3°C
Rome	Fair	13°C	Fair	15°C
Stockholm	Snow	0°C	Cloudy	2°C
Athens	Sunny	7°C	Fair	6°C

12 Search newspapers for weather charts similar to Figs. 4.8 and 4.9. Notice the kind of weather each brings.

13 Study Fig. 4.20.
   a Name the natural vegetation regions you would pass through on a journey from A to B.
   b Which regions would still be untouched, and which would now be mostly farmland?

14 Look at the areas of Europe most affected by acid rain. Compare the area with a pH value of less than 4.3 with maps of population density (Fig. 2.14) and the economic core (Fig. 9.1).
   Can you see a connection?

15 Search newspapers and magazines for photographs and articles about acid rain. What solutions to the problem are being attempted?

Chapter 5 Farming and the changing rural landscape

Mediterranean farming

Because of our urbanized lifestyle, most of us know very little about farming. Its products are increasingly wrapped in cellophane with the price stamped on, picked from supermarket shelves and freezer counters rather than from the market stall. Many of us are so unfamiliar with the land that we take farming for granted.

To remind us of the importance of farming and our (originally) rural roots, we start this chapter by looking at farming in the Mediterranean lands. In Greece, Italy, Spain and Portugal more of the population live and work in the countryside than in the Netherlands or the UK. People live therefore closer to the land, and their food, as the extract suggests, is not just of the packaged sort. It is from the long-established farmscapes of the Mediterranean lowlands that some crops, now grown further north, originally came. Wheat, barley and the grape are three examples.

A Tuscan vineyard

Tomorrow, around seven thirty, dressed in our oldest clothes we will turn up at the big modern farmhouse they have built to replace the old, more beautiful one, armed with baskets with iron hooks on them so that we can hang them from the pergole, the horizontal wires on which vines are trained, while we cut the grapes with scissors, secateurs or just sharp knives . . . We always start at the most distant vineyard, which may be a mile or more away from the house, up or down the hillside, often separated from it by other people's properties and usually only reached by the roughest and steepest of tracks . . . Pergole are picturesque and shade you from the midday sun but they no longer accord with modern wine-making theory. No more trellises are being constructed, and new vineyards are planted in regular, widely-spaced parallel rows in fields bulldozed out of the hillside, and the pretty terraced fields one above the other will soon be no more.

At about ten o'clock . . . we have a 'merenda', a picnic in whichever field we happen to be in . . a very un-English breakfast . . . with lots of fresh pecorino, cheese made with ewe's milk, prosciutto (ham), and what is here called mortadella (salami) and bread baked in the outside wood oven which every house possesses, and wine.

At about a quarter to one we go back to the house for the midday meal . . . We eat brodo, broth made with beef or chicken stock with pasta in it, followed by manzo bollito (boiled beef), stuffed with a mixture of spinach, egg, parmigiano cheese and mortadella; and also roast or boiled chicken . . ., the chickens being the best sort that have scratched a living in the yard, roast potatoes, the bitter green salad called radici, mixed with home produced olive oil and vinegar, and plates of delicious tomatoes, eaten with oil, salt and pepper.

(from *On the Shores of the Mediterranean* by Eric Newby, 1985)

Assignments

1 (*General*) Referring to an atlas and/or page 163, briefly describe the main features of a Mediterranean climate. Suggest some advantages and disadvantages of this climate for the farmer.

2 (*Page 165*) Draw bar diagrams to show the percentage of the working population employed in the primary sector in the countries of Mediterranean Europe.

3 (Extract: 'A Tuscan Vineyard') a) Pick out phrases which suggest that farming is changing. b) Make a list of the sorts of foods and drink mentioned. How does the diet compare with your own? Try to explain any differences.

Farming and settlement on the Plain of Hellas

The information shown in Fig. 5.1 refers to the Plain of Hellas, Greece. Settlement dates back to 5000 BC and by looking at the maps, graphs and tables, you will get an introduction to many of the features of lowland Mediterranean farming and life.

Assignment

Referring to the material provided, copy the following paragraphs, selecting the correct 'left' or 'right' and completing the blanks.

The Plain of Hellas lies in the north/south of Greece. Along its coast there runs a line of sand dunes/cliffs, broken by the River _____ which rises in the mountains of the _____ Peninsula to the south/north. The river meanders/flows straight across a broad coastal plain lying below _____ metres and with a very steep/gentle gradient. This plain consists of a very fine, fertile alluvial soil which has been spread by the winter/summer floods. During the long, hot summer, however, when average temperatures are as high as _____°C and precipitation as low as _____mm in _____, the river is almost dry. Wells have had to be sunk, springs exploited and a network of irrigation canals developed in this area of cool temperate/mediterranean climate.

Land use is very varied. On the level coastal plain most of the land is given over to cotton/wheat. Close to the settlements and near the river, areas of level land are given over to

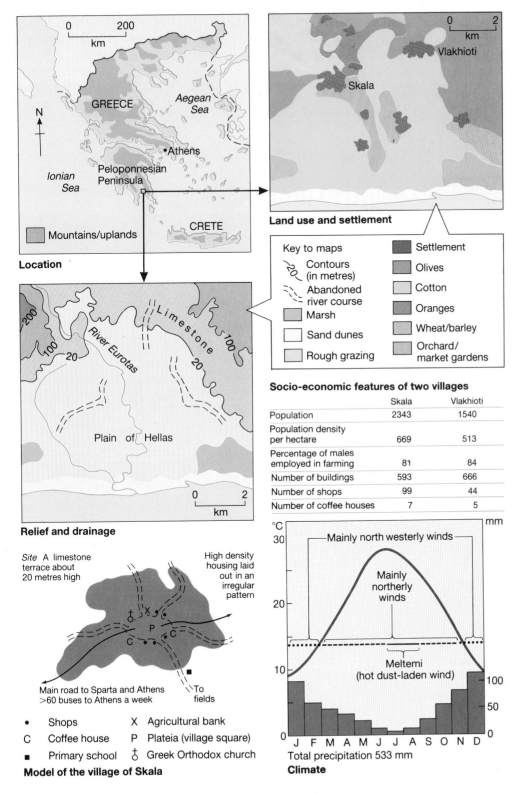

Location

Land use and settlement

Key to maps			
Contours (in metres)		Settlement	
Abandoned river course		Olives	
Marsh		Cotton	
Sand dunes		Oranges	
Rough grazing		Wheat/barley	
		Orchard/ market gardens	

Relief and drainage

Socio-economic features of two villages

	Skala	Vlakhioti
Population	2343	1540
Population density per hectare	669	513
Percentage of males employed in farming	81	84
Number of buildings	593	666
Number of shops	99	44
Number of coffee houses	7	5

Site A limestone terrace about 20 metres high

High density housing laid out in an irregular pattern

Main road to Sparta and Athens >60 buses to Athens a week

To fields

- Shops
- C Coffee house
- Primary school
- X Agricultural bank
- P Plateia (village square)
- ☩ Greek Orthodox church

Model of the village of Skala

Mainly north westerly winds

Mainly northerly winds

Meltemi (hot dust-laden wind)

Total precipitation 533 mm

Climate

Fig. 5.1 Farming and settlement on the Plain of Hellas

The west coast of Mani

rough grazing/market gardening/orchards. There, encouraged by the fertile soil and cold/mild winters, vegetables are extensively/intensively cultivated, especially tomatoes. These are taken by road to the Greek capital _____ which lies some _____ km to the south-west/north-east. On the gently sloping ground cereals such as _____ and _____ are grown, as also _____ and _____ trees. On the areas of steepest slopes the land is given over to _____ grazing. Sheep and goats have traditionally grazed these granite/limestone hills with their tough wiry drought resistant plants during the winter/summer months.

Almost all the farms are found in the villages. Settlement is nucleated/dispersed and this has been encouraged by: (1) the need to group houses around the limited/plentiful water supply; (2) the insecure history of the area; (3) avoidance of the summer/winter flooding and the now shrinking coastal marshes, once home to mosquitoes which spread _____ (cured by DDT spraying in the 1940s) and (4) the need to leave as much/little land as possible for crops.

The two largest and oldest villages of Skala and Vlakhioti grew up at about 200/20 metres. Over many years as the swamps were drained newer villages developed on the plain.

In all these villages some 10 per cent/80 per cent of the people work the land. Housing density is low/high with many traditional houses. These are of one or two storeys, built of rough cast limestone, with sloping roofs (why?) which overhang (why?). The streets are irregular, focussing on the plateia or square, with its Roman Catholic/Greek Orthodox church, the shops and the coffee houses frequented by the men in the village. (See also Ambeli, pages 12–13)

Shepherds of the Camargue

Lowland areas such as the Plain of Hellas are not the only Mediterranean farming environment. The peninsulas and islands of the area are dominated by plateau and mountain rather than plain. Farmers from the lowland areas have pastured their livestock in the uplands, sometimes driving sheep and goats over long distances. Such seasonal migration is known as *transhumance* and over many years well established routes have developed, linking upland and lowland (see Fig. 5.2). Today transhumance is declining. Some of its main features and reasons for decline are described in this excerpt and photographs (Figs. 5.2 to 5.6).

Assignments

1 (*Text*) **a)** Explain what is meant by transhumance. **b)** Suggest why farmers practise transhumance.

2 (*Fig. 5.2 and atlas*) **a)** Name the main upland areas numbered 1 to 6. **b)** What advantages do these upland pastures offer the lowland farmers?

3 (*Text*) In what ways have the methods of transporting the animals changed in the past 100 years?

4 (*Text*) Suggest at least three reasons why shepherds in the Camargue are finding it more difficult to obtain summer grazing rights.

5 (*Fig. 5.6, text and atlas*) Make a large copy of the map. Show the River Rhone and label the cities. Show the route taken and add notes about the Camargue and the Alpine pastures.

6 (*Text*) Can small-scale sheep farming survive in the Camargue?

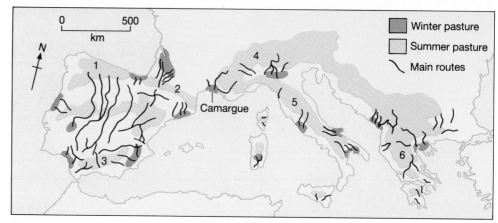

Fig. 5.2 Main routes of transhumance in northern Mediterranean lands

Fig. 5.3 The cabin where the shepherd and his family stayed

Fig. 5.4 The steep, slow climb up into summer pastures

Fig. 5.5 The flock in a mountain valley

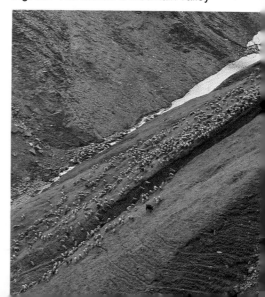

Transhumance

Transhumance is practised all around the Mediterranean as the hot summers of this region dry out the grass. The heat and flies inhibit the animals from feeding properly, so the pastoralists take their animals up into the cool of the mountains where the pastures are rich for the summer period. The shepherds of the Camargue begin to leave for the Alps from the second week of June, but those with Alpine pastures as high as 2000 metres may leave as late as the beginning of July to be sure that the snow has melted.

Before the twentieth century, the only way of reaching the Alps was on foot, and with a large flock of sheep this could take anything up to a month. After World War 1, some flocks went by train to the Alps. In the 1950s the mode of transport for many changed from trains to large multi-decker trucks.

I have twice accompanied a shepherd and his wife ... When I travelled with them it was the first year that the shepherd had taken his sheep to this particular mountain. This year the shepherd was outbid for the usual pasture, which he had used for 12 consecutive years.

The number of available pastures has been declining for several reasons. A re-afforestation programme for the mountains is taking large areas out of grazing. The National Park Authorities are not keen on the core areas of the parks being grazed, and charge a high rent which discourages many shepherds. This particular summer the only pasture my friend could get was one in the Parc National des Ecrins which cost far more than usual.

Large areas of pasture are also disappearing due to the development of ski-resorts, as the mountain sides are disturbed by the building of ski-runs and access roads. With an increased concentration of people in the main valleys since the late 1960s water supplies have had to be improved by tapping streams high up in the mountains; to prevent fouling of the water by animals the pastures around the streams are fenced off.

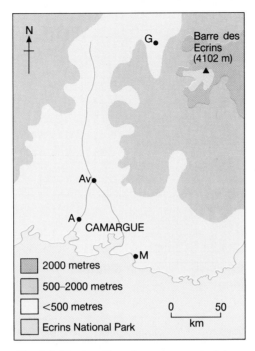

Fig. 5.6 The location of summer and winter pastures mentioned in this extract

Depopulation of the high mountains in the mid to late 1960s has led to the current government policy of preferential treatment for shepherds who live permanently in the mountains. This has meant that a local shepherd with only a limited number of animals can rent a large summer pasture and increase his flock with groups of sheep sent up by small farmers from the Camargue.

Shepherds also compete for grazing with cow herdsmen, who keep animals for milk production to make the famous Alpine cheeses such as Beaufort. Rivalry is such that cattlemen will not allow sheep to graze the same pasture as their cows even after they have returned to the lower valleys.

When in the mountains the shepherd goes out before dawn each day to climb up to where the sheep sleep, usually under the rocky crags just below the summit. The jingling of the sheep's bells guides him in the right direction. On reaching the sheep the shepherd will check for any dead or wounded animals, hurt by falling rocks or an accidental slide; he then brings them down to their grazing for the day.

Living conditions in the mountains are rudimentary. The cabins are often only one room, without piped water and with an earthern or rocky floor. Replenishing food stocks that year was a major expedition for the shepherd's wife. She had to set off early in the morning to walk down to the main valley, with one of the donkeys, to where their van was parked. After driving to the supermarket in the nearby town, she returned to load up the donkey and walk back up the mountain before darkness fell.

Bad weather can make life very difficult. One year so much snow fell in August that the shepherd had to take his sheep several hundred metres down into the valley where he and his wife lived in the back of their van for a month. The sheep were able to graze on the lower slopes only due to the kindness of the local villagers whom the shepherd and his wife knew well.

At the beginning of October, before the snow arrives, the sheep come down from the mountains to the plains. *L'hivernage* (this term now includes autumn, winter and spring), is the busiest time of the year for the shepherd, with lambs being born and later shearing to be done. Finding winter grazing in the Camargue is now also becoming difficult as the landowners find crops such as rice, wheat and oilseed rape more profitable. The shepherds are also in competition for pastures with the bull and horse owners who raise their animals for the tourist market which is proving more economic than lamb production. Previously sheep were welcomed on to the land to provide essential manure for the fine silty soils of the Camargue; today artificial fertilisers replace the sheep.

(From *Nomads of Europe* by Alison Duncan)

Note: See also page 42 about the Rhône Delta.

Irrigated landscapes of Spain

The Valencia area

In certain respects the Mediterranean climate is perhaps the best in Western Europe for agriculture. Firstly, compared to the cooler temperate lands of North-west Europe its lowlands offer a full year growing season. Consequently a wide range of fruit and vegetables (*primeurs*) can be sold earlier during the higher priced winter period. Secondly, the high, almost desert-like, summer temperatures experienced in the southern areas in particular can be exploited to produce four to six crops per year of certain vegetables.

The key to this, given the summer drought, is irrigation. The high yielding, intensively cultivated landscape of the area around Valencia shown in Fig. 5.9 would be impossible without irrigation. First the Romans, and then especially the Moors, were originally responsible for the irrigated landscape of today.

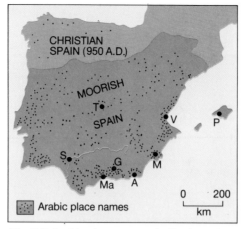

Fig. 5.7 Arabic place names in Spain and Portugal

Equivalent terms in different languages

Arabic	Spanish	English
Wadi al Kabir	Guadalquivir	'The big river'
al mizz	arroz	rice
al zait	aceite	olive oil
al naraij	naranja	orange

The Moors and irrigation

Fig. 5.7 and the table below it show that some seven centuries of Moorish (that is, Arabic) rule, from 711 to 1482, throughout much of Spain and Portugal, left a legacy of place names.

The greatest impact of the Moors, as Fig. 5.7 shows, was in the south and south-east. Using irrigation skills they learned in North Africa, the lowland landscape around cities such as Valencia was transformed (see Fig. 5.9). Nature helped them in two ways. Firstly, the Valencia lowland is the largest of the coastal areas of South-east Spain, over 80 kilometres along the coast and up to 20 kilometres wide. Secondly, the rivers entering the area, for example the Jucar and the Turia, are relatively long and have a more reliable flow. In addition there are numerous springs where the limestone hills meet the lowland plain.

But it was the Moors who engineered the intricate system of water channels, ditches and aqueducts and introduced new water lifting devices. In these ways the limitations of only 425 mm of precipitation per year were overcome. Small intensively culti-

Fig. 5.8 A field irrigation system in the Valencia Huerta

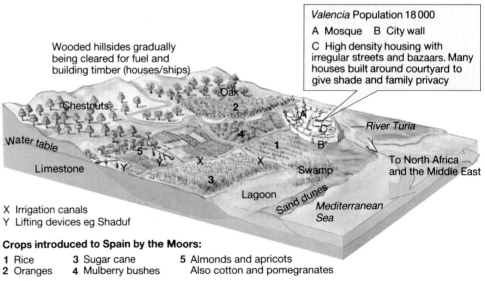

Wooded hillsides gradually being cleared for fuel and building timber (houses/ships)

Valencia Population 18 000
A Mosque   B City wall
C High density housing with irregular streets and bazaars. Many houses built around courtyard to give shade and family privacy

X Irrigation canals
Y Lifting devices eg Shaduf

Crops introduced to Spain by the Moors:

1 Rice   3 Sugar cane   5 Almonds and apricots
2 Oranges   4 Mulberry bushes   Also cotton and pomegranates

Fig. 5.9 Valencia and its surroundings in Moorish times (c. AD 900)

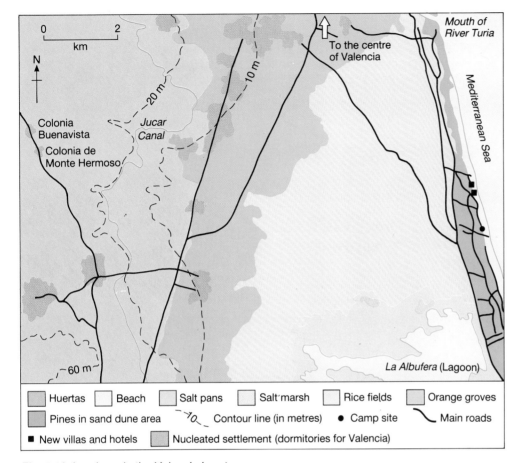

Fig. 5.10 Land use in the Valencia huerta

Key:
- Huertas
- Beach
- Salt pans
- Salt marsh
- Rice fields
- Orange groves
- Pines in sand dune area
- Contour line (in metres)
- Camp site
- Main roads
- New villas and hotels
- Nucleated settlement (dormitories for Valencia)

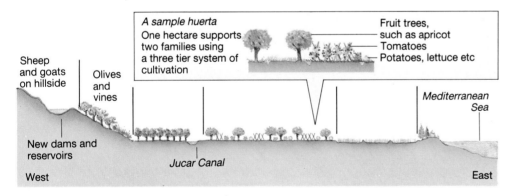

Fig. 5.11 Transect through the Valencia huerta

Assignments

1 (*Fig. 5.7 and atlas*)
   a) Name the cities shown by their initial letter and the river.
   b) Where are the main areas of Moorish settlement?

2 (*Fig. 5.9*) Describe the main features of the Moorish landscape mentioning:
   a) the layout and buildings of Valencia;
   b) the fields, crops and irrigation methods;
   c) the interior hill areas.

3 (*Text*) What are the advantages and disadvantages of the Valencia lowlands for farming?

4 (*General*) Explain why this area has a mean precipitation only of 425 mm per year.

5 (*Figs. 5.10 and 5.11*) Complete this paragraph about the land use zones in the Valencia area. (Fig 5.11 is only partly completed.)
At the coast _____ covered sand dunes are being developed by the tourist industry, shown by new _____ and _____. To the north of La Albufera _____ there are intensively cultivated fields of _____, one of the crops originally introduced by the _____. Then the land rises to around 10 metres where there is a zone of _____ which compete with the southern _____ of Valencia for space. To the west lies a wide area of _____ groves. Through this zone passes the _____ canal which almost follows the _____ metre contour line. Finally, the lowland climbs to the lower foothills with _____ yards and _____ trees, often grown on terraces. High up are the mountains, formed from _____ rock, grazed by _____ and _____. There, the construction of major _____ and reservoirs has ensured even greater control of water for purposes of _____.

6 Copy and complete Fig. 5.11 by adding the land use types.

vated plots called *huertas* were created. On these plots, little larger than gardens, a wide range of crops was grown. Some of these were introduced to Spain (and other Mediterranean areas, for example Sicily) by the Moors.

Today the Valencia area is one of the main centres of agricultural production in Spain, while Valencia (population 750 000) is the third largest city. Fig. 5.10 shows part of the lowland plain immediately south of the city. This map allows us to see some quite well marked land use zones.

Land use patterns and cultivation

The distribution of land use zones in the Valencia area is the result of various factors. These include: (i) relief: the contrast between the upland and the lowland; (ii) soil: the poorer and thinner soils of the upland, compared to the normally fertile alluvium of the lowland; (iii) the availability or non-availability of irrigation; (iv) the value of land: land values are generally higher nearer the city.

Over the years, as the importance of these factors has varied, the boundary between the land use zones has changed. The Valencian suburbs, for example, have expanded at the expense of the farmland. On the other hand, certain areas of poorer quality lowland are now intensively cultivated. The *Colonia Buenavista* (see Fig. 5.10) is one of three new villages developed since 1960. People displaced by new reservoirs created in the mountains have been resettled in new houses and on five hectare units of land.

Perhaps the broad pattern of land use in the Valencia area can be compared to the land-use model (Fig. 5.12). The three 'scapes' are separated by two 'fringe' zones where change and land use conflict occur.

Farming in the Valencia area is one of the success stories of Spanish agriculture. Al-

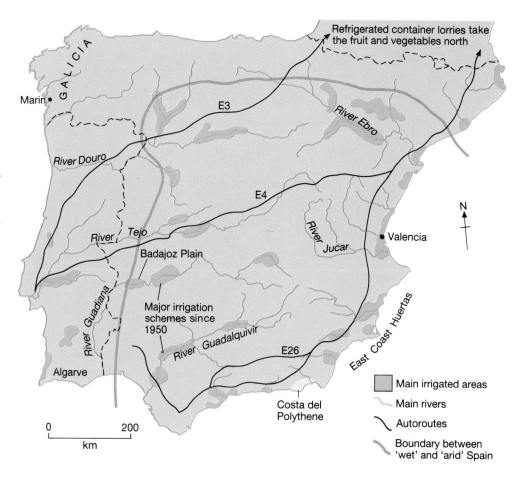

Fig. 5.13 Irrigated lands of Spain and Portugal

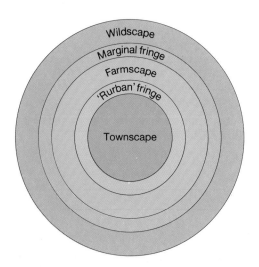

Fig. 5.12 Model of land-use zones

though the holdings (see Fig. 5.11) are typically small the yields are high. By using a system of two- and three-tier cultivation, every centimetre of space is used. Thanks to high temperatures and irrigation a very wide range of vegetables and fruit is cultivated all year round. Marketing is made much easier for the commercially-oriented farmers, thanks to co-operatives. The Valencia regional co-op, with about 4000 members, handles some 60 000 tonnes of oranges through one marketing point. Other vegetables and fruits are handled in a similar way. From intensive zones such as Valencia, much of the produce is now trucked north, using refrigerated containers for destinations in the cooler countries of the EC.

Since Spain and Portugal joined the EC in 1986, the intensively cultivated zones have benefited most. The newspaper extract and photograph describe a completely new irrigated landscape which is also prospering. (see Fig. 5.13 for its location).

Assignments

1 (*Fig. 5.11*) Explain what is meant by 2/3 tier cultivation. What are the advantages of such a system?

2 Co-operative farming was pioneered in Denmark. From page 84 explain what is meant by a co-operative. What are the benefits of membership for the owner of a huerta?

'Costa del Polythene'

On Wednesday, as Spain's King Juan Carlos and Felipe Gonzalez, the prime minister, played host to Common Market leaders in Madrid's royal palace for the country's formal signing of the treaty of accession to the EC, some 60 juggernauts laden with agricultural produce left the country's Almeria region on a regular run into northern Europe.

Almeria, which forms the south-east corner of Andalusia, had until recently been known as an arid expanse of scrubland and mountains where vegetation was rare.

Popularly known as 'culo', a colourful term for backside, Almeria missed out on the country's post war economic surge. Ignored both by Madrid and by investors, the area became the poorest of Spain's 52 provinces. Today the province is number 20 in Spain's economic league and still climbing, thanks to an agricultural revolution over the past 12 years that has turned Almeria into the greenhouse of Europe.

Marion Roe, Conservative MP for Broxbourne in the Lea Valley which has an important greenhouse industry, described Almeria's growth as 'the plastic miracle' after a recent visit with the House of Commons agriculture and fisheries select committee.

Others have likened Andalusia to the California of the Common Market and have even described its expansion as an 'agricultural Klondike'.

It is Almeria that is leading the gold rush. There are 11 600 hectares (27 840 acres) of greenhouses in the region, the world's biggest concentration of plastic. It is stretched on 9ft high steel or wooden frames partly open at the sides to allow ventilation and it covers beds of lush green produce growing in a hothouse environment. By comparison, there are just 3,000 hectares of greenhouse in the whole of Britain.

The Almeria greenhouses are largely controlled by some 15 000 peasant farmers. The smallholders – the average size of a plastic greenhouse is 750 000 sq metres – form 40 cooperatives which auction the produce and organise the use of technical equipment. The giant in the area is a company called Quash, which has 640 hectares under plastic. Quash, which refuses to discuss its business affairs and is not popular in the area, employs 1 300 people and is believed to be owned by Swiss business interests.

From the greenhouses of Almeria come tens of thousands of tons of tomatoes, peppers, cucumbers, green beans, Chinese cabbages, melons, water melons, aubergines and courgettes. The crops are harvested twice-yearly when they are out of season in northern Europe.

Exports to Europe totalled 178 761 tons last year, earning Spain 35 billion pesetas (£155m). Exports have doubled in the last four years, while earnings have more than tripled.

The speed of Almeria's transformation has been remarkable. In 1958, just 30 hectares were under plastic. The province can thank a rare natural combination for the boom – clear light, sunshine, fairly strong winds and huge deposits of water 100 metres below the scrubland.

For the traveller on the main coast road that leads to the holiday playgrounds along the Costa del Sol, El Ejido, the region's capital, is a town best seen from the rear mirror as it fades into the distance. It is an eyesore. Yet El Ejido, with a normal population of 35 400 plus 12 000 emigrant workers, is the most prosperous town in Spain. In a region where unemployment is as high as 25%, there are no jobless in the town.

Senor Juan Callejon, the Socialist mayor, says: 'El Ejido is like a wild west town. It's been built on a boom and needs roots, an identity. Many streets lack pavements and lighting, and some houses do not have proper sanitary conditions. We are not rich but prosperous'.

But now for the first time since the boom started, danger signs are appearing. After an inspection by the Spanish department of mines, a ban was imposed last May on any further expansion. Seawater was found to be contaminating two of the three vital underground water supplies because of low levels.

(*Sunday Times*, 16 June 1985)

3 (*Figs. 5.10 and 5.12*) Compare the land use model with the Valencia area. Do you agree that it summarizes the main land use patterns and trends in the area?

4 (*Extract: 'Costa del Polythene; and Fig. 5.14*) Read the extract and write an account of this new landscape. Cover the following: (i) location; (ii) past economic circumstances; (iii) features of the landscape, crops grown and main markets; (iv) advantages of the area; (v) ownership; (vi) problems.

Fig. 5.14 The Costa del Polythene

The Badajoz plain: A large-scale irrigation scheme

The Plain of Badajoz is part of the valley of the River Guadiana. This is just one of the large river valleys of the Meseta – the plateau and mountain area of central Spain – which has been affected by major irrigation schemes. In the past fifty years Spain has created more irrigated land than in the previous 2000 years since Roman times.

Schemes such as the Badajoz plan were part of a series of integrated plans to transform all aspects of life within these river basins. The plan, which aimed to change the economy of Spain's largest province (21 657 square kilometres, almost as large as Belgium), was very ambitious but its problems were many and typified much of the Meseta.

The problems of Badajoz

a *Environmental* (Mostly shown on Fig. 5.15). The broad flood plain, the Vega, offers good soil but it was underutilized.

b *The land-holding system* Enormous estates called *latifundia* dominated the area. The landowners were often absentees, not interested in achieving the maximum potential from the land, as the diagram below suggests.

At the other end of the scale there were 57 000 *yunteros* – peasants with very small plots with little equipment, and 66 000 labourers who only obtained work for about 180 days in the year.

c *Social and economic* Limited industrial development and low-yielding extensive farming based on dry farming and grazing (see Fig. 5.15); the high birth rate (39

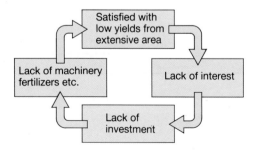

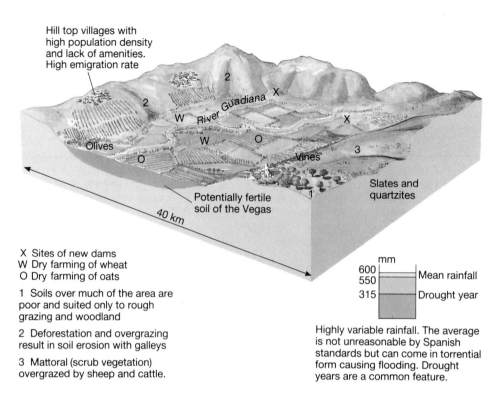

X Sites of new dams
W Dry farming of wheat
O Dry farming of oats

1 Soils over much of the area are poor and suited only to rough grazing and woodland

2 Deforestation and overgrazing result in soil erosion with galleys

3 Mattoral (scrub vegetation) overgrazed by sheep and cattle.

mm	
600 550	Mean rainfall
315	Drought year

Highly variable rainfall. The average is not unreasonable by Spanish standards but can come in torrential form causing flooding. Drought years are a common feature.

Fig. 5.15 A new irrigated landscape on the Guadiana plain

per thousand) and illiteracy rates (30 per cent male/35 per cent female) low per capita income and lack of infrastructure e.g. many towns and villages had no electricity at all.

The Badajoz scheme

In 1952 development started, involving government investment of over £1000 million and the compulsory purchase of stretches of land from landlords at fair rates.

Thanks to the construction of five large dams and a network of major and minor canals, an area of irrigated land, larger than all the Valencia lowland, has been created on the Vega.

The former semi-desert plains now yield a wide range of fruit and vegetables, and dairy cattle are reared on irrigated pastures. Food-processing factories and a textile plant deal with farm produce. Some 12 000 people have been re-settled in new villages (about 3000 houses) which have a good range of services.

Re-afforestation is proceeding on non-productive land.

Assessment of the Badajoz scheme

Millions have been invested and the land certainly yields more. But have those in the greatest need really benefited? It seems that the question of land ownership is not yet resolved. The latifundia owners now control 60 per cent of the irrigated land, while small landowners struggle on plots of five to six hectares and earn less than the national average. Far more people have left the area than have resettled on the new lands.

Assignment

Make a large copy of Fig. 5.15, showing relief, drainage and existing villages. To it add: dams with new reservoirs at sites marked X; electricity pylons; a canal network; four new lowland villages; new road to link the villages; a food processing factory; crops of vegetables and fruit trees.

Farming and competition for water in the Algarve

Switching to intensive agriculture can result in competition for scarce water resources. Fig. 5.16, for example shows the coastal strip of southern Portugal – the Algarve (see also Chapter 8). Here, as the extract suggests, farming, housing, tourism and industry all compete for water. This situation has not been helped by: (i) the summer peak demand and (ii) below average rainfall in the early 1980s.

Assignment

Read the extract and then match numbers 1–11 on Fig. 5.16 with the following: New electric wells; intensive irrigated farmland growing citrus, peaches, vegetables; new flats and hotels; salt water seepage; factories for soft drinks/food processing; mains piped water; new golf courses; irrigation canal; new dam; new villas with swimming pools; water table 40–60 metres deep.

The thirsty Algarve

Agriculture is still the main user of water in the Algarve, accounting for about 90 per cent of the available water resources and leaving only 10 per cent for domestic and industrial uses. Agricultural demand has increased massively. Traditional 'dry' trees, figs, almonds, olives and carobs, have been replaced by 'thirsty' trees e.g. citrus crops, peaches and others which depend on intensive irrigation. At the same time there has been a switch from traditional winter wheat, beans and barley to irrigated vegetables, often with greenhouse cover. These changes have occurred as a result both of private initiatives, mainly through co-operatives of small landowners and sharecroppers, and of public initiatives, following state investment in the major irrigation schemes.

As a result the Algarve now has one third of the Portuguese citrus crops but accounts for 62 per cent of the production. The net effect of these developments has been a huge increase in the land area using water for irrigation.

Domestic demands for water, although smaller, are nevertheless increasing very rapidly. Population growth in the last ten years has been spectacular, but the effects have been all the greater because much of this has been concentrated on the narrow coastal strip where water is most scarce.

The tourist industry accounts for 40 000 users in registered accommodation at any one time, and tourist demands peak in the two months of July and August when water supplies are at their lowest. Water supplies for the residential and the tourist developments have to maintain higher standards of chemical purity than are traditionally accepted in rural communities. The improvement and modernisation of facilities through the installation of mains drainage and piped water supply aggravate the problem since this alone can account for an increase of as much as 2000 per cent in the water consumption of the average household. Finally, the heavy investments in golf courses and swimming pools have pushed up the demand higher still.

Industry also makes great demands on water resources and requires particularly high quality supplies. Fruit and vegetable canning and preservation is a major growth industry in the Algarve but the most rapidly growing industries are those manufacturing alcoholic and non alcoholic drinks.

In both agricultural and tourist development *drilling for ground water* has proceeded at a rapid rate. Inland, co-operatives of small farmers are opening up old wells and financing new boreholes, often from the receipts of part-time employment in the tourist industry. Nine new wells have been bored to supply the town of Portimão and its tourist development of Praia de Roche.

The major problem is the proximity of development – and hence of drilling – to the coast. As the water table is lowered, denser saltwater lying under the fresh ground water moves inland to equalise the loss.

(From 'The Thirsty Algarve', *Geographical Magazine*, June 1984

Fig. 5.16 Competition for water in the Algarve

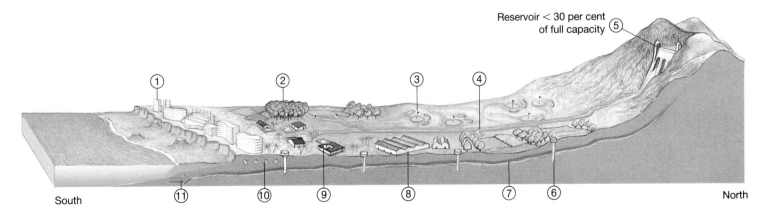

South   Reservoir < 30 per cent of full capacity   North

Minifundia and Latifundia

Minifundia

We have seen that much of the rural planning has involved enormous new irrigation schemes such as the Badajoz plan. But in both Spain and Portugal there are still deep rooted problems to be tackled if they are to become the 'California of the EC.' Perhaps the main problem is that of the small farm, with many very small 'fields' which barely gives a living for the farmer. Such *minifundias*, as they are called, are the dominant type of holding in Spain and Portugal.

The province of Galicia in North-west Spain is, for the most part, a landscape of minifundia. The second paragraph of the extract explains how the tiny fields and farms came about. In this poor 'problem' region the average farm size is only three hectares, composed of some 25 scattered 'fields'. These farms are grouped in an estimated 30 000 small villages, (see Fig. 5.17). The map shows that this is a very densely-settled area. Indeed, with a figure of over 400 people per square kilometre of farmed land, this is the highest rural population density in Western Europe.

As the population grew the number of farm holdings increased, thanks to the inheritance laws. Every square centimetre of land had to be used. Terraces were carved, and cultivation climbed as high as the climate allowed. Tiny garden-like plots have resulted (Fig. 5.19).

On the upper slopes cattle are reared, taking advantage of the mild but damp climate of the region.

Given the small size of these farms, it is essential for the families to find another source of income. There are several possibilities.

a Perhaps the husband is able to find work in a local factory. In such a case it is often his wife and children who do a lot of the farm work.
b Alternatively, he may find work elsewhere, as many did in France during the 1960s and 1970s, for example. Remittances would be sent home, helping to buy a TV, washing machine, etc.
c Working as a fisherman. Because of the overcrowded land resources, the coastal people of Galicia have long looked to the sea for a livelihood. Scattered the length of the sheltered ria coastline (see page 36) are over 70 ports, the largest of which is Vigo. Marin (see Fig. 5.17) is another

A journey through Galicia

The two excursions take me through the countryside of Galicia. I like it very much, a hard, cold, dour land resembling Scotland. Even a few miles travel into the countryside of Galicia, shows the observant traveller the secret of this land: the granite rock which is both the glory and the curse of the region. From deep quarries which seem to abound, the Galician digs out a gray-and-white-flecked granite which he uses for everything. A farmer wants a barn? He builds it of granite. He wants a corncrib to protect his grain from rats? He builds one of solid granite. Garages, lean-tos, small homes and large are all built of this fine stone. This sounds ridiculous, but in the fields even fences, which in other parts of the world would be

built of wood, and here built of granite; long thin slabs, beautifully cut and stood on end to form stony pallisades. Galicia is the granite land.

But this prevalence of stone is also the curse of the region, for the land is inherited not by the eldest son alone but by all, so that fields are divided and subdivided so often in the course of a hundred years that the resulting areas are scarcely big enough to support a family. What makes it worse is that each canny Galician insists upon outlining his new field, however small, with granite walls, until the area absorbed by stone equals about 30% of the tillable land. And with each death, the fields grow smaller and the fences bigger.

(from *Iberia* by James A. Michener)

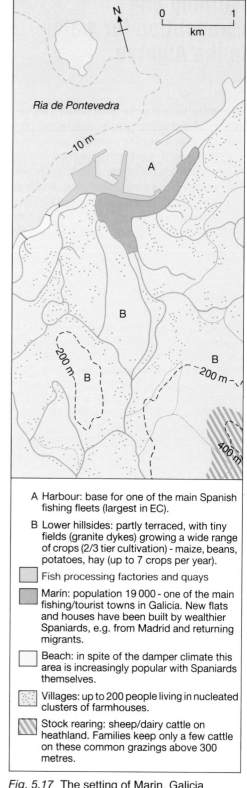

A Harbour: base for one of the main Spanish fishing fleets (largest in EC).

B Lower hillsides: partly terraced, with tiny fields (granite dykes) growing a wide range of crops (2/3 tier cultivation) - maize, beans, potatoes, hay (up to 7 crops per year).

Fish processing factories and quays

Marín: population 19 000 - one of the main fishing/tourist towns in Galicia. New flats and houses have been built by wealthier Spaniards, e.g. from Madrid and returning migrants.

Beach: in spite of the damper climate this area is increasingly popular with Spaniards themselves.

Villages: up to 200 people living in nucleated clusters of farmhouses.

Stock rearing: sheep/dairy cattle on heathland. Families keep only a few cattle on these common grazings above 300 metres.

Fig. 5.17 The setting of Marin, Galicia

important centre. Although Spain joined the EC in 1986, the Spanish fleet (by far the largest) is denied access to EC territorial waters until 1996. This had lead to a recession in fishing, and in associated occupations such as the canning and curing of fish.

Rural development plans are under way, encouraged by the Government acting through its agency – the IRYDA. So far it has only had a limited success in trying to achieve: (1) larger farms; (2) a massive reduction in the number of fields; (3) an improvement in the rural infrastructure, i.e. upgraded roads, improved electricity supplies and provision of piped water.

One difficulty has been the lack of capital, but perhaps the main obstacle to change is the attitude of many of the farmers. Often they have a conservative attitude and, rather like the granite slabs described in the extract, are reluctant to move with the times. Membership of the EC, however, may mean the end of minifundia like these.

Latifundia

At the other end of the scale there is the issue of the large estates or latifundia. Fig. 5.18 shows some of the features of an estate in Andalucia, Southern Spain.

Various attempts have been made in Spain, Portugal and Italy, to take land away from the generally inefficient large landowners and re-distribute it to landless peasants.

a In Spain the Socialist Government passed land reform laws in 1983. Inefficient landowners can be bought out and the land re-distributed. In spite of the traditional inefficient image, the vast majority of landowners, however, have been investing in their estates, mechanising and achieving higher yields.

b In Portugal in 1974 the right-wing dictatorship was overthrown. Landless labourers in the south of the country (the area with the strongest communist vote)

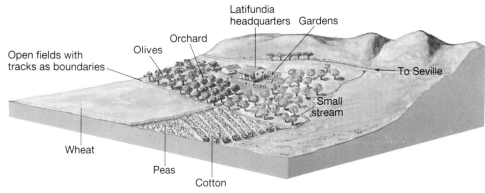

Area: 1600 hectares
Owner: Lives in Seville, 32 kilometres to the north
Main crop: Olives for table use and oil
Animals: Pigs and mules

Labour: Foreman and four men employed full time as well as 35 day labourers from a nearby village and up to 100 at harvest time.

Fig. 5.18 A large estate, or latifundia, in the Guadalquivir valley

have taken over the estates and created collective farms. Northern Portugal, with a similar farming system to Galicia, remains a stronghold of conservative peasants anxious to retain their minifundia.

c Land reform measures have been passed for eight areas in Italy. Six of these areas were in the Mezzogiorno region. These were part of a programme to improve living standards (pages 144–148). By the 1960s some 113 000 families had been resettled on plots of four to ten hectares (arguably, not all that many), and at a very high cost. Mafia corruption, and conservatism on the part of the peasants, who did not like to leave their hilltop 'agro-towns', have limited progress in Sicily. On the other hand, for some it has meant new economic opportunities and a chance to improve their living standards.

Assignments

1 (*Text/excerpt*) What is meant by Minifundia? Explain their size.

2 (*Fig. 5.17*) Describe the main physical and human features of the landscape around Marin.

3 (*Fig. 5.18*) Describe the location, size, relief, land use and labour force of the latifundia.

Fig. 5.19 A typical small terraced plot

4 (*Text*) Suggest why latifundia owners are more efficient farmers now than 20 years ago.

5 (*Text/research*) What are the obstacles in the way of land reform in the Mediterranean area?

Farming landscapes of the North European Plain

The European Community and the Common Agricultural Policy

Spain and Portugal became members of the European Community (EC) in 1986. The addition of these two Mediterranean countries came at a time when a great many criticisms were being directed at the Common Agricultural Policy (CAP) of the EC.

What is the CAP?

The aims of the CAP are quite desirable: to increase agricultural output; to ensure a steady and regular supply of food at reasonable prices; and to create a reasonable standard of living for people employed in farming. Such aims were drawn up in the mid 1960s when the original six EC countries had some 17.5 million farmers, farming generally was not particularly efficient, and memories of food shortages during and after the war were still fresh.

How are the CAP aims achieved?

1 The CAP gives farmers a steady income by a system of guaranteed minimum prices.
2 Traditionally, the CAP protects farmers against falling prices due to over-production of farm produce, by buying up surplus production and storing it in massive freezers and warehouses.
3 The CAP together with national and regional funds, has given grants to create larger, more mechanised farms.

What are the criticisms of the CAP?

Figs. 5.20–2 and the extract give some idea of the questions which are being asked

Fig. 5.20 Food surpluses in 1985 led to storage of vast quantities of produce

Scenic view of Lake Wine
WINE LAKE - 1.7 billion litres
MOUNTAINS IN ORDER OF DISTANCE:
BEEF MOUNTAIN 789 000 tonnes
SUGAR MOUNTAIN 7 000 000 tonnes
GRAIN MOUNTAIN 19 000 000 tonnes
BUTTER MOUNTAIN 1 017 000 tonnes
DRIED MILK MOUNTAIN 965 000 tonnes

concerning the CAP. These are to do with costs, surpluses, and who benefits.

a Costs: Even before Spain and Portugal entered, the CAP accounted for 70 per cent (in 1985) of the whole EC budget. At that time there were only eight million farmers. Critics suggested that the CAP merely cushioned inefficient farmers.

What about the cost of subsidies for example, on sugar beet? This allows overpriced EC sugar to be exported at reduced prices often undercutting producers of cane sugar in the Third World.

b Surpluses: Fig. 5.20 shows the surpluses in storage in 1985. The EC warehouses were so full that cold-storage owners in Switzerland were paid to house unsold surpluses. Various views are expressed about this state of affairs.
   1) 'Surely it's immoral to have such food surpluses when there are some 800 millions suffering starvation in the world?'
   2) 'But a flood of food to areas such as the Sahel only destroys local farming?'
   3) 'Production should be cut back.

Spain is the world's biggest producer of olive oil and there is an olive oil "pond" already. And what about a spare 100 million gallons of Iberian plonk ready to be poured into the EC wine lake? sea? ocean?'
   4) 'Politicians have to back up the farmers. Think of the votes. 30 per cent of Portugal's labour force works on the land!'

c Who benefits? A fundamental criticism is that the large farmers benefit far more than the smaller ones. It is maintained that larger farms are better able to take advantage of the price support system. In some areas for example, the Paris Basin (see page 78) the landowners are sometimes large investment and insurance companies who have removed trees and hedges in an effort to get as much land under cereal cultivation as possible.

Attempts to reform the system are not easy. A 15 per cent cut back in milk caused angry French farmers to dump loads of dung outside the Agricultural Offices in Paris. Farmers, as the Beauce extract suggests, have a strong influence on politicians.

Fig. 5.21 Surplus tomatoes left to rot

The sweet smell of excess

To the hungry, the EC must seem a magic land where, apart from those butter mountains and wine lakes, even the ponds are olive oil and the hillocks barley. The surpluses are part of the EC's Common Agricultural Policy. Farm spending dominates the EC budget . . . Surpluses dominate farm spending.

Some food (see Fig. 5.21) is simply destroyed. Other produce joins the mountains, or is exported at knock-down prices. The Russian housewife is a major beneficiary . . . The most wasteful areas are milk and cereals. The average Euro-cow is pumping out twice as much milk as it did 20 years ago . . . There has been a swing to cereals, even in unlikely and marginal areas. But with fewer livestock to feed, there is less demand and a growing mountain.

(The Sunday Times)

Fig. 5.22 An EC grain store ('grain mountain')

Assignments

1 (*Text*) What do the letters CAP represent and what are CAP's aims?

2 (*Text*) **a**) Make a list of the advantages and disadvantages of CAP **b**) What are your views on Food Aid from EC surpluses to the 'South'?

3 (*Excerpt*) **a**) Draw up a table to show the changes at M. Vorimore's farm from 1950 to 1985. You should look at: size; type of farm; crops/livestock; labour and machinery. **b**) What do you think his attitude is to the CAP?

Jean-Jacque Vorimore: A farmer in the Beauce Region

The Beauce region lies south west of Paris (see Fig. 5.23). It is one of the most prosperous of all French farming regions. Any unfavourable change in the CAP would meet with hostility from farmers such as Jean-Jacque Vorimore whose farm is described in the extract that follows.

The 220 hectares of fat corn lands which Jean-Jacque Vorimore farms near Chartres serve as a good example of the recent transformation of French farming. When his father was in charge of the farm (then only 140 hectares) in 1950, it produced cereals, lucerne, rape and maize, had 15 milk cows and fattened some beef cattle; horses pulled the ploughs and four full-time workers lived in on the farm. Now Vorimore and his brother-in-law employ only two workers on a farm almost entirely given over to cereals and grassland, worked with machines owned jointly by a mini co-operative of four farmers. The local Beauceronne co-op, of which Vorimore is the president, can store 55000 tonnes of cereals produced by the 400 members in its giant silos; it employs 30 staff, owns 20 lorries and uses three railway sidings; it has shares in the giant dockside grain terminal at Rouen, which in turn has shares in a large American cereal co-op.

The successes of technocrat farmers like Vorimore have made cereals France's major export-earner after armaments; and this has given French farmers greater political weight than their 8.3 per cent of the population would seem to merit.

Vorimore also points out that 'France is still essentially a rural country. And although they are elected by local communities, the mayors become civil servants paid by the state. Now in the area covered by my co-op, 300 of the mayors are farmers, and 250 of them are members of the co-op. Neither the mayors nor the government are ever left in any doubt about the way we farmers feel'.

(The Sunday Times)

Farming contrasts in the Paris Basin

Cereal farms such as M. Vorimore's are typical of the Beauce region. Picardy and Artois are two other areas where grain production is important.

These are just some of the distinctive areas or 'pays' which are found in the Paris Basin. Fig. 5.27 shows some of the main features of this syncline, with its variety of different slopes, soils and farming traditions. The differences between the 'pays' are not so marked nowadays, thanks to modern farming technology and EC policies. It is still possible, however, to see differences in the farming landscapes as shown in the following three examples.

Beauce

Lying to the southwest of Paris, Beauce is one of the best known regions or 'pays'. Its underlying rock is limestone but this has been covered since the Ice Age by fertile deposits of *limon* (limon/loess are of the same origin). Most of this land is given over to arable farming with crops such as wheat, barley and sugar beets. Fields are large and farming is mechanised. Most of the farms are located in the nucleated villages such as Moriers and Aigneville. Often these are built around the market place. Settlement takes this form because wells have been sunk to obtain water from the very permeable underlying limestone.

Brie

As Fig. 5.24 shows, Brie has a quite different landscape. Unlike Beauce, much of the limestone has been worn away, leaving a surface mantle of clay. On these heavier, damper soils dairy farming is common, encouraged also by the proximity to the Paris conurbation. Woodland and orchards are common, often surrounding the more

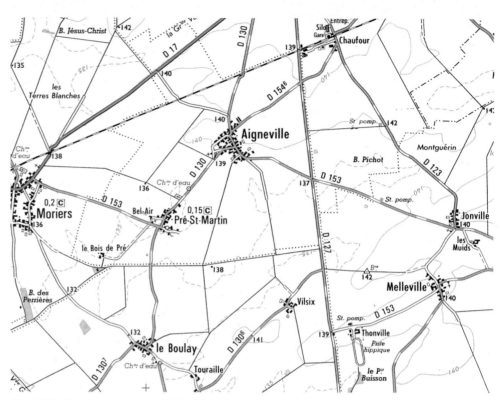

Fig. 5.23 The Beauce region (1:50 000)

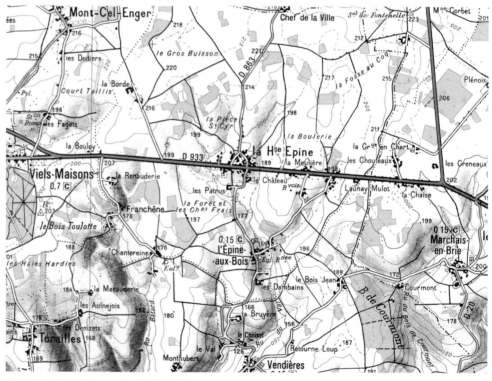

Fig. 5.24 The Brie region (1:50 000)

dispersed settlement pattern of villages and farms. As shown in the south east of the extract the word 'Brie' is quite common throughout the pays. It is, of course, the name of the distinctive cheese produced from the area.

Côte de Champagne

Another well-known name is that of champagne; perhaps the most famous product of the whole Paris Basin, yet confined to only a small area. Part of this area is shown in Fig. 5.26.

The champagne grape, as Fig. 5.25 shows, is grown close to the northern limits of vine growing or viticulture. There are various reasons for its success.

a The cooler temperatures are compensated for by the south and south-east facing scarp slopes which give a favourable aspect.

b Forests, such as the one above Trépail, give shelter while the slopes give protection from the danger of late frosts.

c The loamy, chalk based soil is warm and well-drained. Its colour helps to reflect light which speeds up the maturing of the grapes.

d Above all else, there is a long tradition of skill in viticulture. Many of the high standards were set by the Benedictine monks, especially Dom Perignon. Wines from many local vineyards are skilfully blended, and undergo a double fermentation to produce the finished sparkling wine.

Vineyards are small (over 70 per cent of those around Trepail are of less than one hectare). Usually, some 10 000 vines are planted per hectare. They are laid out in rows about a metre apart, and each vine is about 80 centimetres from its neighbour. The result is the orderly, intensive landscape shown on Fig. 5.26, with access roads breaking up the pattern of small fields.

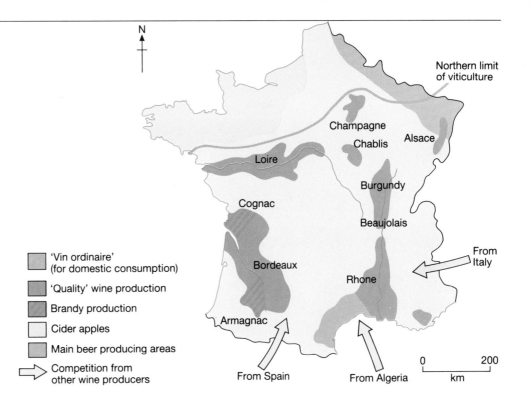

Fig. 5.25 Alcohol producing areas of France. Alcoholism and related diseases are major causes of death in France

Assignments

1 (*Text, and Figs. 5.23 and 5.24*) Draw up a table to compare Beauce and Brie. You should consider: location, soil, farming and settlement.

2 (*Fig. 5.26*) Draw an annotated sketch to show (a) the main landscape features and (b) the factors which have encouraged vine growing.

Fig. 5.26 The Côte de Champagne, near Trépail

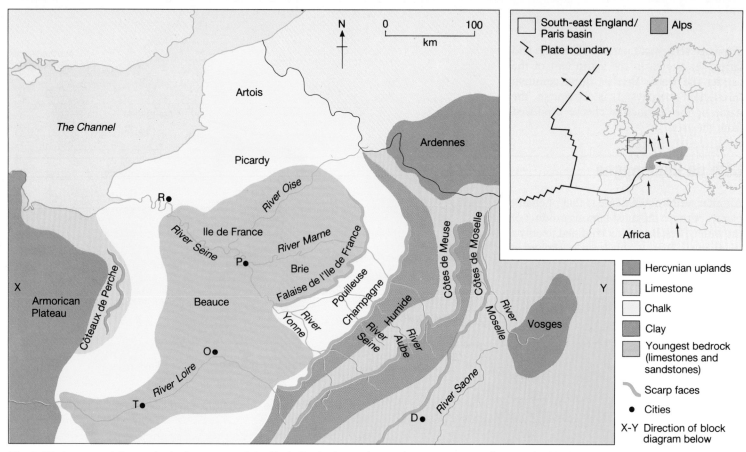

Fig. 5.27 Aspects of the geological structure of the Paris Basin. Inset shows plate movements that resulted in Alpine folding 25 million years ago

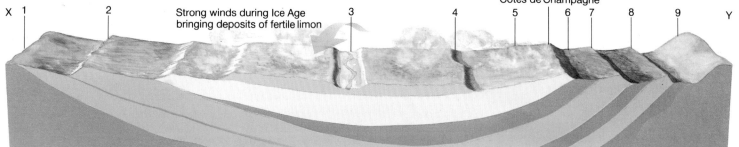

Fig. 5.28 Simplified block diagram of the geology of the Paris Basin

Assignments

1 (*Fig. 5.27 and 5.28*) Compare the block diagram with the map and match each of the numbers with the following: Vosges; R. Seine; Côteaux du Perche; Champagne Humide; Côte de Meuse; Côte de Moselle; Champagne Pouilleause; Armorica; Falaise de L'Ile de France.

2 (*Figs. 5.27, and 5.28*) Study these diagrams and complete the following:

The Paris Basin is a fertile circular lowland of metamorphic/sedimentary origin. Escarpments/clay vales have scarp slopes mainly facing southeast and east/ northwest and west. The outermost escarpments such as the Côtes de Meuse and Côtes de Moselle are formed from chalk/limestone; nearer Paris, the Côtes de Champagne is mainly chalk/limestone while the Falaise de L'Ile de France consists of geologically young deposits of limestone and sandstone. Separating the escarpments are moist clay/sandstone

vales such as Beauce/Champagne humide. Masking these underlying rocks are more recent deposits of river gravel and over large areas, fertile, stoneless deposits of wind blown moraine/limon. Various rivers drain the region creating gaps in the escarpments and encouraging routes to converge on the capital _____. The area is drained to the west by the River Moselle/ Loire and to the north west by the River Seine/Saone and its main tributaries such as the _____ and the _____.

Computerised flower growing in the Netherlands

Another intensively cultivated landscape is shown in Fig. 5.29. This is part of the famous Dutch bulb fields, visited by thousands of tourists each year. It lies between Leiden and Haarlem on the warm, lime-rich sandy soils sheltered by the coastal sand dunes. To ensure that the bulbs are of the highest quality, the flowers are cut off at an early stage.

So great is the speed of change, however, that tulips in fields may come to be just for the tourists. Two thirds of all the world's exports of cut flowers come from the Netherlands, but increasingly from glass-houses. Even in the famous Westland district (Fig. 5.30), the production of cut flowers and pot plants is now more important than that of vegetables (for example, tomatoes, lettuces, cucumbers). In this 'city of glass', a typical holding is about 1 hectare in size, employing two or three people.

Such a landscape represents an enormous investment. This is because greenhouses are not just to provide warmth and protection. They represent a computerised, artificial environment. According to the instructions keyed in by the grower, watering, fertilising, temperatures and lighting levels are determined by the computer. The use of subsidised Dutch gas helps to keep heating costs down.

The value of flower exports from the Netherlands rose from £250 millions in 1965 to £900 millions in 1985, and is expected to grow at 13 per cent per year.

Most of the flowers are sold at one of a dozen auctions. But dominating the export market is the Aalsmeer auction market (see Fig. 5.31). Handling some 12 million flowers and 900 000 pot plants daily is an enormous task, as the extract suggests. Needless to say, the computer again plays an important role.

Aalsmeer: the world's biggest flower auction

As you look down the length of the vast building – in area the equivalent of 300 soccer pitches – you see more flowers than you're likely to see in the rest of your life. And they're all moving automatically on computer-controlled trolleys on rails, to or from six great auction rooms seating 2 000 buyers.

Before the buyers, in their steeply-tiered seats, are two vast clocks on the wall denominated in Dutch cents (100 of them to the guilder). Trolleys packed with warm bursts of colour in the form of roses, freesias, sunflowers, statice, ferns and narcissi move relentlessly past the clocks. Nine hundred transactions an hour are made on each clock, requiring of each bidder the special skills of a Space Invaders champion.

The computer which has guided the trolleys into the auction room like gaudily-decorated Daleks automatically registers the sale and within another 15 minutes has directed the blooms to the buyers' warehouses which line the half-mile length of one side of the co-operative. There, they are re-sorted, re packed and despatched by road, rail and air all over Europe and the world.

Flowers cut by hand in greenhouses in the afternoon start reaching the Aalsmeer Auction by 6.30 pm and then onwards through the night. The auctioneering begins the next morning at 6.30 am and closes by midday. Most of the flowers leave Holland by nightfall in refrigerated containers or pre-chilled boxes. By the next day they are on sale throughout Europe and in America and Asia.

Aalsmeer and its flowers give a glimpse of what the future technological Europe will be like. At Aalsmeer, it is colourful, but in other fields of endeavour, the implications are deeper and could even be frightening.

(*The Scotsman*, 7 January 1986)

Fig. 5.29 Outdoor floriculture in the Netherlands

Fig. 5.30 Westland: the 'City of Glass'

Fig. 5.31 Bidding in progress at the Aalsmeer flower auction

Ex Undis: an arable farm in East Flevoland

Ex Undis is an example of a highly intensive farm in the New Polderlands (see Fig. 5.32). Appropriately its name means 'from the waves' for it was in 1957 that the water was finally drained from the East Flevoland polder.

The farm is run by Mr de Boer, who went to an Agricultural College and trained for a year in the USA. His father was originally responsible for the farm, leasing the land from the Dutch Government in 1970. The de Boers moved from the Groningen area but it took three unsuccessful applications before Mr de Boer Senior, then aged 49, was accepted as a farmer on the New Lands.

Like all other neighbouring farms set in this 'geometric' landscape (see Figs. 5.33 and 5.34) Ex Undis is rectangular in shape. It consists of 2 blocks of land each 300 × 1000 metres giving an area of 60 hectares. Such a shape helps to reduce the costs of access and drainage while making it easier to use machinery. Drainage ditches mark the field boundaries while trees around the farm buildings provide useful shelter and help to break up the horizontal landscape.

Fig. 5.33 Aerial view of East Flevoland

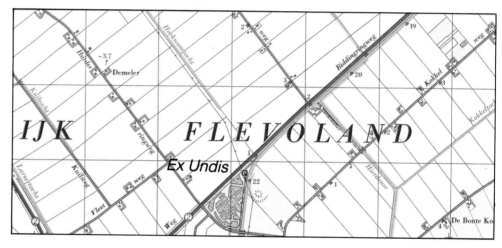

Fig. 5.34 Area around Ex Undis (1:50 000)

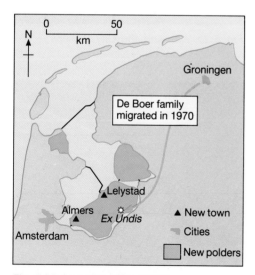

Fig. 5.32 Location of Ex Undis

Fig. 5.35 shows that Ex Undis is purely an arable farm. Wheat, potatoes and sugar beet are the main crops. This is because of the suitable soil conditions. As Fig. 5.36 shows the soil is rich in lime and potassium. After all, Mr de Boer is ploughing up a former sea bed with its shell and fish remains. The choice of the remaining crops depends on Mr de Boer's assessment of the market. Beans, peas and oats have been grown.

Yields are very high (see Fig. 5.37), even by Dutch standards which are among the highest in the world. The farm is a highly mechanised, scientifically-run unit with a large input of fertilisers and pesticides.

Often this involves hiring an aircraft for aerial spraying.

Unlike many other Dutch farmers, Mr de Boer does not buy or sell through a co-operative. His high quality seed potatoes are sold to France and West Germany via a potato merchant; wheat is sold at Groningen while the sugar beet is processed near Amsterdam. Mr de Boer feels that he has greater freedom of action by not joining a co-operative. Perhaps this is to be expected of someone who is really a 'sea bed pioneer farmer'. He is reminded of this by his annual 'harvest of shells' (Fig. 5.38) after ploughing. During World War II what is now Flevoland was on a bomber flightpath between the U.K. and Germany!

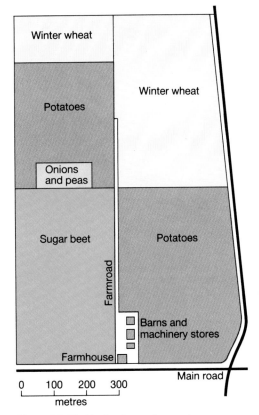

Fig. 5.35 Ex Undis: farm plan and crop patterns

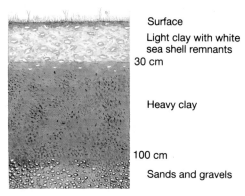

Surface
Light clay with white sea shell remnants
30 cm

Heavy clay

100 cm
Sands and gravels

Fig. 5.36 Ex Undis: soil profile

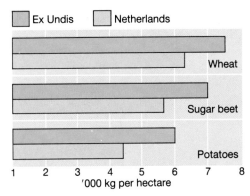

Ex Undis   Netherlands

Wheat

Sugar beet

Potatoes

'000 kg per hectare

Fig. 5.37 Crop yields of Ex Undis compared with the Netherlands as a whole

Fig. 5.38 A bomb harvest at Ex Undis

Fig. 5.39 Ground view of fields of Ex Undis

Services in East Flevoland

For many of their daily needs the de Boers use the village of Biddinghuizen (see Fig. 5.40B), seven kilometres away. Higher order services, especially concerning the farm, are obtained from the small town of Dronten. The main shopping centre which is the New Town of Lelystad is not popular with the de Boers at all. They prefer to travel to the older town of Harderwijk or to Amsterdam (about an hour's drive away).

It is interesting to compare the present day settlement pattern with the original plan drawn up in 1954 (Fig. 5.40A). There were to be 10 villages with low order services; a small town with higher order services – Dronten, and finally, serving as the New Polderlands 'capital', the New Town of Lelystad. However, because of (i) the reduced significance of farm employment and (ii) increased car ownership, the original ten villages were reduced by the 1965 plan to only two.

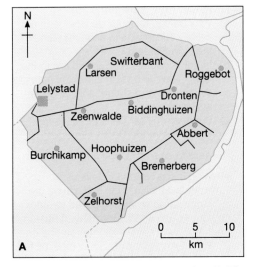

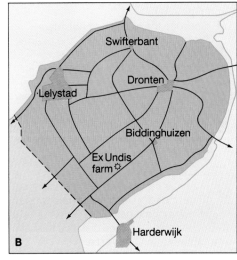

Fig. 5.40 A: The 1954 settlement plan B: The reality of the 1980s

Fig. 5.41 Land use conflict: urban encroachment on farmland

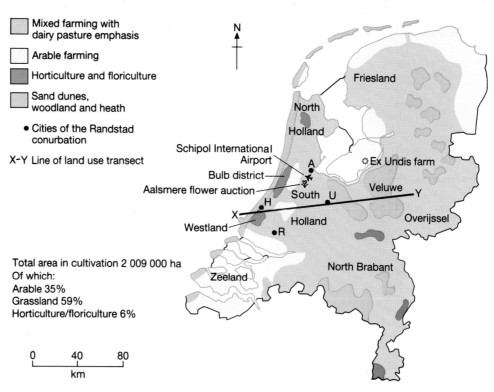

Mixed farming with dairy pasture emphasis

Arable farming

Horticulture and floriculture

Sand dunes, woodland and heath

● Cities of the Randstad conurbation

X–Y Line of land use transect

Total area in cultivation 2 009 000 ha
Of which:
Arable 35%
Grassland 59%
Horticulture/floriculture 6%

0   40   80
km

Fig. 5.42 Agricultural land use in the Netherlands

Fig. 5.43 Transect showing land use in the Netherlands

Assignments

1 (*Text, atlas and Fig. 5.30 and 5.42*)
   a) Describe the location of the Westland district, mentioning the neighbouring cities.
   b) In what way does the presence of large cities influence land prices?
   c) What is the average size of holding in Westland and why are they expensive to run?

2 (*Text and 5.42, atlas, newspaper extract and Fig. 5.31*)
   a) Describe the location of Aalsmeer flower auction, mentioning the nearby airport.
   b) Explain why this is the largest commercial building in the world.
   c) Why is quick marketing from Aalsmeer so important?
   d) What are the advantages of the Netherlands' location for the export trade?

3 (*Fig. 5.32, 5.34 and text*)
   a) Describe the position of Ex Undis farm.
   b) What does 'Ex Undis' mean and why is it an appropriate name?
   c) Work out the average distance between farm houses in this area.
   d) List the ways in which the area is a 'man-made landscape'.

4 (*Text, and Figs. 5.35 and 5.36*)
   a) Why do you think Mr de Boer was not initially successful in acquiring land in the New Polders?
   b) Imagine you were on a field trip to the farm. Draw up a set of summary notes to cover: size and shape; soil; land use and markets.
   c) Suggest why Mr De Boer achieves yields above the Dutch average.

5 (*General/research*) Copy and complete:

   Farming in the Netherlands is very intensive/extensive. This is because the country is large/small compared to other countries such as W. Germany. It has an area of _____ square kilometres and on this land a population of _____ must be fed, housed and employed. This gives a population density of _____ per km². In places such as South Holland it is as high as _____ per km². Here agriculture has to compete with the urban land of the south Randstadt cities of Amsterdam/Rotterdam and Utrecht/The Hague. Because of land shortage, therefore, the Dutch have been forced to turn to the more intensive forms of farming i.e. floriculture/horticulture/sheep rearing, orchards and rearing of beef/dairy farming.

6 (*Fig. 5.41 and 5.39*) How does this photograph show land use conflict?

7 (*Figs. 5.42 and 5.43*) Copy and complete the land use transect. Replace the numbers with the following: Utrecht; coastal sand dunes; mixed farming with dairying; heathland (with National Parks); arable farming; Westland area of intensive horticulture/floriculture under glass.

Danish agricultural exports

One feature which both Dutch and Danish farming have in common is that in these countries agricultural goods make up a significant part of the total value of exports (24 per cent – Netherlands, 26 per cent Denmark in 1984). Fig. 5.45 reminds us, for example, of the large bacon export trade from Denmark to Britain. The traditional 'British breakfast' with bacon, eggs and butter used to be based to an important extent on Danish pigs, poultry and dairy cows. Although Britain is now self-sufficient in egg production there are still strong trading links with the Danish farming landscape (Fig. 5.44).

Assignments

1 (*Fig. 5.44*)
   a) Which words best describe the Danish landscape shown in the photograph: flat, hilly or undulating?
   b) Describe the distribution of the farm houses.
   c) In what way does the land appear to be suited to grain crops?
   d) What is the function of the woodland?
   e) What are the main differences/ similarities between this landscape and that of East Flevoland? (see page 80)

2 (*Fig. 5.45*)
   a) Which four countries, in rank order, are the leading importers of Danish agricultural products?
   b) What are the two main categories of agricultural imports into Britain?
   c) Comment on the likely effect of a change in British diet on the import of agricultural imports from Denmark.

3 (*Atlas/research*) Draw a map of the main export routes from Denmark to Britain.

4 Draw an annotated sketch of Fig. 5.44 and mark the following: undulating land; hedgerow boundaries, arable fields; woodland; dispersed farmhouses.

Fig. 5.44 An agricultural landscape in Denmark

Fig. 5.45 **Geographical distribution of Danish agricultural exports in 1984 (in million krone)**

	Cattle and meat	Pigs and pig-meat	Butter	Cheese	Poultry and eggs	Canned milk and meat	Other agric. products	Sugar, mink skins, etc.	Total agric. products
Belgium, Luxembourg	10.6	7.4	0.6	99.2	1.3	5.0	354.9	47.1	526.1
France	69.1	780.9	9.1	15.5	3.6	156.6	408.2	142.6	1585.8
Netherlands	21.8	6.0	0.1	22.9	0.6	40.3	763.3	53.7	908.6
Italy	1844.1	672.8	23.8	225.3	1.1	148.6	387.8	47.9	3351.2
West Germany	404.0	1274.3	177.8	885.9	109.8	327.9	2901.4	554.3	6635.4
United Kingdom	119.6	3881.8	980.8	351.5	148.6	1181.6	911.7	456.1	8031.7
Ireland	–	8.9	0.0	3.1	3.3	8.4	18.3	–	41.9
Greece	72.7	95.7	6.1	139.2	14.3	94.3	10.9	5.1	438.3
EC	2541.8	6727.8	1198.3	1742.5	282.5	1962.8	5756.4	1306.8	21519.0
Sweden	4.0	87.4	0.4	70.0	2.0	15.6	757.7	130.3	1067.3
Norway	10.1	3.9	0.0	43.0	4.7	8.1	227.6	223.1	520.5
Finland	1.5	0.3	0.0	17.0	0.8	1.4	150.2	46.0	217.3
Other EFTA countries	4.1	18.8	0.9	39.2	12.9	9.0	161.3	344.5	590.8
EFTA	19.8	110.4	1.3	169.2	20.3	34.2	1296.8	743.9	2395.9
Eastern Europe	31.3	0.3	7.8	1.3	0.1	31.5	644.8	0.5	717.4
Other European countries	30.6	9.5	3.8	76.1	6.2	32.9	69.6	26.0	254.8
USA	61.1	953.0	9.3	545.5	5.9	2361.3	143.4	432.4	4511.9
Other countries	358.4	2684.5	395.3	1542.5	373.6	2685.1	626.7	517.5	9183.6
Total world	3043.0	10485.4	1615.8	4077.1	688.6	7107.7	8537.8	3027.1	38582.4

The adaptable Danes

The pattern of Danish agricultural trade dates from major changes that took place in the 1870s. Danish farming showed that it could adapt to changing circumstances.

Competition from the Prairies

Up until the 1870s, Danish farmers concentrated on growing grain and rearing beef cattle. With the building of the trans-continental railways and the opening up of the North American Prairies, the Danes could not compete with the cheap flood of grain imports from the USA and Canada.

So the Danes switched to dairy farming, with related pig and poultry rearing. In Britain and Germany there was a growing demand from the increasing industrial population for butter, cheese and bacon. On the west coast of Denmark a new port, Esbjerg, became the main trading link with Britain.

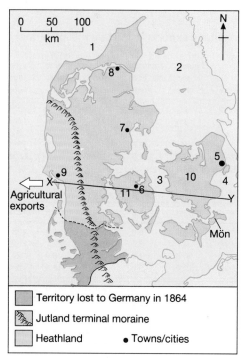

Fig. 5.46 A base map of Denmark (X and Y indicate line of transect)

Map legend:
- Territory lost to Germany in 1864
- Jutland terminal moraine
- Heathland • Towns/cities

Scale: 0 50 100 km

Agricultural exports (X — Y)

Mön

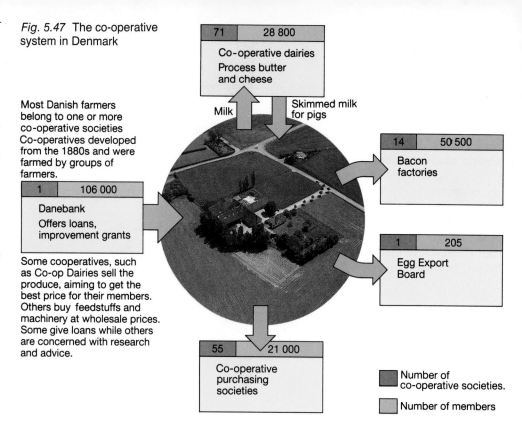

Fig. 5.47 The co-operative system in Denmark

Most Danish farmers belong to one or more co-operative societies. Co-operatives developed from the 1880s and were farmed by groups of farmers.

Some cooperatives, such as Co-op Dairies sell the produce, aiming to get the best price for their members. Others buy feedstuffs and machinery at wholesale prices. Some give loans while others are concerned with research and advice.

- Co-operative dairies: 71 / 28 800 — Process butter and cheese
- Danebank: 1 / 106 000 — Offers loans, improvement grants
- Bacon factories: 14 / 50 500
- Egg Export Board: 1 / 205
- Co-operative purchasing societies: 55 / 21 000

Milk / Skimmed milk for pigs

Legend:
- Number of co-operative societies.
- Number of members

The dairy farming era: the 1870s to the 1960s

During this period this small country with a population of just over five millions built up a very successful, export oriented farming industry. Various factors help to explain the very high productivity and success of the Danes.

a By the 1870s the Danish farmers were mainly owner-occupiers. It was therefore in the interest of the farmers to adapt to new circumstances and invest in new technology.

b New technology was adopted, for example, the new cream separator (invented in the 1870s). This allowed large scale separation of cream and skimmed milk in dairies such as the one shown in Fig. 5.49. The skimmed milk was then returned to the farms to help feed the new breeds of pigs.

c New livestock breeds were introduced and existing breeds were improved by selective breeding. High milk yields were achieved from the Friesian while the Danish Red gives a very high butter fat content. Careful breeding also produced the Danish Landrace pig suited to the British demand for lean cuts of bacon.

d High standards were ensured through strict systems of quality control. This was encouraged by: (i) the co-operatives (see Fig. 5.47), which insisted that only the best quality butter, cheese, bacon and eggs were exported; (ii) the Government, whose LUR mark is the official seal of approval.

e The standards of agricultural education and research in Denmark are very high. Only after a full training course are Danish farmers issued a 'Green Licence' allowing them to run a farm.

Although dairy farming dominated, the farming landscape was mainly an arable one, especially in the east (see Fig. 5.44). The cattle were mainly stall-fed for most of the year; home produced crops being supplemented by imported maize and soya beans. Outdoor grazing was controlled by electric fences or tethering.

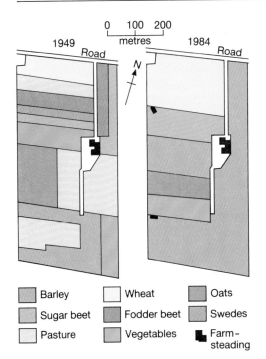

Barley Wheat Oats
Sugar beet Fodder beet Swedes
Pasture Vegetables Farm-steading

Fig. 5.48 Changes in a sample farm on the Island of Mön

Increased specialisation: the 1960s to the present

In the past thirty years Danish farming has changed (Fig. 5.48). Some Danes maintain that 'Agribusiness' has taken over. There is an increased emphasis, especially in the east, on larger, more specialised farms, often using 'factory techniques' (but no battery-cage hens).

Cereal production, especially barley, has increased, encouraged by the CAP (see page 74) and the growing demand from the Danish brewing industry. Responding to criticism of CAP, one Danish agricultural expert maintained that it was a very welcome food subsidy for the consumers.

Dairy farming has been affected by EC milk quotas, and butter production has been cut. New markets have been found, however, especially in the Middle East. Technology now allows the Danes to produce Feta cheese from cow's milk instead of sheep's milk.

There may be fewer of them, but Danish farmers are as adaptable as ever as they approach the 21st century.

Trends in Danish agriculture

	1960	1970	1980	1984
Number of farms	196 076	140 197	114 213	92 018
Average farm size (ha)	15.8	21.0	25.3	30.7
Area of agricultural land ('000 ha)	3 074	2 941	2 884	2 855
Agriculture's share of the working population (%)	16	9	6	5.7
Number of dairy cows ('000s)	1 438	1 153	1 104	1 010
Number of pigs ('000s)	6 147	8 361	9 957	8 717
Cereals (as % of agricultural land)	46.7	59.1	63	60
Root crops (as % of agricultural land)	18.3	9.8	8.4	8.2
Grass (as % of agricultural land)	31.7	27.2	23.1	22.5
Use of nitrogen fertilizer (kg per ha)	40.0	91.0	135	136

Assignments

1 (*Atlas/Fig. 5.46*) Name stretches of sea 1–4; towns/cities 5–9; islands 10–11.

2 (*Text*)
   a) Explain why the Danes switched to dairying in the 1870s.
   b) What is meant by co-operative farming (Fig. 5.47)?
   c) What do you think are the advantages and disadvantages of belonging to a co-operative?

3 (*Text*) What ensures the high quality of Danish agricultural exports?

4 (*Text/Fig. 5.48*)
   a) Describe and explain the main trends in Danish farming (1960–84) with regard to (i) number and size of farms, (ii) the size of the labour force, (iii) livestock and grain cultivation.
   b List the changes on the sample farm and try to explain them.

5 (*Fig. 5.50*)
   a) Match the numbers with: Copenhagen; the Jutland moraine; sand dunes; North Sea; Zealand; Funen; the Sound; the Great Belt; outwash sands.
   b) Explain the farming contrasts between West and East Denmark.

Fig. 5.49 The world's first co-operative dairy at Hjedding, West Jutland in the 1880s

Fig. 5.50 Transect of Denmark (X-Y see Fig. 5.46) showing soils and agricultural activity

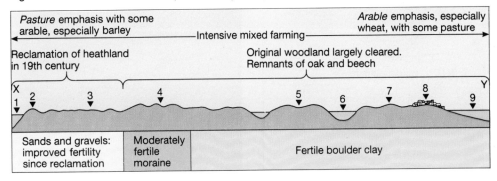

Farmscapes of upland areas

Denmark, East England, Benelux and North East France form a zone with high agricultural yields (see Fig. 5.51). This is partly explained by the presence of much of Western Europe's urban population. In addition, the conditions of relief and climate are favourable, while the standards of farming technology and organisation are very high.

Away from this core, yields begin to diminish for various reasons. The Mediterranean areas have already been considered so we will look at the upland, marginal areas of North-west Europe out with the European Community, starting with a Norwegian farm.

Fig. 5.51 Intensity of land use in Europe

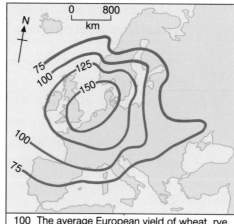

100 The average European yield of wheat, rye, barley, oats, maize, potatoes, sugar beet, hay

Fig. 5.52 **Main features of land use in selected countries**

	A	B	C	D
Denmark	4237	62.6	5.9	11.6
Norway	30 787	2.6	0.4	21.7
Finland	30 547	7.9	0.5	76.3
France	54 563	34.2	23.6	26.7
West Germany	24 434	30.7	19.5	30.0
Italy	29 402	42.4	17.5	21.6
Austria	8273	17.6	24.7	39.7
Belgium/Luxembourg	3282	26.8	21.5	21.4
Netherlands	3396	25.4	34.2	8.6
Portugal	9164	38.7	5.8	39.7
Spain	49 954	41.1	22.1	30.6
Sweden	41 162	7.2	1.8	64.2
Switzerland	3977	9.9	40.9	26.5
Ireland	6889	14.1	70.1	4.6

A: Total area ('000 ha)   B: Arable and cropland
C: Permanent pasture   D: Forest and woodland

Field study notes of Nes farm, Hardangerfjord

Location: On the south east facing side of Hardangerfjord, about 75 kilometres east of Bergen (see Fig. 5.53).

Owner: Her Torstein Nes – married with a family of four (3 boys/1 girl). Farm has been owned by the family since 1644.

Size/land use: Main farm covers an area of twelve hectares. Her Nes also owns two areas of summer grazing, called saeters. The lower one is three kilometres away and 230 metres high; the higher saeter is at 700 metres and lies above the tree line (Fig. 5.56).

Fig. 5.53 Location of the Nes Farm, Norway

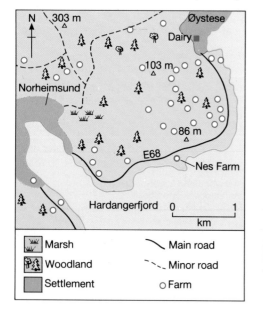

Marsh
Woodland
Settlement

Main road
Minor road
Farm

Fig. 5.54 General view of Nes Farm from above the main road

Pasture/grass: still cut for hay rather than silage. Although tractor/mower are used, small patches are still cut by scythe. After a damp spell the hay is still 'hung out to dry' on lines slung between poles.

Orchard: plums, apples, pears, raspberries and strawberries form an important part of the farmer's income. This area specialises in pears, and Her Nes is a member of one of the long established fruit co-operatives (dating from 1889). Membership means that he will receive as good a price as any fruit farmer in Norway.

Vegetable plot: carrots, potatoes, cabbage etc. – grown for family use. Nes family are almost self-sufficient in foods – flour, sugar and coffee are their main purchases.

Livestock: 4 cows, 5–10 sheep, 1 pig. During summer months cows (often tethered) graze in the orchard, but are indoors and stall fed for 9–10 months (see sketch below).

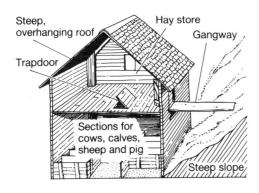

Milk is taken to the dairy in Øystese to be made into milk and cheese.

Sheep are taken to the lower and then the upper saeter during the summer (that is, transhumance) and are kept indoors for eight months.

Labour/machinery: Family labour, including one son who is a mechanic. Summer help is taken on at haymaking. For its size Nes is well equipped with machinery – a tractor, a forage-harvester, a muck-spreader, a plough, a hay wagon and electric milking machines.

Other sources of income: Another son, Otto, has established and manages a camping and

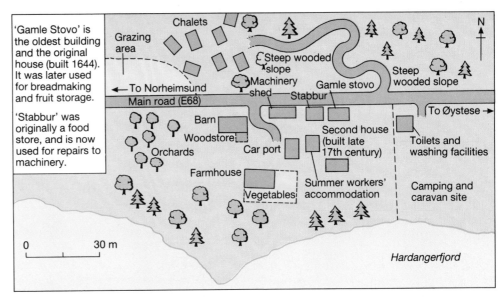

'Gamle Stovo' is the oldest building and the original house (built 1644). It was later used for breadmaking and fruit storage.

'Stabbur' was originally a food store, and is now used for repairs to machinery.

Fig. 5.55 Sketch plan of the Nes Farm

Fig. 5.56 Nes Farm: the high saeter

Fig. 5.57 The caravan site on the Nes Farm

caravan site (see Figs. 5.55 and 5.57) as well as eight wooden chalets.

The chalets are built in a traditional style, and were erected by the farmer who made use of the woodland on the farm. During the summer they are let as part of package deal holidays involving crossings from the UK on Olsen-Bergen Line ships. In winter Norwegian skiers use them.

A probable change: Mr Nes may give up dairying. Most farms have invested in milk pipelines connected to a large tank. Her Nes still uses milk churns but the dairy at Øystese has decided to stop accepting them. He has to balance the cost of new investment against his income from milk.

Assignments

1 (*Fig. 5.52*) Draw divided bargraphs to compare land use in Denmark and Norway. Referring to an atlas explain the differences.

2 (*Fig. 5.55 and atlas*) **a**) Describe the location of the Nes Farm. **b**) Suggest why Mr Nes tries to grow as large a crop of hay as possible. **c**) Describe and explain the design of the barn. **d**) Why have the Nes family developed a camp/caravan site? **e**) (*Fig. 5.57*) What advantages does this site have? **f**) Explain the relatively large amount of machinery on such a small farm.

3 (*Discussion*) If you were Her Nes would you give up dairying? What factors would influence your decision?

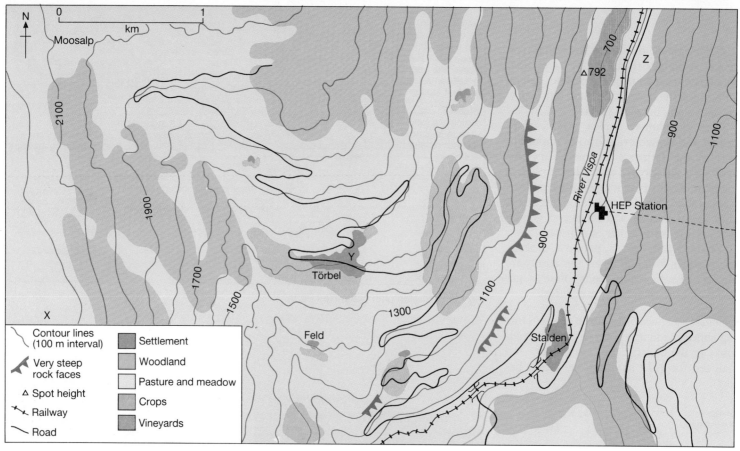

Fig. 5.58 Relief, land use and settlement in the Törbel area of the Swiss Alps

Fig. 5.59 (below) Törbel: influence of altitude and seasonal rhythms

Farming in the Alps: the village of Törbel

A critical factor influencing change is the improvement of transport links. The Swiss village of Törbel (Fig. 5.62) was only accessible by footpath until 1937, when the new road was built. Only in 1955 were the first mechanical devices (for example, garden rotovators) introduced. This village still displays many of the traditional features of Alpine farming.

Assignments

1 (Fig. 5.60) Using an atlas, name the following: rivers 1–2; cities 3–6; neighbouring countries 7–10; peak 11; ski-resort 12.

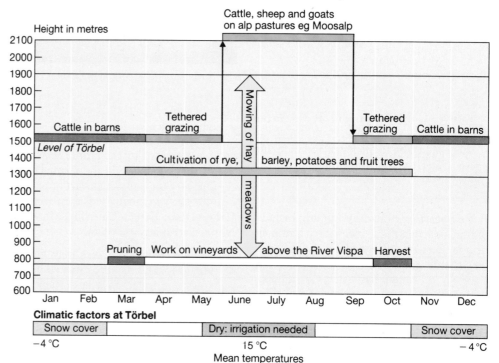

2 (*Figs. 5.58 and 5.59*) Copy and choose the correct 'rights' or 'lefts'.

Törbel lies west/east of the Vispa valley which links the Rhine/Rhone valley with the resort of Basle/Zermatt to the south. The village lies on a valley bench about 1800/1500 metres high. Fortunately for the village it faces towards the north/south giving it a favourable aspect. Even in winter it can have 7 hours of sunshine/day compared to only ½ hour at the lower/higher village of Stalden nearby.

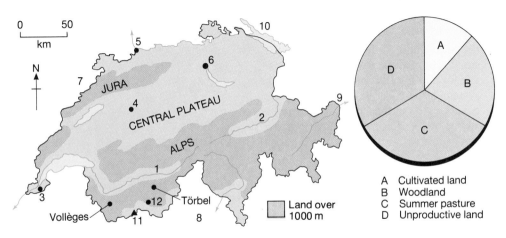

Fig. 5.60 A base map of Switzerland

A Cultivated land
B Woodland
C Summer pasture
D Unproductive land

Fig. 5.61 Land-use in the Swiss Alps

Using the mountain slopes at Törbel

There are many environmental problems to overcome in mountainous areas and over hundreds of years the people of Törbel have created a landscape which is as much man-made as natural.

Various factors have been taken into account. *Aspect* (i.e. the direction that the slope is facing) is important. In this German speaking part of Switzerland (see page 6) they say that Törbel is on the *Sonnenseite* (sunny side) as opposed to the *Schattenseite* (shadow side). Elsewhere *L'Adret* and *L'Ubac* are, respectively, the corresponding French terms. *Altitude* and the steepness of *slope* are other physical factors as well as *precipitation*. Fig. 5.59 shows the length of snow cover. Remarkably the average precipitation is only 540 mm per year. This relatively low figure occurs because the mountains create a localised *rain shadow* effect. To overcome the summer drought, a series of water channels called *bisses* have been built, tapping distant springs and glacial meltwaters.

Over the years a distinctive mountain economy has developed with farmers using a wide range of slopes with different aspects from the valley bottom to the mountain top. Four main land uses are involved (see Fig. 5.58).

a *Woodland* Originally a great deal more of the land below the treeline (the maximum altitude of trees) was wooded. In fact the name Törbel is from the Celtic

Fig. 5.62 Törbel: Note the steep wooded slope, nucleated settlement and scattered fields

word *dorwia* meaning 'larch forest'. Today, thanks to skilful management, the spruce, fir and larch woodland can: (i) provide building timber and fuel; (ii) retain both soil and moisture on the steeper slopes; (iii) enhance the scenery, and (iv) protect Törbel from avalanches. Avalanches occur from November to April and are especially threatening when the *Föhn* wind blows (see page 57) down the Vispa valley.

b *Pasture* From one point of view the

warmth of the Föhn is welcome because it clears the snow from the pastures. Fig. 5.58 shows that pastures extend beyond the treeline, reaching a maximum of 2600 metres. Although it is declining, the system of *transhumance* is still carried out. Traditionally this involved the movement of cattle, sheep and goats to the summer pastures or *alpages*. In some areas this involved several intermediate pastures but Törbel is fortunate in having the Alpage pastures close by. On the rich grazing of the Moosalp (Fig. 5.58)

89

the Simmental cattle were herded by a small group of men who were responsible for milking and cheese making. This system freed the rest of the village to concentrate on the crops, hay making and irrigation during the long days of the brief summer.

c *Crops* While the alpages are owned by the whole village, giving each farmer the rights of common grazing, fields are individually owned. Where slope, soil and aspect are favourable the land is cropped for rye, oats, barley and potatoes. On the steeper slopes hay is mown for winter fodder. Each farmer's fields are scattered and not grouped together. This can involve an average round trip time of fifty minutes walking from house to field.

d *Vines and fruits* Longer journeys, with overnight stays in log huts, are involved in looking after the terraced vineyards above the Vispa river. In addition cherry, apple and plum trees are grown on the borders of the grain fields.

Changes in alpine farming

Although some of the traditional rhythms of farming life can still be seen, Alpine farming has steadily been changing over the past forty years. People have left, attracted by the jobs in the cities and the chemical and metallurgical industries of the Rhone valley. Those people who wish to stay have had to adapt to various changes.

a *Land consolidation* One problem facing farmers is that the fields are scattered and too small to be suitable for modern, time-saving machinery. Fig. 5.63 also shows that access to individual fields is along narrow paths.

This picturesque 'patchwork quilt' landscape is a result of: (i) a traditional sharing out of good and poor quality land, and (ii) the division of land between all the children when parents die.

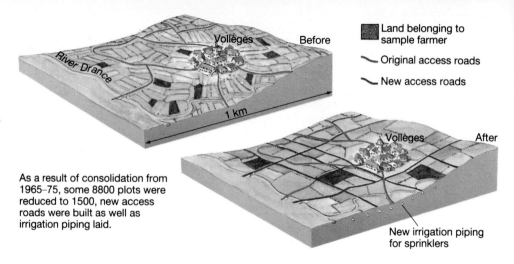

As a result of consolidation from 1965–75, some 8800 plots were reduced to 1500, new access roads were built as well as irrigation piping laid.

Land belonging to sample farmer
Original access roads
New access roads
New irrigation piping for sprinklers

Fig. 5.63 Land conservation in Switzerland in Vollèges Commune

Over a period of some ten years land consolidation was carried out in the commune of Vollèges. New access roads, and unified fields with sprinkler irrigation were created. This programme of modernisation was, however, expensive and involved government subsidies. Some farmers, such as those specialising in intensive vegetable and strawberry cultivation may benefit from small fields.

b *Decline of transhumance* Fewer people and fewer cattle make the seasonal migration to the lower *mayen* and upper *alpage* grazings. In some areas the cattle are kept in the valleys, close to the co-operative butter, cheese, yoghurt and condensed milk factories. With improved road links to the pastures, the hay is brought down and extra foodstuffs for example cattle cake, soya etc. purchased. For those men still involved new cowsheds and living quarters have been built. Rather than convert the milk to butter or cheese on the alpage it is sent directly by pipeline to the dairy in the valley below.

c *Impact of tourism* (see pages 134–136) With the decline of transhumance, chalets on the lower 'mayen' pastures have been converted to holiday accommodation or second homes. A new type of tourist transhumance has provided additional sources of income for the Swiss mountain farmers.

One major problem, however, is the loss of land as suggested below.

Loss of farmland in the Swiss Alps

Every second	1 square metre
Every minute	60 square metres
Every day	10 hectares
Every year	350 hectares

Such a loss, for tourist services such as ski-lifts, access roads and parking means that a key feature of the Alpine landscape, its beauty, is under threat.

Assignments

1 (*Fig. 5.58*) **a)** What is the height of the treeline? **b)** Give the heights of the vineyards and Moosalp. **c)** Work out the straight line distance, road distance, and detour index between Standel and Törbel.

2 (*Text*) **a)** Why do dairy cattle spend only a few months on the alpages? **b)** Why do farmers grow as large a crop of hay, etc. as possible?

3 (*Fig. 5.58 and text*) Draw a cross-section between points X, Y and Z. Add notes and symbols to show the main features of land use and settlement.

4 (*Text*) Write brief notes explaining **a)** the decline of transhumance **b)** the advantages of land consolidation.

5 (*Discussion/research*) Is it worthwhile to preserve upland farming communities?

Chapter 6 Resources and power

Protest in Samiland

Where is Samiland? Possibly you know it better as Lapland, the home of Western Europe's remaining nomadic herder, who prefer to be called the Sami rather than the Lapps. By changing their name, the Sami are trying to maintain their *identity*. This involves retaining as much as possible of their traditional style of life and language. But as the extract (written by a Sami) suggests, it is not easy.

In 1979 matters came to a head, attracting international attention. After many years of debate the Norwegian Parliament passed a plan to build a major hydro-power scheme on the Alta-Kautokeino river (Fig. 6.1).

A strong Sami protest campaign was built up, receiving support from Norwegian environmental groups. Non-violent demonstrations were mounted, with at one stage 6000 people from 20 countries demonstrating at the Alta site. Throughout

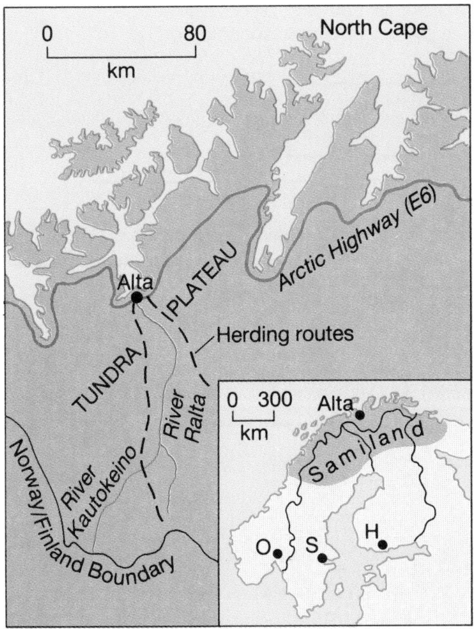

By taking land and water, the basis for making a living is destroyed. By destroying the basis of livelihoods, one destroys the conditions necessary for living in the traditional manner. In taking land and water, one is taking fish and reindeer. When the reindeer are gone, a vital part of the Sami culture is gone.

In making schooling compulsory, one transfers the children to boarding school . . . the children are taught to think in the Western manner, educated. The bond with Nature is broken, they're taught to be masters over Nature, not part of it. After many years of education, it is difficult for anybody to make contact with Nature in the way one does growing up as part of it. Besides which, after the construction of mines, dams, power stations and military bases, there won't even be very much left of Nature.

Schools have been created to realize the needs and ideals of society. School is for man, and it tries to turn dreams into reality. And of course, those who have power and authority also know what is good for the small and the primitive.

That's how small Sami children also learn to have a nose for money, to think of time in terms of money, of land as money . . . Learn that one must have idols, learn to watch idols like new waves, Saturday night fevers, follow the top ten, chew gum. Instead of lasso and reindeer horns they got new toys like machine guns and Hunter jets. That's education that is.

And education has reached the mountain highlands too. The first generation of Samis to use snowscooters and cross country motorbikes is now moving over the highlands. Cars, planes and helicopters make daily life easier. Turf huts and tents have given way to centrally heated houses equipped with TV and electricity. Money is in the thoughts of reindeer owners rather often, and reindeer are valued in terms of money. That's education for you.

(from *Greetings from Lapland* by NilsAslak Valkeapää)

Fig. 6.1 Location of Alta and the Kautokeino River

Government viewpoint	Sami viewpoint
1 The river is an untapped source for HEP	1 The dam and reservoir will flood an important reindeer calving area
2 Electricity supplies are essential for everybody who lives in the North	2 Access roads and pipelines will disrupt our traditional routes
3 Future off-shore oil developments require electricity for related on-shore activities	3 Salmon (on what is the richest salmon fishing river in Western Europe) will not reach their spawning grounds
4 In this northern area we have to import some electricity from the USSR	4 We have grazed our reindeer in this area for centuries. It is part of our birthright

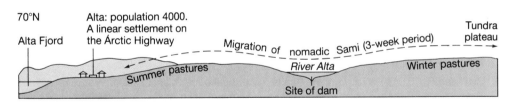

Fig. 6.2 The site of the Alta dam and resource issues at stake

Norway the motto 'elva skal leve' (the river shall live) was heard. Arguments, such as those shown in Fig. 6.2 were put forward by both sides. But, in the end, the Government went ahead, and the scheme has been completed. Measures have been taken to prevent damage to fish and the environment. According to the Government, compensation was given to the Sami, many of whom 'are in favour of the project'. 'The majority (of the Sami) are integrated into Norwegian society.' Most of the Finmark plateau 'where the nomads live, is protected as a National Park'.

This issue shows the different interests involved in resource development. These include:

a *Local interest* versus *national interest*;
b *Traditional life style* versus *dominant culture*.

Lifestyles for the Sami have been changing for many years. Only a small remnant are today reindeer herders. Most are sedentary – farmers, foresters, miners or office workers. Those who are involved in reindeer herding can make a good living. The sleigh has given way to the skidoo (Fig. 6.3) and the bungalow has replaced the cabin.

But there is still the issue of identity. Although the governments involved have set up Sami schools and radio/TV broadcasts in their language, many of the Sami feel that they need more representation. Among the majority population of Norwegians, Swedes and Finns who live in the north, many would argue that the Sami interests are more than adequately catered for.

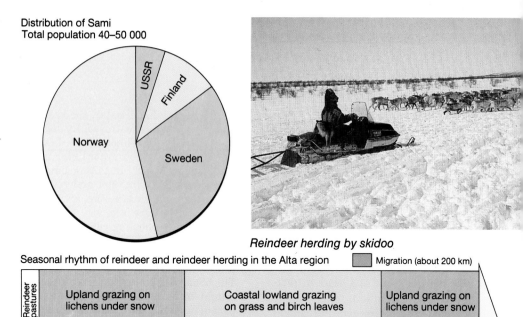

Distribution of Sami
Total population 40–50 000

Reindeer herding by skidoo

Seasonal rhythm of reindeer and reindeer herding in the Alta region   ▨ Migration (about 200 km)

Reindeer pastures	Upland grazing on lichens under snow	Coastal lowland grazing on grass and birch leaves	Upland grazing on lichens under snow
Reindeer management	Slaughtering and sale of reindeer	Calving · Reindeer tend to be scattered	Rutting · Gathering of reindeer

Jan Feb Mar Apr May Jun Jul Aug Sep Oct Nov Dec

Fig. 6.3 Aspects of Sami life

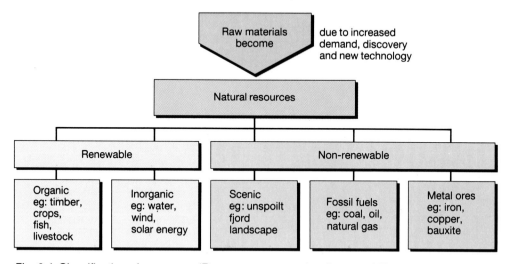

Fig. 6.4 Classification of resources. 'Resources are not, they become.' *Zimmerman*

Assignments

1 (*Fig. 6.1 and atlas*) **a)** In which 4 countries is Samiland located? **b)** Describe the location of Alta, mentioning its distance from Oslo.

2 (*Text and Fig. 6.2*) **a)** What were the Samis' objections to the hydro-scheme? **b)** Do you think that the Norwegian Government was right to go ahead with the scheme?

3 (*Research/discussion*) **a)** Name other minority groups in the Arctic area. **b)** Can groups such as these maintain their identity?

4 (*Figs. 6.3 and 6.4*) **a)** Describe the traditional Sami seasonal rhythm. **b)** How would you classify the type of resources they use?

Labels on image:
RAILWAY SIDINGS ON CAUSEWAY
PELLETIZING AND CONCENTRATING PLANT
KIRUNAVAARA 'IRON MOUNTAIN'
FORMER OPEN CAST WORKINGS
HEAD OFFICE AND ADMINISTRATIVE BUILDINGS
KIRUNA
LAKE LUOSSAJÄRVI
MODERN HOUSING ESTATES
SCRUB BIRCH WOODLAND

Fig. 6.5 Kiruna, Northern Sweden

Resources in Norden

Norden is the name given to Denmark, Finland, Iceland, Norway and Sweden. All these countries, except perhaps Denmark, have certain features in common. These include: a peripheral northern location; a difficult, mainly upland environment; low population density; a similar historical, religious and language background (Finnish is, however, related to Hungarian) and a high standard of living, with an advanced welfare state. Yet less than a hundred years ago many districts of Norden were very poor, with famine and emigration quite common.

Many factors explain Norden's transformation, not least the high educational standards of the people themselves. Also important has been the availability of a wide range of resources, both renewable and non-renewable (see Fig. 6.4). Fish, timber, hydro-power, metallic ores, agricultural products and scenic resources have all provided work and income.

Of the main power resources, Norden lacks significant coal deposits, but this has been a blessing in disguise. Industrial growth has mainly taken place in the twentieth century, using hydro-power at first and then oil and gas. In this way, the towns and cities of Norden have been spared the worst effects of the coal-based industrial landscapes found elsewhere in North-west Europe.

The Northern iron ore fields: a non-renewable resource

One of the largest settlements in Northern Sweden is the town of Kiruna. Lying almost 68°N, it is one of the most northerly towns in the world. Dominating Kiruna, and explaining its very existence, is the Kirunavaara iron ore mountain, split by former open cast workings. Since 1962 the ore has been mined underground and Kiruna now boasts what is claimed to be the world's largest underground mine. From this highly mechanised complex (along with the mines at Gallivare-Malmberget) come 90 per cent of Swedish iron ore exports. These export figures allow Sweden to rank sixth in the world iron ore export league.

Fig. 6.5 shows a landscape typical of a 'robber economy.' It is a landscape which will continue as long as there is a demand for the estimated 3000 million tonnes of reserves of iron ore in these northern fields. What factors explain the growth of this a landscape?

a *Presence of a raw material* In this case high grade iron ore resources had formed in ample quantity in the ancient rocks of the Baltic Shield (see page 18).

b *Markets* Although people were aware of

93

the iron deposits they did not start mining until the 1890s. By then there was an ever increasing need for iron for the expanding steel industries of Western Europe.

c *Technology* Demand could not be met without the invention of the Gilchrist-Thomas steel converter in 1878. This enabled the iron and steel mills to use the Swedish ore. The converter was able to deal with the high phosphorous content of the very rich (60 per cent–70 per cent) in iron ore.

d *Capital* The large amounts of money for mining equipment, paying wages, transport and costs came originally from the Swedish company LKAB. Since 1907, LKAB had been partly owned by the state. In 1957 it was completely nationalised, not only because exploitation of this remote resource was expensive, but it was also seen as an important national asset.

e *Labour supply/settlement* A labour force had to be attracted to this remote location with its harsh winters. January temperatures are as low as −40°C and there are up to six weeks of continuous winter darkness. Above average salaries are paid as an incentive and the town of Kiruna (population 27 000) has a very high standard of housing and amenities.

f *Power supplies* Electricity for Kiruna, the other mining settlements, the mines and the railway comes from hydro-power schemes at Porjus and Harspranget on the River Lule.

g *Transport* With the completion of the Narvik-Lulea railway (see Fig. 6.7) in 1902 Kiruna was able to export most of the ore through the ice-free Norwegian port. Daily, freight trains carry thousands of tonnes of ore along this electrified line. Moving large volumes of bulk traffic makes rail transport (with lower costs per tonne-kilometre) cheaper than road transport for longer distances. Making the journey even more economic is the concentration of the ore into a purer form by a process of pelletisation. Finally, from Narvik, taking advantage

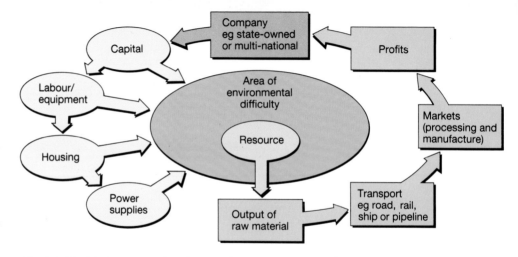

Fig. 6.6 Model of resource development in an area of environmental difficulty

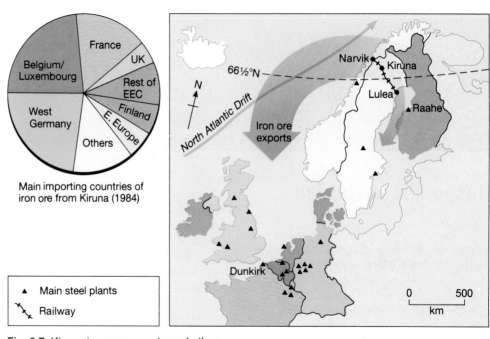

Main importing countries of iron ore from Kiruna (1984)

▲ Main steel plants
✕ Railway

Fig. 6.7 Kiruna iron ore exports and other main steel plants in North West Europe

of its fiord location, bulk ore carriers (up to 235 000 tonnes) export the ore to the markets shown in Fig. 6.7.

The main problem facing Kiruna and the other mining settlements is the decline in demand for iron ore because of the recession. This has increased unemployment. With a location remote from main markets, it is difficult to attract alternative sources of employment.

Assignments

1 (*Fig. 6.7 and atlas*) Describe, as fully as possible, the location of Kiruna. You should mention how far it is from Kiruna to Stockholm.

2 (*Fig. 6.7 and atlas*) **a)** From which two ports is the Iron ore from Kiruna exported? **b)** Which of these ports exports most of the ore? **c)** Give as many reasons as possible to explain your answer to (b). **d)** What are the main countries which import Swedish ore?

Swedish timber: a renewable resource

The sketch map below shows a forested landscape in Central Sweden around the coastal town of Skutskär. The woodland in the area belongs to STORA, one of Sweden's largest forest industry groups. Companies such as STORA own 25 per cent of all Swedish forests; the remainder is

Fig. 6.9 STORA's pulp mill at Skutskär

either publicly or privately owned, as shown on Fig. 6.10.

Employing some 14 500 people in Sweden alone (3,400 abroad), STORA produces a wide range of products: sawn timber, woodpulp, packaging materials, newsprint and special papers. A key part of their organisation is the Skutskär pulp mill. (see Figs. 6.8 and 6.9). Like other such mills it is the main source of employment for the inhabitants of Skutskar.

STORA, as Fig. 6.11 suggests, controls a very wide range of operations. From the raw material the whole way through to the finished product STORA owns the various means of production. Such an arrangement is known as *vertical integration*. The firm also owns a pyrites mine and hydro-power schemes linked to the national grid as well as serving the STORA enterprises.

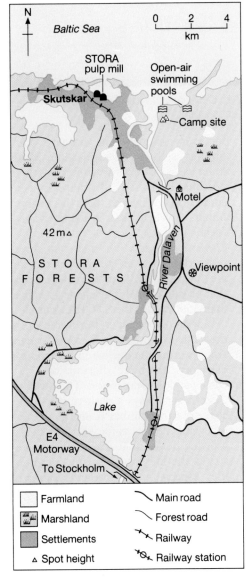

Fig. 6.8 The forested area near Skutskär

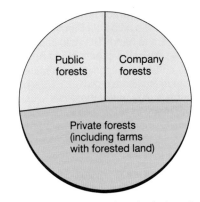

Fig. 6.10 Ownership of Sweden's forests

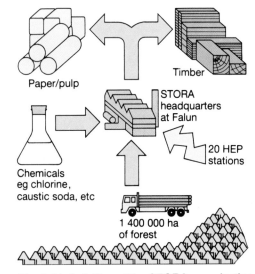

Fig. 6.11 Activities of the STORA organisation

Assignments

1 (*Fig. 6.8*) **a**) What is the main land use in the Skutskär area? **b**) Give three other land uses in the area. **c**) What evidence is there that this area is popular with tourists? **d**) Would there be any advantages or disadvantages if the marsh areas were drained?

2 (*Figs. 6.8 and 6.14*) Complete this paragraph, selecting from the words provided and picking the correct 'lefts' or 'rights'.

Skutskär's pulp mill is located on the west/east coast of Sweden, _____km north/south of Stockholm. The mill has developed here for several reasons.

a) It occupies a large/small area of sloping/level land, about two kilometres north-east/north-west of the mouth of the River Daläven. b) In the past such a location allowed timber to be floated down the river from November/April onwards. Today, however, the timber is taken to the mill by means of a good network of _____ and _____ which focus on the town. c) Raw materials are available, especially: (i) an ample supply of _____ from Stora's own forests or purchased from _____ forests or local _____. Spruce is chiefly used, shredded into chips. (ii) Plentiful supplies of _____ are at hand. The pulp is obtained by treating the chips chemically in huge vats. d) Power supplies are relatively cheap using Stora's own _____ electric schemes. e) Locally there is a _____ force, many of whom live in _____ itself. f) Finally, there has been an essential input of _____, thanks to STORA investing millions of kröner.

Select from: water, hydro, Skutskär, roads, timber, state, railways, farmers, labour, capital.

Fig. 6.12 Mechanised cutting and clearing

Swedish forestry: a success story

Although dwarfed by such coniferous giants as the USSR, Canada and the USA, and with only 0.6 per cent of the world's timber reserves, Sweden is a key country in the world's timber trade (see below).

Swedish share of world timber trade 1983 (per cent)

Paper: 13   Pulp: 15   Sawn timber: 10

Every fifth merchant ship leaving a Swedish port carries a cargo of forest industry products, most of which are destined for EC countries. Several factors help to explain Sweden's success.

a *Accessibility* Fig. 6.14 shows that the main forested areas are less than 200 km from the coast. In northern Sweden especially, the parallel rivers converge upon the Gulf of Bothnia, allowing easy floating in the past to the coastal mills. Today, however, although some sea floating between mills continues, river floating is found only on the R. Klar. Apart from the effect of the water (shrinkage, sinkage and loss of brightness) hydro-power schemes created bottlenecks. Today the bulk of the timber harvest is carried by road (see Fig. 6.16). New forest roads have, of course, made the woodlands more accessible for recreation.

b *Timber growth rate* The forests of Southern Sweden, thanks to a more favourable climate, can be harvested quite rapidly by world standards. Fig. 6.15 shows that conifers can mature in about 70 years. In the north, however, the slower growing conifers provide quite a dense timber for exploitation.

c *Good forest management* Fig. 6.15 shows the various stages involved from planting to felling. Thanks to good organisation, backed up by education and research, Sweden's stock of growing timber has increased during the 20th century.

Drainage of marsh lands has helped (five hectares of forest land can be made

Fig. 6.13 New plantings in a forested landscape

for every kilometre of drainage ditch dug) as well as soil fertilisation. Maximum use is made of the whole tree where possible. Branches and stumps are consumed as fuelwood, part of energy-hungry Sweden's search for alternative fuels.

d *Ownership pattern* The fact that forest industries such as pulp/paper-making are integrated with timber growth means that private capital is available as well as State money (see the STORA example).

Nor are the farmers slow to recognise the value of timber. In Sweden farmers are offsetting the decline in demand for dairy products by re-afforestation.

e *Government encouragement* The Swedish Government plays a positive role in recognising that timber is one of the few renewable resources for which there is a growing demand. It also sees that forestry is the lifeblood of many communities especially in Norrland. Forestry also has an important role to play in nature conservation and recreation on the one hand, and at the same time account, for 19 per cent of Swedish exports on the other. Forestry's role as a form of *multiple land use* is therefore recognised.

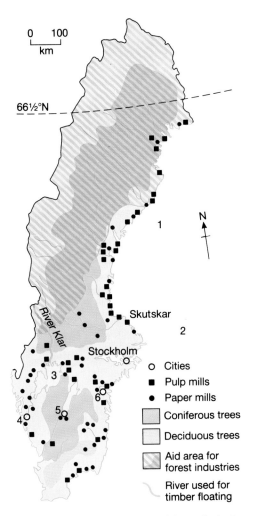

Fig. 6.14 Swedish forestry and forest industry

Map legend:
- ○ Cities
- ■ Pulp mills
- ● Paper mills
- Coniferous trees
- Deciduous trees
- Aid area for forest industries
- River used for timber floating

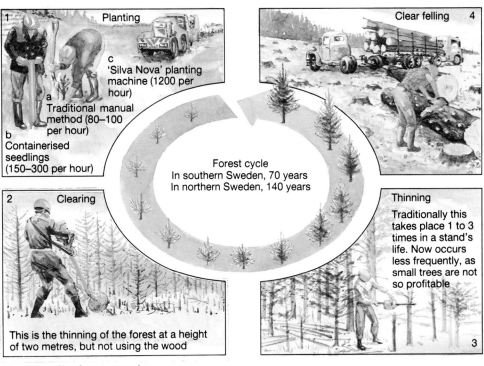

1 Planting
c 'Silva Nova' planting machine (1200 per hour)
a Traditional manual method (80–100 per hour)
b Containerised seedlings (150–300 per hour)

2 Clearing
This is the thinning of the forest at a height of two metres, but not using the wood

Forest cycle
In southern Sweden, 70 years
In northern Sweden, 140 years

4 Clear felling

3 Thinning
Traditionally this takes place 1 to 3 times in a stand's life. Now occurs less frequently, as small trees are not so profitable

Fig. 6.15 The forestry cycle

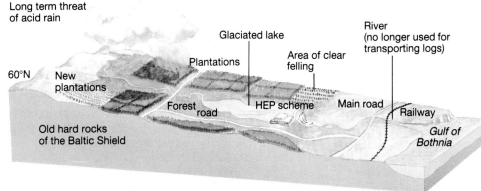

Long term threat of acid rain

New plantations
Old hard rocks of the Baltic Shield
Forest road
Plantations
HEP scheme
Glaciated lake
Area of clear felling
Main road
River (no longer used for transporting logs)
Railway
Gulf of Bothnia
60°N

Fig. 6.16 A forested landscape of Northern Sweden

As a result of such factors Sweden helps to meet the growing demand for world timber. Efficiency has, however, changed the landscape and rhythm of forest life. Thirty years ago axes were the main tool of a largely part time labour force (farming most of the year, forest work in winter) while horse-drawn sledges took the timber to the floatways to await the spring thaw. Increasingly it is the specialist forester using chain saw, harvesters and forwarders (see Figs. 6.12 and 6.15) who is employed all year round. Pine and spruce are still the main species but large areas are thinned or clear-felled nowadays. In many ways the new plantations appear more regimented and lack the birches and alders which gave more variety to the taiga landscape of forty years ago.

Assignments

1 (*Fig. 6.14*)
  a) Use an atlas to help you identify the following: gulf 1; sea 2; lake 3; cities 4, 5 and 6.
  b) Describe and explain the location of the timber-using mills.

2 (*Fig. 6.15*) **a)** Suggest why Swedish foresters are keen to increase the planting rate, especially in Norrland. **b)** Why has the amount of small scale thinning of trees decreased? **c)** Write a paragraph describing the main stages involved in the Forest Cycle.

3 (*Text/research*) Write an essay on the Swedish forest landscape: past, present and future.

Energy resources in in Norden

Sweden is encouraging the use of wood wastes, such as branches and stumps, as a form of energy. It is estimated, for example, that after trees have been felled there are some 23 million cubic metres of wood left to waste every year (equivalent in energy terms to 5 million tonnes of oil).

This is part of a long-term scheme (started in 1981) to reduce Sweden's dependence on imported oil. Although we tend to think of hydro-power as the main source of energy in Sweden and the other Nordic countries it was, in fact, oil. Sweden's energy mix was similar to that of Norden as a whole (see Fig. 6.17).

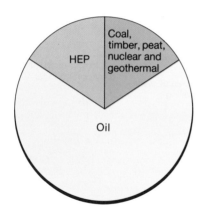

Fig. 6.17 Energy resources in Norden

The dependence on oil during the 1950s and 1960s era of 'cheap energy' brought benefits to the affluent peoples of Norden.

a Oil had encouraged the era of car transport and had mechanised farming and forestry.
b Norway's large shipping industry had grown with a particularly large tanker fleet. Cheap fuel had made it easier for Finnish ice breakers to ease winter communications.
c Domestic air services had expanded in Norden helping to reduce time distance

Fig. 6.18 Natural hot springs are used to heat greenhouses in Iceland

between the isolated north and more populous south.

d Oil-fired thermal power stations, along with the hydro schemes, ensured that winter cold could be met in comfort.

It took the massive rise in oil prices of 1973–74 and 1978–79 to encourage a switch in energy policies. Policies varied from country to country, according to their location, governmental policies and the availability of energy resources.

Geothermal energy

This is a part of daily life for many Icelanders. Thanks to Iceland's location on the mid-Atlantic ridge, hundreds of hot springs and geysers are found on the island, particularly in the south. More than a third of Iceland's 200 000 inhabitants live in centrally-heated homes, using hot water at 55–90°C, from the natural hot springs. The Reykjavik area has benefited particularly, and the demand for imported oil has been reduced.

Geothermal energy has also been used to heat greenhouses. About 140 farmers grow

a wide range of vegetables such as tomatoes, cucumbers, and lettuces as well as flowers (see Fig. 6.18).

So far, less than 2 per cent of Iceland's geothermal energy has been used. So there are virtually inexhaustable sources of this type of energy.

Hydro-power

Iceland has so far only utilised about 7 to 10 per cent of its hydro-electric power potential. There are very large water power resources in Iceland, Finland, and particularly, Sweden and Norway.

Of all the countries, perhaps Norway comes closest to the ideal conditions for hydro-power (see Fig. 6.19). Its greatest potential is in the south, that is, near the main centres of population. This, of course, helps to reduce the costs of transmission.

In Sweden and Finland, although hydropower provides 70 per cent and 27 per cent respectively, of the electricity consumed, conditions are not as favourable as in Norway. Nonetheless, the potential is there, and undeveloped falls and rapids in the

Fig. 6.19 Ideal conditions for efficient production of hydro-power

High and reliable precipitation throughout the year

No significant evaporation or water freeze

Deep steep-sided valleys which can be dammed

A large head of water

Large and suitable catchment areas

Stable hill slopes

A steep slope down which water can be piped

A ready market, not too distant and accessible by power cables

A suitable site for a power house with turbines

Hard, impermeable rock

A suitable outfall, such as a lake or fjord

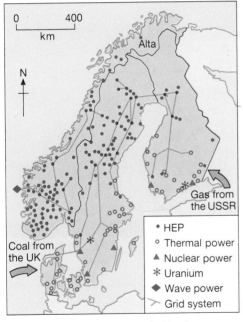

Fig. 6.20 Electricity sources in Norden (excluding Iceland)

Scale: 0 — 400 km

- • HEP
- ○ Thermal power
- ▲ Nuclear power
- ✳ Uranium
- ◆ Wave power
- ⊱ Grid system

Alta

Gas from the USSR

Coal from the UK

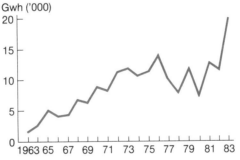

Fig. 6.21 Power exchange among NORDEL countries

NORDEL

Fig. 6.20 shows that the electricity grids of the four countries are linked up. This system of electricity interchange is called NORDEL, and, as the graph (Fig. 6.21) shows, the exchange of electricity has been increasing.

Altogether, about 8 per cent of all the electricity which is generated, is exchanged via the NORDEL grid. One factor which makes peak demand times a bit easier is the fact that Finland is in a different time zone.

Assignments

1 (*Text*) What have been the advantages and disadvantages of oil as the main source of energy in Norden?

2 (*Text*) a) Why is Iceland the only Nordic country with geothermal energy? b) What benefits has such energy brought Iceland?

3 (*Atlas, Figs 6.19 and 6.20*) Copy the following, selecting the correct 'lefts' or 'rights'.

In Sweden and Finland hydro-power has less favourable conditions than in Norway because: (i) The main hydro schemes and longer rivers are in the south/north whereas most of the people live in the north/south; (ii) in Sweden and Finland the rainfall (about 750/1500–1000/2000 mm) is higher/lower compared to Norway, while (iii) as these countries are away from the influence of the North Atlantic Drift, lakes and rivers are less/more likely to freeze.

4 (*Fig. 6.19*) Suggest ways in which glaciation favours ideal conditions for the generation of hydro-power.

Fig. 6.22 A hydro-power station in Norway

north present possible hydro sites. This can result in land use conflict, as we saw in the case of the Alta scheme. Scenery is a recreational and tourist resource in its own rights so conservationists can argue against further hydro-power expansion.

The search for alternatives

Of all the Nordic countries Denmark was the most affected by the oil price rises of the 1970s. Lacking, until recently, a domestic source of energy, Denmark has been successfully aiming to reduce its dependence on imported oil and to conserve energy. Various measures have been tried and these include:

a Switching from oil-fired power stations to coal. This has increased coal imports, including low sulphur content coal from Scotland.

b An increase in 'imported' electricity from Norway (hydro-power and nuclear) via NORDEL.

c Using oil from the Danish sector of the North Sea.

d An intensive programme of energy conservation including house and office insulation funded by the Government. In addition there are district heating schemes.

e Finally, Denmark leads Western Europe in *wind power*. Wind is one of the oldest forms of energy and it is making a comeback.

Today there are over 1 500 private or communal wind systems in Denmark. The machines are small (around 65 kw), and many are linked into the Danish electricity grids. Backed up by Government research,

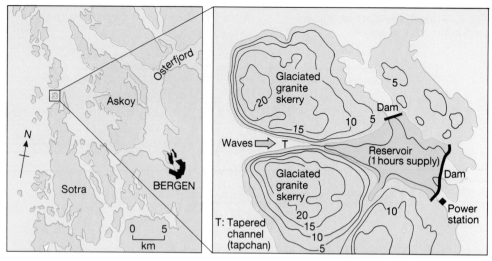

Fig. 6.24 Location and site of Norway's first wave-power station

Fig. 6.25 The wave-power scheme in Norway

Fig. 6.23 A wind power station in Denmark

the Danes now lead Western Europe in exporting wind turbines to markets both in the 'North' and the 'South'.

Another interesting form of small scale 'clean' alternative energy is that of *wave power*. Figs. 6.24 and 6.25 show the location and site of the world's first commercial wave power station.

On a skerry near Bergen, Norway, a cone-shaped channel or Tapchan was blasted out of the solid granite rock. The channel is 170 metres long, and at its mouth some 55 metres wide, tapering to zero inland. As waves enter the channel their height increases and they spill over into a reservoir. The water has, in effect, pumped itself up. After that it will fall from the reservoir and operate the power station generators.

Such a power unit, although initially expensive, is ideal for remote coastal communities. Unlike the offshore oil deposits wave power will always be available as an energy resource.

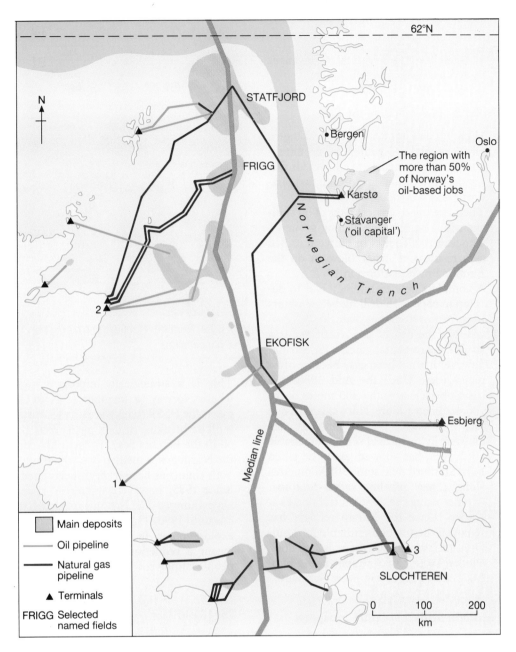

STATFJORD

• Bergen

Oslo•

FRIGG

The region with
more than 50%
of Norway's
oil-based jobs

▲ Karstø

N
o
r
w
e
g
i
a
n

• Stavanger
('oil capital')

T
r
e
n
c
h

EKOFISK

▲ Esbjerg

Median line

1

Median line

3

SLOCHTEREN

Main deposits
Oil pipeline
Natural gas
pipeline
▲ Terminals
FRIGG Selected
named fields

| 0 | 100 | 200 |

km

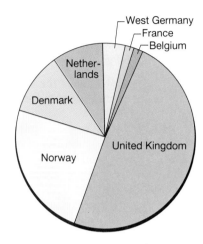

Fig. 6.26 North Sea oil and gas fields

West Germany
France
Belgium

Netherlands

Denmark

United Kingdom

Norway

Fig. 6.27 Ownership of North Sea gas and oil

Ownership of North Sea gas and oil

The resources of the North Sea continental shelf were divided up after the 1958 United Nations Conference on the Law of the Sea. For once, agreement was reached between the countries concerned with the UK and Norway receiving the largest sectors as Fig. 6.27 shows.

Development phases

a The story really started at Slochteren in the Netherlands with the discovery of one of the world's largest natural gas fields in 1961. As similar geological structures were likely to be found in the North Sea, multinational companies such as Royal Dutch Shell and Texaco were encouraged to start surveying and test drilling.

b By the mid 1960s natural gas had been found in the southern North Sea and in 1970 oil was first discovered in the Norwegian sector by Phillips Petroleum in the Ekofisk field.

c Discoveries have continued to be made with a northward movement of exploration and exploitation. South of 62°N there are very large deposits (up to 5000 million tonnes of oil equivalent); while

Norway and North Sea oil and gas

Norway, after the UK, has the second largest share of the North Sea oil and gas resources. The wealth from exploiting fields such as Ekofisk, Frigg, and Statfjord (Fig. 6.26) has brought undoubted material benefits to a country with just over four million people and well endowed with hydro-power resources. In 1985, oil and gas contributed 18.2% of Norwegian GNP and

35% of all exports. Living and welfare standards have improved for all Norwegians, not only the 58 000 employed in oil-related activities. Large subsidies have helped farming, fishing and manufacturing, particularly in the North. Some would argue, however, that the economy has become too dependent on oil and gas.

Whatever the advantages and disadvantages the present situation has involved many issues and stages over the past thirty years.

there are no official figures for the area to the north, the deposits may well be larger.

d By 1984 some 61 million tonnes of oil equivalent (t.o.e.) were produced (35 million in oil; 26 cubic million gas).

Developing the oil/gas fields

a Using geophysical surveys the oil companies assess the presence of oil/gas bearing rocks.

b Once the companies have confirmed the presence of suitable quantities of oil/gas using drill ships or semi-submersible rigs, production platforms are towed to the site (see Fig. 6.28).

c Large concrete platforms of the type found in the Ekofisk field are able to store the oil in their structure, receiving oil from up to forty wells in the vicinity.

d Oil is taken ashore by (a) transferring it to tankers (b) special steel pipelines with protective coatings. The sections of pipe are joined together by teams of welders on laying barges.

e Tankers have taken the oil ashore to Norway. A pipeline for oil runs from the Ekofisk field to Teesside, and a gas pipeline to Emden in West Germany. From the Frigg field two pipelines, one British and one Norwegian, carry the gas to St. Fergus in Scotland.

f Maintaining these platforms and rigs is an enormous task. Thousands of tonnes of material (steel, food, fresh water etc.), not to mention teams of workers, have to

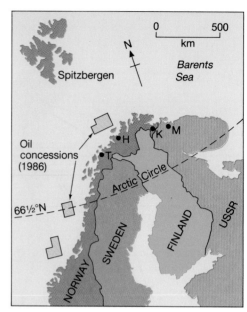

Fig. 6.28 Oil platform being towed to its site from a Norwegian fjord

be taken from the oil capital of Stavanger by service vessel and helicopter.

Problems in developing the fields

a High waves (up to 20 metres high), strong winds, fog, winter ice and unreliable weather systems are all hazards facing the exploration rigs, production platforms and service crews.

b There are the ecological risks of oil spillage which can damage fishing grounds. Thousands of tonnes of oil were spilled as a result of a major blowout on the Ekofisk Bravo platform in 1977.

c A complete new technology had to develop to cope with drilling below waters from 70 to 190 metres deep.

d Overall, the bed of the North Sea is a shallow continental shelf. Pipelaying, however has not been easy because of irregularities. Until the mid 1980s the main obstacle was the 300 metre deep, 100 kilometre wide Norwegian trench (see Fig. 6.26). New technology, for example in the form of semi-submersible lay barges, has allowed gas to be taken from Statfiord field some 308 kilometres along a new pipeline called Statpipe. After crossing the trench it terminates at Karstø. Once the Karstø refinery has removed the fractions suitable for liquifying the remaining ethane is fed along another section of Statpipe via the Ekofisk field, to Emden in West Germany.

Northern fields and future prospects

In 1980 the first oil concessions north of 62°N were granted (see Fig. 6.29). Test drilling off Hammerfest has revealed promising gas accumulations. It will, however, be the mid 1990s before oil and gas are actually produced.

a Operating so far north will require new technology and very high safety standards.

b On shore the communities are very dependent on a single source of income, for example, fishing and oil/gas exploitation while bringing advantages may destroy the traditional economy.

Fig. 6.29 Northern Norway, showing oil and gas concessions

c This is a strategically-important area where Norway (a member of NATO) meets the USSR (which is using Finnish-built ice breaking drill-ships to probe for oil in the Barents Sea). So far, unlike in the North Sea, a median line which suits both countries has not been negotiated. Since 1985, however, world oil prices have slumped and are not expected to rise until 1990. This has slowed down oil exploration in the North Sea and has meant a reduction in the number of people employed.

Assignments

1 (*Fig. 6.26*) Identify, using an Atlas, the terminals for Norwegian oil/gas numbered 1–3.

2 (*Text*) Explain why the gas/oil from Ekofisk has been mainly piped to Britain and West Germany.

3 (*Fig. 6.26 and text*) What are the various problems involved in developing Norwegian oil/gas fields?

4 (*Fig. 6.26 and text*) In what way was the laying of Statpipe a technical breakthrough?

5 (*Text*) Has the development of oil/gas been worthwhile for Norway?

Nuclear power and governments

Forecasts are made of future energy requirements. Fig. 6.30 shows two forecasts for the year 2000 for Europe as a whole. In both nuclear power is seen to be more important than in 1980.

How reliable are such forecasts? A great many factors will influence the long-term situation. These will vary from country to country but in the case of nuclear energy perhaps the key factor is the role of the Government. This can be illustrated from Sweden, France and West Germany.

All three countries were keen from the early 1970s to use nuclear power to provide electricity and to reduce the use of oil and/or coal. Nuclear power stations were located on sites by taking into account factors shown in Fig. 6.31. But by the mid 1980s the long-term plans were being modified in different ways.

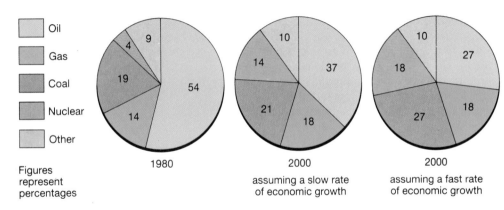

Fig. 6.30 Present and possible future energy demands in Europe

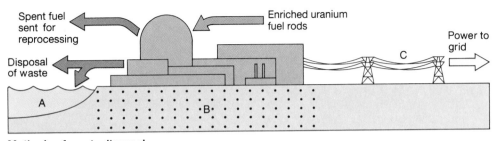

Methods of waste disposal

1 Low level radioactive wastes are released into the air, water or ground to be diluted to 'safe' levels.

2 High level radioactive wastes need to be stored for thousands of years by, for example, burial of sealed containers in solid rock foundations.

Fig. 6.31 Model of the location of a nuclear power station

Sweden

By 1981 Sweden was using more electricity from nuclear power per capita than any other country in the world. There were six nuclear stations and another six being constructed. But as a result of a referendum held in 1980 nuclear energy is to be phased out after 1990. As stations reach the end of their working life (in theory 20 years) they will not be replaced. The Swedish Government had listened to public opinion.

France

France has taken the lead in Western Europe in exploiting nuclear energy. During 1984, 60 per cent of French electricity came from nuclear stations; a figure expected to rise to 75 per cent by 1990. French nuclear progress has been made possible by three things.

a Governments have been fully committed to an ambitious nuclear programme originally announced in 1973. With the coming to power of the Mitterand Socialist Government a review was made of the plans and a station due to be built at Plogoff was cancelled. But although the pace of construction has slightly slowed, 38 plants have been installed and 24 are still to be built.

b An absence of large scale domestic supplies of energy and overdependence on imported oil and gas has influenced government thinking. Hydro-power (both high level schemes in the Alps and Pyrenees and low level schemes along the Rhone and Rhine) cannot meet demand nor does French coal. It is planned to reduce the present workforce (56,000 in 1985) by 50 per cent by 1990 and reduce production from 18.5 million to 12 million tonnes in the same period. Cheap imports of coal will be encouraged; in 1985 France was the second largest importer of coal in the world.

c Unlike the situation in Britain, the programme of planning and construction has gone ahead smoothly. There is not the same scale of public enquiries; licensing money is paid to the local community and electricity is supplied at a 10 per cent discount for those living within 10 kilometres of a nuclear station.

As a result of such a vigorous programme, with relatively little opposition from the environmentalist groups (compared to West Germany), France has a glut of electricity. Surplus power is exported and since 1987 Britain has been plugged into the French grid with the completion of the cross Channel link. France aims to export some 10 per cent of its electricity output to neighbouring countries by 1990.

West Germany

Rather like France, the West German Federal Government welcomed nuclear power in the early 1970s. By 1983 there were 15 nuclear reactors operating and another 12 being built. This was well short of the original target because of political factors.

a Government is decentralised. Before a nuclear station is built the local state (land) has to award a licence.

b There is no centralised electricity industry in West Germany. While France has a single nationalised organisation there are 13 separate electricity supply groups in West Germany.

c Opposition to nuclear power has been stronger. The rise of the 'Greens', political parties which are interested in ecology and have anti-nuclear policies, has raised many questions (see below) in the mind of the public. At certain sites there were savage clashes between police and anti-nuclear groups.

The rate at which nuclear power stations are built varies from country to country. Nuclear energy raises many fears, especially the prospect of another Chernobyl and the question of waste disposal. Equally, it is argued that such stations create jobs locally; in France, for example, 160 000 are involved, directly or indirectly, in the nuclear energy industry.

Questions about nuclear power

a What about a nuclear leak and the danger of radiation?

b If we don't use nuclear energy then surely we'll use up fossil fuels and then there will be no energy left?

c Could these plants be sabotaged and the fuel shipments hi-jacked?

d Are the costs really cheaper? There are surely huge capital costs involved?

e Nuclear power is alright as a stop-gap but surely more should be spent on renewable resources?

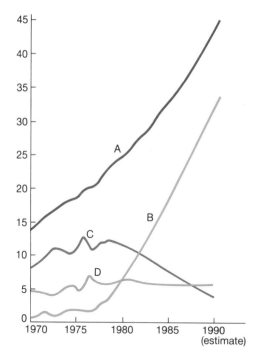

Fig. 6.32 Electricity production in France

Assignments

1 a) (*Fig. 6.32*) Study this graph showing electricity production in France. Replace the letters A, B, C and D with the following labels: from nuclear energy; from coal and oil thermal stations; from hydro-power; total electricity production.

b) (*Text*) Explain why the French have made such progress in the production of electricity from nuclear power stations.

2 (*Fig. 6.31*) Make a large copy of this diagram. Name three important locational factors (A, B and C on the diagram) for the siting of a nuclear power station.

3 Make a list of the main arguments for and against nuclear power. Conduct a class debate on the subject. You can obtain additional material from **a)** the CEG Board, the SSE Board etc. **b)** anti-nuclear groups such as 'Friends of the Earth'.

4 (*Research/discussion*) Comment on these thoughts.
'There is much public reaction which is emotional and quite irrational . . . This was made quite clear by the public outcry at the Three Mile Island incident (which killed no one, injured no one and . . . damaged no one) compared to the equanimity with which the news of the death of a dozen miners in a Lancashire pit was received'. (Rowland Moss, '*The earth in our hands*' (Inter-Varsity Press)).

5 (*Text*) Read all the material on nuclear energy again. Was the writer in any way biased towards one side or the other?

6 (*Fig. 6.30*) Two energy forecasts are shown for the year 2000. Which do you think is the most likely? What factors influenced your decision?

Fig. 6.33 A nuclear power station on the Rhône. Comment on the choice of site and the impact of the station on the environment

Coal and industry: past and present

Coal is not a particularly attractive fuel. It is dusty, contains impurities and contributes to acid rain and smog. In the older established coalfields of Western Europe coal is worked from seams that are often faulted and thin. Much of Western Europe's coal-mining industry is highly subsidised to allow it to compete with the cheaper imports (see Fig. 6.34). In addition, the numbers employed in coal mining are falling. Such issues raise questions about coal's future.

Yet this was the fuel of the Industrial Revolution of the eighteenth and nineteenth centuries. The adoption of the steam engine involved huge amounts of coal for the boilers while coking coal was essential for the blast furnaces producing iron and steel. Coal was the key factor underlying the type of landscape we find in areas like the Sambre-Meuse coalfield of Belgium. But many of the features were (and often still are) found on the other main coalfields of Western Europe. These areas were transformed into industrial regions. Although each area, such as the Ruhr or the Saar coalfield, is unique, it is suggested there are common various stages of development shown in Fig. 6.34.

Infancy Industry was organised on the 'domestic system' (family based) weaving or spinning of cloth

Youth Manufacturing industry developed in factories, usually located near water power. Most people were still rural dwellers

Maturity Growth of factories and towns, usually located (but not always) on a coalfield. Development of canal and rail transport. Migration of people to form a new urban workforce

Old age Increase in unemployment with decline of the traditional 'key industries' due to competition from other areas or abroad (eg coal, steel and textiles)

Rejuvenation Intervention by governments, regional bodies, or the EC to encourage new growth industries and service employment. Problems of inherited landscape (such as derelict buildings, pit heaps and inadequate infrastructure)

Fig. 6.34 Stages of industrial development

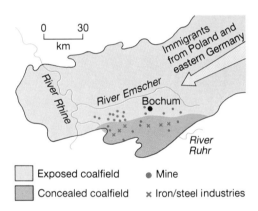

Fig. 6.35 The Ruhr in the 1860s

Fig. 6.36 The growth of Bochum in the Ruhr

The Ruhr coalfield: an industrial region

Fig. 6.35 shows certain of the features of the Ruhr coalfield. This is Western Europe's largest coalfield and industrial region, covering an area of 4500 km² and with a population of some 5.5 million. The vast majority live in a series of cities which form a polycentric conurbation. The map (Fig. 6.37) only hints at the main urban, industrial, transport and mining features of this region, which has played a critical role in the economic history of West Germany. How did it all begin?

Beginnings

Until well into the nineteenth century the lowland to the north of the Sauerland plateau was mainly a farming district. Wool and flax were made into cloth in the villages, and in market towns such as Essen and Bochum. Originally, spinning and weaving took place in the family home, but with the introduction of new machinery from Britain, small textile factories appeared.

This was true of metalworking industries. Iron forges also took advantage of water power from the swift-flowing streams draining the Sauerland plateau. In addition, charcoal was available from the forested slopes, so that specialised towns such as Solingen grew up, producing scythes and swords.

1850 to 1945

Up until this period the amount of coal mined was very small. Most mining was in the south of the coalfield where the seams outcropped at the surface in the valley of the River Ruhr. From the 1870s, however, various changes were under way.

a Germany was emerging as an industrial power. A large new market was created, when the separate German states united to form the German Empire in 1870.

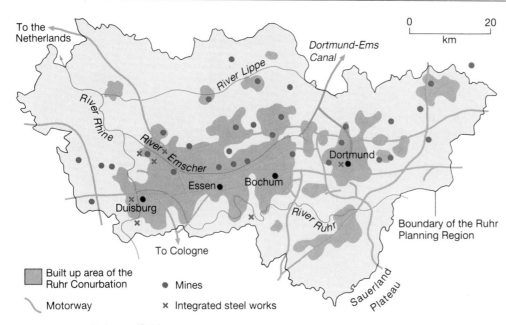

Fig. 6.37 The Ruhr coalfield

b As a result of increased demand and improved technology (new drainage and ventilation systems), mines were exploiting deeper seams. Fig. 6.35 shows that these were on the 'concealed' coalfield where later geological deposits covered the coal. This northward movement was worthwhile. Although expensive to mine, the seams were thicker and contained a richer variety of coal: coking coal (for iron/steel plants); anthracite (for household fuel); and 'gas coal' (a raw material for the chemical industry).

c The presence of blackband iron ore and coking coal was a key factor in the emergence of an iron and steel industry, mainly located on the exposed section of the coalfield in towns such as Essen, Duisburg and Dortmund.

d Population was rapidly growing in the Ruhr. 'Pushed' by the poor conditions of the rural areas and 'pulled' by the availability of jobs, thousands (see Fig. 6.35) were migrating to the area. A new industrialised urban landscape was emerging – both in old established medieval towns such as Essen and in 'new' towns such as Bochum, which grew rapidly.

e Large industrial companies emerged, often dominating a particular city. Perhaps the best known firm was that of the

Krupp family, who established their first iron foundry in Essen in 1811. The city then had a population of some 8000 but by 1939 it had swollen to 600 000 with 270 000 employed at the Krupp works. This was possible because the firm had expanded (as Fig. 6.38 shows) into a wide range of related operations.

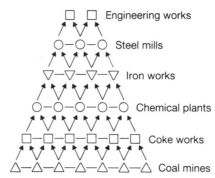

Fig. 6.38 Vertical and horizontal organisation in Krupps of Essen

As a result of these changes the Ruhr became the industrial heart of pre-war Germany. Although local raw materials such as blackband ores became exhausted, alternative sources were found. Ore was brought from Lorraine, Sweden and Luxembourg, making use of the excellent river and canal links. Barges were also used to export coal.

1945 to the present day

In 1945, as a result of widespread bombing, the Ruhr was severely damaged, and the people were on the verge of starvation. Some 15 years later the industries had more than recovered, cities were rebuilt, and the Ruhr was playing an important role in the West German 'economic miracle'. A combination of determination, skilled refugee workers from East Germany (see page 8), American aid, and membership of the EC from 1957, made West Germany into a prosperous economy.

By the 1970s, however, the economy of the Ruhr (along with the other coalfield areas of Western Europe) was showing signs of decline, notably in the traditional industries.

a Coal, the mainstay of the Ruhr, was in trouble. Production peaked in 1956 and then its share of the energy market began to shrink as shown by these figures for the Ruhr.

Year	Coal production (million tonnes)	Numbers employed (000)'s
1956	125 000 000	393 831
1982	70 000 000	140 536

Coalmining has come under pressure from two directions: (i) competition from cheaper alternative fuels: oil, natural gas and nuclear energy: (ii) competition from cheaper imported coal (see Fig. 6.42).

As a result, a programme of rationalisation has been carried out. The smaller, inefficient coalmines south of the River Emscher were closed. Today production comes from fewer, larger and highly mechanised, mines in the northern section of the coalfield. Some of these (see Fig. 6.37) are found in semi-rural areas.

b Likewise, the steel industry has declined – this time in the face of competition from Japan, Eastern Europe and newly industrialised countries of the South such as South Korea. The solution has been similar; the closure of uneconomic plants and the concentration of production and investment in modern integrated works, notably at Dortmund and Duisburg.

c Changes have also come about in the other manufacturing sectors. Oil encouraged the chemical industry to switch from carbo-chemicals (i.e. based on coal) to petro-chemicals. Textiles also benefitted from oil by the development of synthetic fibres such as rayon and nylon.

In many respects then the Ruhr is a region of industrial decline and change. It is undergoing the process of *deindustrialisation*. Service industries (see page 129) are now more important. In Essen, for example, some two thirds of the working population are employed in the service sector. Many, however, are not employed at all. In 1987 over 250 000 were unemployed, with some cities more affected than others. Likewise, some groups of people are more affected, notably the 'guestworkers' (see page 9), many of whom prefer to receive West German social security payments rather than return to their home countries.

Various measures have been undertaken to try to diversify the traditional Ruhr industries and to try to relieve the hardship of unemployment. Two branch factories were set up by Opel (part of General Motors) at Bochum which once employed 65,000 miners. Investment in textiles, electrical engineering, electronics, consumer goods, aluminium works and chemicals have been encouraged by Government investment and the EC. Industrial estates and also the dense network (499 kilometres) of autobahns play an important role.

The Ruhr today is still West Germany's main industrial core. In the long run its traditional industries of coalmining and steel will continue to decline. It will continue to be one of the world's major industrial regions but with a greater variety of types of employment.

Changing images of the Ruhr

As we have seen, the key to future development in the Ruhr lies in attacting fresh investment. The people who take decisions about locations for branch factories take many factors into account. Often they are influenced by their *image* of an area, that is what they imagine it to be like. The Ruhr unfortunately has a 'Black country' image – slag heaps, derelict factories, soot-belching fires. Often this is based on dated (but once accurate) descriptions and a limited range of photographs or press releases (see extract and Fig. 6.34).

Although there are environmental problems, much has been done to rehabilitate the Ruhr environment.

a A great deal of derelict colliery and factory land has been reclaimed. For example at Gelsenkirchen a huge pit site has been turned into a recreational area (see Fig. 6.40).

b Green wedges of land separate the towns and cities.

A German's image of the Ruhr coalfield in the 1950s

. . . and on the surface planning was most precise where transportation and production (of coal) were concerned. Man, however, had to get by somehow. He had, of course, to have a place to live, to eat, drink and pray; shops, schools, pubs, churches, hospitals, chemists' shops – he lacked nothing. But for a hundred years without anyone paying the least heed, dust and soot were allowed to pour down on him, making the landscape in which he lived atone for this, drenching him in vapour, putting a gag on the climate, robbing him every year of a whole month's sunshine; an industrial landscape was created, but this notion, which sounds so rational, is only a romantic glossing over of the fact that here industry has killed the landscape without creating a new one.

(from *In the Ruhr* by Heinrich Böll, translated by G. L. McCorkindale)

c New purification plants are helping to reduce the level of river pollution while air pollution has generally fallen. The extract on page 108 shows, however, that there is still some way to go.

d A wide range of leisure zones, regional and nature parks have been created.

The key question is which image, Fig. 6.39 or Fig. 6.40, will most influence the industrial decision makers?

Fig. 6.39 A Ruhr steelworks landscape; the smokestacks once belched soot and fumes

Fig. 6.40 Recreation area on a reclaimed pit site

A glowing future for coal?

Fig. 6.30 suggests that by the year 2000 coal will be playing a more important role in Europe's energy scene. The main market will continue to be thermal power stations. Rightly or wrongly, in spite of fears about acid rain, such stations are seen as a less objectionable alternative to nuclear energy, in countries such as Denmark and West Germany.

Health alert over Ruhr smog

West Germany's industrial region was put under a maximum smog alert yesterday with private cars barred in city centres and power stations and other industrial polluters ordered to curb operations.

Atmospheric pollution due to a temperature inversion, in which a layer of warm air above much colder air pins pollution to the ground, continued to mount in the Ruhr Valley for the third successive day, and reached its crisis level of 1.7 milligrams per cubic metre yesterday afternoon.

Schools in the seven cities affected by the smog were closed and the authorities appealed on radios for children and people suffering from heart disease and asthma to stay indoors. The health ministry in Dusseldorf said drivers were responding well to the appeal not to use private cars.

(*The Guardian*, 19 January 1985)

Most of the coal that is produced in West Germany for power generation is lignite or 'brown coal'. It is a low grade fuel with poor calorific value and a high moisture content, but it is suitable for thermal power stations. The main source is the Ville Ridge field (see Fig. 6.41) located to the west of Cologne and extending for some 35 kilometres.

The field has been worked by open cast techniques which involve: (1) the removal of the overburden and (2) extraction of the lignite using enormous excavators (Fig. 6.41). Such highly mechanised techniques have proved to be very economic, have but raised conservation issues especially in the

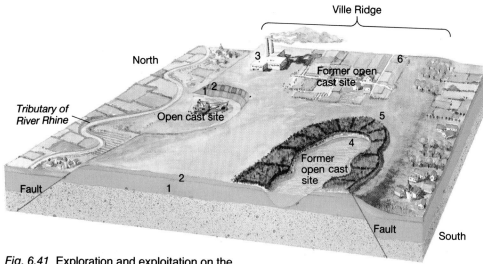

Fig. 6.41 Exploration and exploitation on the Ville Ridge

fertile areas of loess soil in the north of the field. As a result various remedial measures have been undertaken. These include: (1) replacing the soils; (2) re-afforesting the southern areas of poorer soil with coniferous plantations; (3) wholesale removal and rebuilding of over 3500 farms and 15 villages, with a completely new network of roads and other services.

Greece is another country with significant lignite deposits. Although located in the Mediterranean hydro-power belt (see (Fig. 6.42), it is anticipated that by 1990 some 80 per cent of its electricity will come from lignite and 20 per cent from hydro-power.

Assignments

1 (*Text*) Why was coal such an important source of energy in the nineteenth and first half of the twentieth century?

2 a) (*Atlas and Fig. 6.35*) Describe the location of the Ruhr coalfield. b) Why was the early phase of coalmining concentrated in the south of the coalfield? c) (*Fig. 6.36*) Describe and explain the growth of Bochum from 1852 to 1939. d) (*Fig. 6.38 and text*) Explain how the Krupp family came to dominate the economy of Essen. e) (*Fig. 6.37*)

Describe and explain the location of the Ruhr coalmines today.

3 (*Atlas, section on the River Rhine and Fig. 6.37*) What are the advantages of Duisburg as a location for integrated steelworkers? Are there any disadvantages?

4 (*Text/research*) What is meant when describing the cities of the Ruhr as a 'polycentric conurbation'?

5 (*Text*) a) Explain why coalmining has declined in the Ruhr. b) What is the main market for coal from the Ruhr?

6 (*Fig. 6.34*) a) Attempt a summary of the development of the Ruhr coalfield using the five headings given in the diagram. b) Is it a suitable model for the Ruhr?

7 (*Research*) a) What is meant by a temperature inversion? b) How did this influence the Ruhr smog? c) What are the solutions to such smog?

8 (*Extract*) a) What sort of an image does Heinrich Böll give of the Ruhr? b) Is it a fair picture of the Ruhr today?

9 (*Text*) a) What is lignite? b) What is it mainly used for? c) Match the following items with the numbers on Fig. 6.41. Lignite burning thermal power station; lake/reservoir on former working; thick accessible seam of brown coal; overburden; new coniferous plantations used for recreation; reclaimed farmland with new village and access roads.

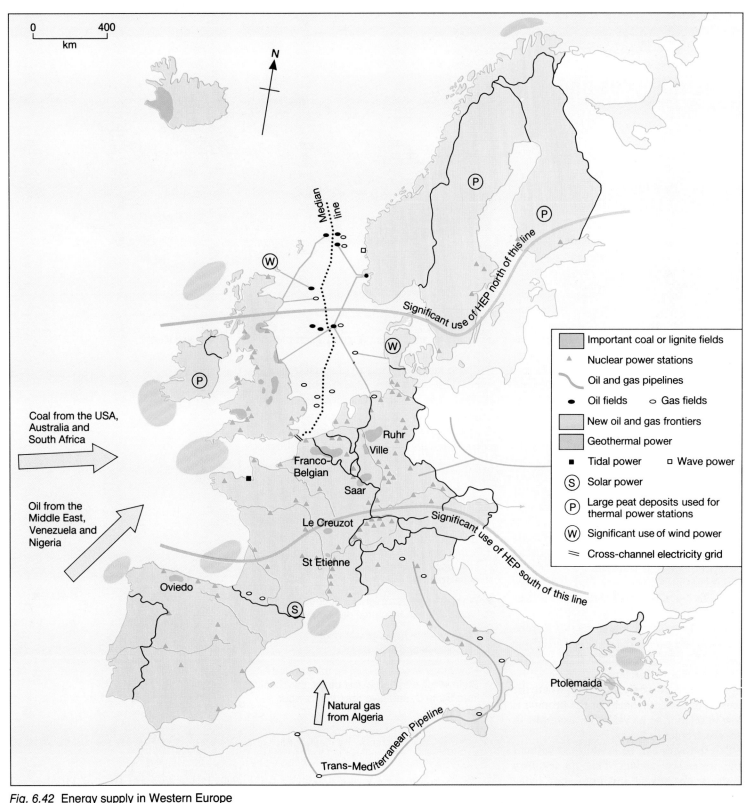

Scale:
0 — 400 km

N

Median line

Significant use of HEP north of this line

Coal from the USA, Australia and South Africa

Oil from the Middle East, Venezuela and Nigeria

Ruhr
Ville
Franco-Belgian
Saar
Le Creuzot
St Etienne

Oviedo

Significant use of HEP south of this line

Ptolemaida

Natural gas from Algeria

Trans-Mediterranean Pipeline

	Important coal or lignite fields
▲	Nuclear power stations
	Oil and gas pipelines
● Oil fields	○ Gas fields
	New oil and gas frontiers
	Geothermal power
■ Tidal power	□ Wave power
Ⓢ	Solar power
Ⓟ	Large peat deposits used for thermal power stations
Ⓦ	Significant use of wind power
═	Cross-channel electricity grid

Fig. 6.42 Energy supply in Western Europe

Chapter 7 Industrial landscapes

Industrial types and locations

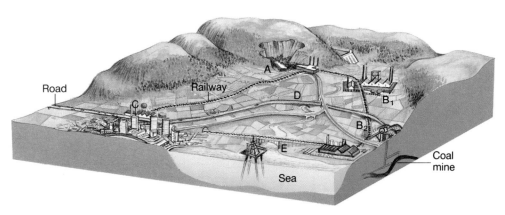

Fig. 7.1 A theoretical industrial landscape

Fig. 7.1 shows a theoretical classification of industries according to location.

A *Raw material*: near an iron ore mine.
B1 *Power* near an HEP scheme
B2 *Power* near a coal mine
C *Market* and *labour* in a large town

This is a very simple classification. There are other factors which are (or were) important. For example, water power and supply. *Water* is often important in processing, for example, paper and textiles, or in the final product itself, such as beer, soft drinks. Before water was used to generate HEP, it was used to turn mill wheels. Thus, in the mountainous and northern areas of Europe, water is a major factor in locating industry. In Southern Europe, adequate supplies of water have to be found if large scale industry is to be established.

Communications are of vital importance in locating industry. The diagram above suggests the importance of railways (as in Belgium), and canals (as in the Netherlands and West Germany). Water transport is cheaper than land transport. This is very significant in Norway (see Fig. 7.2) where access by sea to scattered and remote factories is needed.

The *Euroroutes* or motorways of Europe play a major part in the distribution of raw materials, components and finished products such as motor cars.

Air transport is only important where the weight of the component or the product is low in relation to its value, for example, in the electronics industry.

No industry can be established without the necessary *capital*. This money may come from private investors, but today more and more money comes from *govern-ment grants* and *loans*. A good example of this is Southern Italy.

These factors are not all of equal importance. They may vary in different places, and at different times. Wherever industry is established, it requires an adequate road network; power and water supplies; drainage and telephone systems, and buildings, that is, an *infrastructure*.

Assignments

(*Fig. 7.1*)
1 Name two other raw materials which, apart from iron ore, might attract industrial development.

2 What advantages might locations **D** and **E** have for future industrial development?

3 What other forms of power might become available near the coast?

4 How many ways can coal be transported? State which way you would use to take coal from **B2** to **C**, and give reasons for your choice.

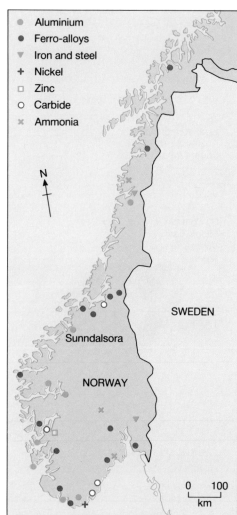

Fig. 7.2 Location of metal and chemical industries in Norway

Legend:
- Aluminium
- Ferro-alloys
- Iron and steel
- Nickel
- Zinc
- Carbide
- Ammonia

SWEDEN

Sunndalsora

NORWAY

0   100
km

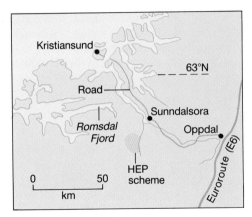

Fig. 7.3 Location of Sunndalsora

Fig. 7.4 The Sunndalsora area (1:50 000)

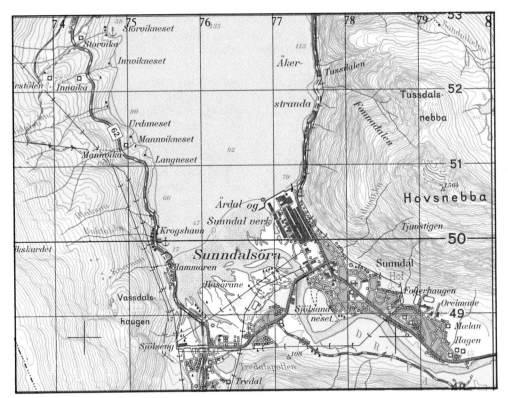

Transport costs are often of critical importance. In some cases, industries can be said to be weight-losing while others are weight-gaining. A good example of a weight-losing industry is making aluminium, as the table below shows you.

Making aluminium	Weight in tonnes
Raw material: Bauxite	4
↓	
Alumina	2
↓	
Final product: Aluminium	1

Norway is one of the world's main aluminium producers. There is no bauxite in Norway, so to save transport costs, alumina is imported, for example to the smelter at Sunndalsora.

Sunndalsora

Fig. 7.2 shows the general location of this small town in Western Norway. Fig. 7.3 below gives more detail about its situation.

Fig. 7.4 shows the actual site of the smelter. This map and Fig. 7.5 both make it clear that another factor in locating industry is the amount of suitable land for building which is available.

Fig. 7.5 View of Sunndalsora, showing maximum use of limited land area

Assignments

1 (*Fig. 7.2*) Which of the factors mentioned were important in the choice of location for these factories on the Norwegian coast?

2 (*Fig. 7.3*) Look at the scale. How far is Sunndalsora **a**) from the E6 **b**) from Kristiansund? Which route is the more important?

3 (*Fig. 7.4 and Fig. 7.5*) In what compass direction was the photograph taken? Describe the site of the smelter [Sunndal Verk] as fully as you can. Mention both physical and human features.

4 (*Fig. 7.4*) Draw a cross section from G.R. 800510 through the Sunndal Verk to G.R. 740490 with a vertical scale of 1 cm to 250 m. Annotate the section to show the main features.

5 (*Fig. 7.4*) Look at the depth of the fjord immediately north of the smelter. Why is the fjord so deep? Why is the fjord so important?

Making aluminium

Look again at Fig. 7.4. Find the electricity pylons which enter the smelter. The availability of vast amounts of power was the most important factor in locating the smelter at Sunndalsora.

The HEP scheme was begun in 1913, but was not completed until 1956. It involved the diversion and damming of the Aura River which flowed into Romsdal Fjord (see Fig. 7.3). Four dams, a 16 kilometre long tunnel, and two power stations had to be built. The larger power station is built 300 metres inside the mountains (GR 765486). Although the water is a renewable resource, the construction involved much expense.

HEP is not therefore cheap, and it becomes even more expensive when firms such as ASV have to pay tax on it. The smelter at Sunndalsora (see Fig. 7.5) is one of many aluminium works owned by ASV which produces almost half of Norway's aluminium.

The smelter was opened in 1954 when the first electricity became available. Alumina (mostly from Jamaica) and cryolite (from Greenland) are imported to Sunnsdalsora, that is, the power source. The smelting of aluminium from alumina is an electrolytic process.

Fig. 7.5 shows that the smelter has had little effect on the landscape. Great care is taken to reduce the discharge of waste into the atmosphere and the fjord to the absolute minimum.

The work available (over 1200 jobs) has resulted in the population growing to 5000. The town has therefore an improved range of services and amenities. The county of Sunndal, 92 per cent of which is unproductive mountain, has gained a great deal from the presence of the smelter. Both ASV and its employees pay local taxes.

The smelter produces about 130 000 tonnes of aluminium each year. Although production and the workforce, declined because of a world surplus, both have since recovered. A major part of the work is research into casting, making alloys and quality control. The smelter, although capital-intensive, is both cost effective and efficient enough to survive in such a remote area as Sunndal.

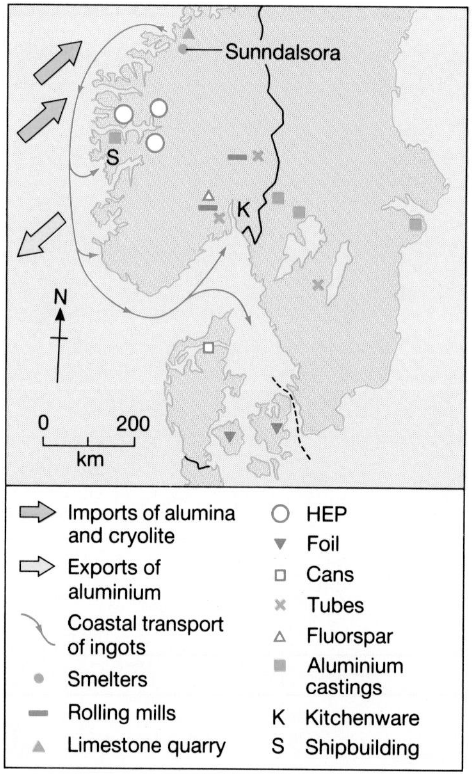

Assignments

1 Draw either pie-charts or bar graphs to show the following:

Number of employees at Sunndal Verk, 1984

a) Manufacturing	719
b) Maintenance and power	272
c) Logistics and engineering	90
d) Administration, etc.	64
e) Research and laboratories	66

Production costs (%) at Sunndal Verk, 1984

a) Raw materials	59
b) Wages and service expenses	16
c) Power	14
d) Capital	9
e) Other	2

2 Complete the following paragraph in your notebooks, under this heading:

Making aluminium at Sunndalsora
Just over _____ people are employed at the smelter. About _____% are involved in making aluminium ingots from imported _____ (from Jamaica). The raw materials amount to over _____ the costs of _____. The making of aluminium is an example of a _____ _____ industry. The most important location factor was the supply of _____, since so much _____ is needed. The smelter is important to the town because it provides _____ and _____ in such a difficult isolated area. The fjord is important to the smelter because it provides a cheap, safe _____ to export the finished ingots. Most of these are sold to countries in the European Community. The rest are sent to other ASV factories in Norway, Sweden and Denmark to be made into_____, _____ and _____.

Fig. 7.6 Location and activities of ASV factories

⇨ Imports of alumina and cryolite	○ HEP
⇨ Exports of aluminium	▼ Foil
↷ Coastal transport of ingots	□ Cans
• Smelters	✕ Tubes
— Rolling mills	△ Fluorspar
▲ Limestone quarry	■ Aluminium castings
	K Kitchenware
	S Shipbuilding

Eindhoven

The map below shows part of Eindhoven, a city in the Netherlands of about 200 000 people. It is similar to Sunndalsora in that it owes most of its employment and growth to one company. In this case it is Philips, the famous Dutch electrical firm. The growth of Philips, and of Eindhoven's industrial landscape, both illustrate other reasons for industrial growth. Eindhoven dates back to the thirteenth century. In 1891 it had a population of 4600, when the Philips company opened its first factory. A small empty textile factory was converted to make electric light bulbs. From that, the company has grown into a world-wide organisation employing more than 340 000, and making a great range of products.

Original factors in growth

1 *Technological change*: the introduction of domestic electricity.
2 *Scientific research*: Anton Philips, one of the founders, had studied with Lord Kelvin.
3 *Family capital* for investment.
4 *Cheap factory premises* being available with a 60 horse-power engine.

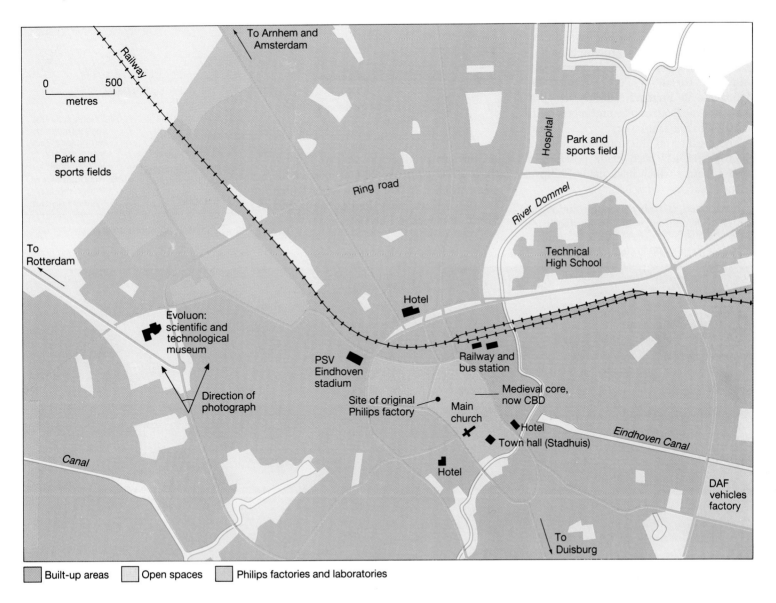

Fig. 7.7 Part of the city of Eindhoven in the Netherlands

The choice of Eindhoven seems to have been a matter of chance. Only ten workers were needed in 1891. Later, as the company grew rapidly, workers travelled daily by train from villages in the surrounding heathland (see page 27) and even from Belgium. The town grew as the company built houses for the carefully selected families brought to Eindhoven from all over the Netherlands.

The map and the photograph (Figs. 7.7 and 7.10) show the industrial landscape which has been created by Philips in the last 90 years. Eindhoven's growth round its medieval core has been on the garden-city principle, based on Port Sunlight and Bournville in England. Philips also provided free medical services and sports facilities for all their employees.

The creation of this unusual industrial environment has been made possible by several factors which have made Philips a financial success (Fig. 7.8).

Eindhoven is today a major industrial centre, with textiles, vehicle manufacturing

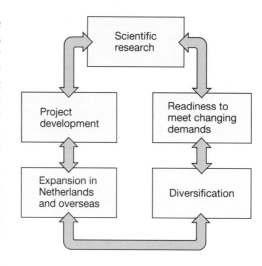

Fig. 7.8 Factors that have influenced Philips' success in the Netherlands

and tobacco products as well as Philips, which alone provides 28 000 jobs in the town. Another 43 000 jobs in other Dutch factories help to make Philips the largest private employer in Europe.

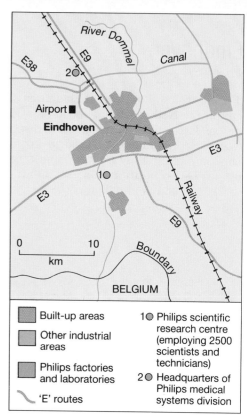

Fig. 7.9 The Eindhoven area

Fig. 7.10 Eindhoven from the air

The development of the electronics industry at Eindhoven has been the result of chance factors, and by careful expansion to meet changing circumstances. The Philips family might have chosen some other location, but the products have never been dependent on particular raw materials. Fig. 7.9 shows how accessible Eindhoven is today. These factors explain the high concentration of the electronics industry here.

Assignments

1 (*Atlas*) Find Eindhoven in the index, and look at the relevant map. How many kilometres (in a straight line) is Eindhoven from **a**) Rotterdam **b**) Amsterdam **c**) the Belgian frontier?

2 (*Fig. 7.7*) The map shows some of the Philips' factories in Eindhoven.
  a) Describe the location of these in relation to (i) the old town (ii) the railway and canals (iii) the ring road.
  b) Where are the open spaces in relation to the other parts of the towns?
  c) How does Eindhoven compare with the model of a Dutch city (page 16)?

3 (*Fig. 7.7 and Fig. 7.10*)
  a) In what compass direction was the camera pointing?
  b) Identify in the photograph Evoluon; the ring road; and the Philips factories and laboratories.
  c) Describe the main features of this industrial landscape, mentioning:
    (i) the design and appearance of the industrial areas;
    (ii) the quality and style of the housing;
    (iii) the road network;
    (iv) the recreational facilities.

4 (*Fig. 7.9*) How accessible is Eindhoven for the transport of components and finished products?

5 (*Fig. 7.11*)
  a) In the last fifty years, Philips have established production centres in over fifty overseas countries. This has been done to avoid import duties and quota restrictions. How has this affected the composition of the workforce?
  b) Suggest reasons for the decline in the total Philips' workforce in the Netherlands since 1970.
  c) In which year did the population of Eindhoven reach 100 000? How do the products made then by Philips differ from those made today?

6 (*Atlas*) Trace a map of the Netherlands, and using suitable symbols show the following information about Philips in the Netherlands.
  Eindhoven: Lighting; glass; radio; gramophone and TV; electronic components; electro-acoustics; industrial equipment; packaging; chemicals; medical systems; and scientific research (*see Fig. 7.11*).
  Baarn: Polygram records.
  Groningen: Small domestic appliances.
  Drachten: Electric shavers; hair driers.
  Hilversum: Telecommunication and defence systems (also at the Hague).
  Apeldoorn: Data systems.
  Amsterdam: Chemical and pharmaceutical products.
  Bearing in mind that there are Philips factories in many other Dutch towns, comment on the distribution shown by the map.

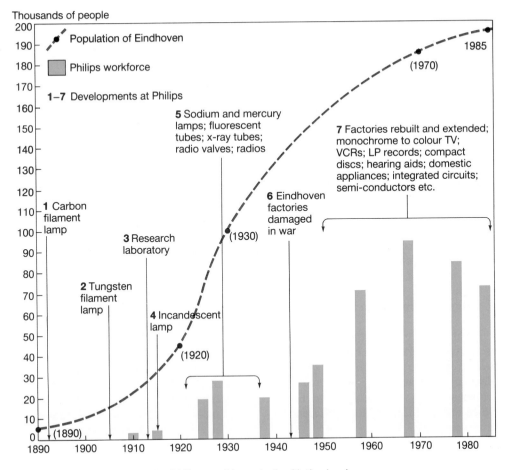

Fig. 7.11 The progress of the Philips workforce in the Netherlands

Making motor vehicles

Eindhoven, as we have seen, is one of the centres of motor vehicle manufacture in Europe. DAF are however, not one of the major car producers in Europe as Fig. 7.12 shows. (The Netherlands is the smallest of the car producing countries in Western Europe).

Fig. 7.12 shows that there is much competition for a share of the car market with six different producers claiming an almost equal share (12%). In 1984, Ford won the largest share of this market. Ford is an example of an American multi-national business with factories in eight different European countries (see Fig. 7.13).

The distribution of these factors illustrates locations:

a near or in the *market* especially the densely populated area centred on Antwerp.

b near other factories making *components*. The motor car industry is an example of an *assembly* industry.

c in *tidewater* locations where land is cheaper, and there is access to sea transport, such as Antwerp, Bordeaux and near Valencia.

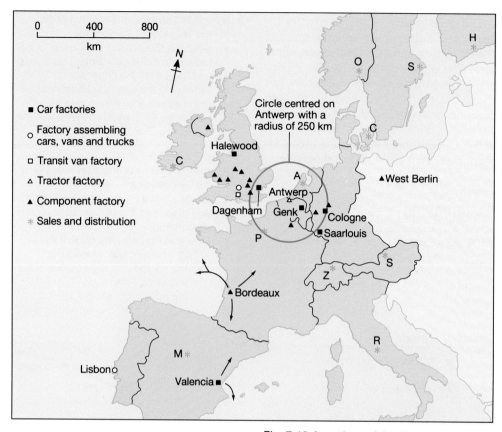

Fig. 7.13 Locations of the Ford Motor Company in Europe

Factory	Car models	No. of workers
Cologne	Granada, Fiesta	27 000
Saarlouis	Escort, Orion	8 000
Genk	Sierra, Transit	10 000
Valencia	Fiesta, Escort, Orion	9 000
Lisbon	Escort, Orion, Transit	1 000

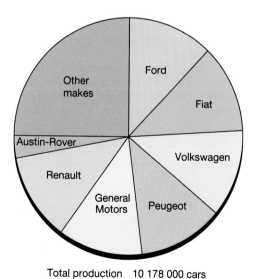

Total production 10 178 000 cars

Fig. 7.12 European car production in 1984

d in areas where labour costs are significantly lower, such as Spain and Portugal. Labour costs in car making in West Germany are the highest in the world, and twice as high as in Spain.

The map also suggests that because of the use of components, assembly factories draw them from several sources. The two Ford plants at Bordeaux make automatic transmissions for the Fiesta and the Escort, which are assembled at four different factories (see Fig. 7.13).

The Fiesta is made both at Valencia (see Fig. 7.13) and at Cologne (see Fig. 7.14). Both places make components as well as finished cars, and both use components from other factories.

The Ford factory south of Valencia is only about one-third the size of the Cologne plant. It produces over 500 000 vehicles annually, as well as Escort and Fiesta engines for other plants. Two possible reasons for locating the Ford factory near Valencia have already been given. The map above shows that the Ford factory has been built on a *greenfield* site i.e. in a rural area which needed massive improvements in the infrastructure.

This factory is part of a rapidly growing Spanish car industry (see Fig. 7.16). Car production has increased by 60 per cent in the last 10 years, and now Spain exports six out of every 10 cars it makes, because of lower costs. This applies even to cars like the SEAT Ibiza, which is designed in Italy and fitted with a Porsche engine.

Assignments

1 (*Fig. 7.12*) **a)** Group the car-making firms according to their country of origin, choosing from: West Germany; USA; France; UK; Italy. **b)** DAF is one of the 'other' car manufacturers in Europe. Can you think of any more?

2 (*Fig. 7.13 and atlas*)
  a) Name the countries in which Ford (i) make cars or components and (ii) have only sales and distribution centres.

Fig. 7.15 The Spanish car industry

1 Ford
2 General Motors
3 SEAT
4 FASA - Renault
5 PCT

▩ Zones of urgent reindustrialization (ZUR)

b) Identify the sales and distribution centres shown.

c) All the factories and centres depend on efficient transport networks especially railways and 'E' Routes. List those which will also depend on sea routes.

3 Explain why car manufacture is described as an assembly industry.

4 (*Fig. 7.16*)
  a) Describe the site of the Ford factory near Valencia. What effect might the factory have on the area?
  b) Draw a sketch cross-section or block diagram to show the site of the factory and the use of the land from west to east (i.e. the coast). Use suitable symbols and annotations.
  c) What improvements have been made to the transport network near the factory?
  d) If you were manager at this Ford factory, what form of transport might you use to send engines to Cologne and Saarlouis?

5 Draw a diagram to show the following figures:

Car production in Spain (millions)

1974	1976	1978	1980	1982	1984
0.70	0.75	0.95	1.03	0.93	1.15

6 Suggest reasons why both SEAT and Volkswagen benefit from working together in Spain to produce VW cars.

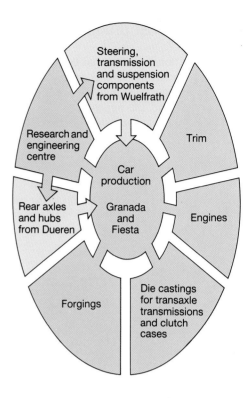

Fig. 7.14 Ford at Cologne, West Germany

Fig. 7.16 The location of the Ford factory on a 'greenfield' site in Valencia, Spain

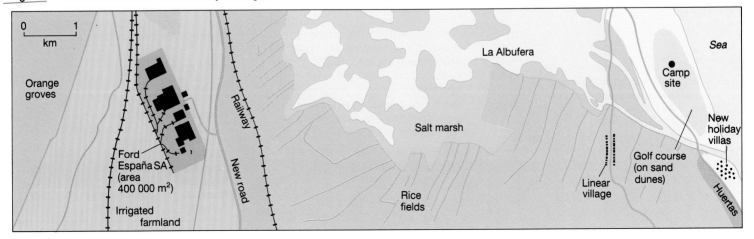

Changes in car production

Car production in Europe has been affected in recent years by several factors. Some have resulted in increased production, others have had the opposite effect. New *technology* as described at Wolfsburg, and higher standards of living resulting in increased demand for cars, have both favoured increased production. The effects of the *depression*, higher oil prices and the opposition of the conservationists to the use of fossil fuels have all reduced the demand for cars.

Making cars at Wolfsburg

... the new Volkswagen production system for the Golf 11 model at its Wolfsburg assembly plant, the 'Hall 54'. In addition to a fully automated and flexible body welding line and robotised paint shop – features common to many factories – the VW facility also takes the first steps to automated final assembly with robots installing the engine, brakelines, battery and wheels. This system can produce not only all the various Golf designs but also Jettas without a change of tools or a halt in production. This flexibility is improved while the use of robots ensures total accuracy by eliminating the human factor of error.'

(*The Economist*, 2 March 1985)

Fig. 7.17 Aerial view of the Volkswagen assembly plant at Wolfsburg, West Germany

Assignments

1 (*Fig. 7.17*)
   a) Trace and identify the main factory building, the railway sidings; parked VW cars; new blocks of flats; low-density housing; farmland; forest.
   b) Calculate the approximate proportions of land in the photograph covered by: industry; housing; farmland and forest. Which of these are **a**) expanding **b**) contracting?

2 (*Fig. 7.19*) Study Fig. 7.18 carefully:
   a) identify beyond the factory: the power station; the village of Aultenbauna; the National Park. In what compass direction was the camera pointing? **b**) If you followed the road (dual carriageway) in the bottom left of the photograph, which 'E' route would you reach? **c**) In what ways is this area typical of a new industrial landscape? Is it a pleasant place to live?

3 (*Atlas*) Find Kassel in your atlas. Find Wolfsburg. How far apart are they?

4 Most of the VW factories are in one part of West Germany. Identify this region and make a list of the advantages and disadvantages of locating a factory there.

5 Use the following information to draw a map showing Volkswagen operations in Europe.

Factory	Products	No of workers
Wolfsburg	Cars	57 900
Hannover	Lorries	18 500
Braunschweig	Machine tools and components	6 300
Salzgitter	Engines	7 300
Emden	Cars	9 400
Kassel	Components	16 500
Ingolstadt	Audi cars	35 400
Brussels	Car assembly	4 700
Sarajevo	Car assembly	2 900

Give the map a key and a title.

Fig. 7.18 Aerial view of the Volkswagen assembly plant at Kassel, West Germany

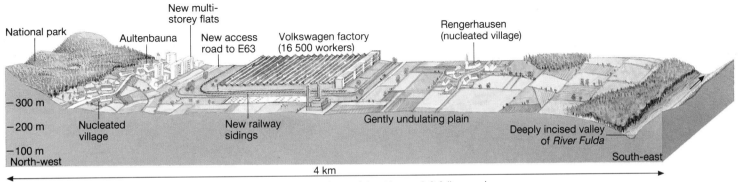

Many of the workers are part time (or 'five o'clock') farmers. As a result, much land is now left fallow each year

Fig. 7.19 Landscape of car production near Kassel. The Volkswagen factory on the outskirts of Kassel was constructed on a 'greenfield' site between nucleated villages. There is good access by road and rail to other Volkswagen factories for the distribution of gear boxes and spare parts

Sunndalsora, Eindhoven and Wolfsburg are all examples of company towns, but they are all dwarfed by Turin (population 1 million). Fiat was established here in Northern Italy in 1899, and it has been responsible for the growth of the city in the last forty years (see panel). Although Fiat have factories in the south of Italy, and there are other car manufacturers in Italy (see assignments), Turin is the largest centre, employing over 80 per cent of Italy's car workers. Of the total workforce in Turin, one third is directly employed by FIAT, with another third employed indirectly. FIAT has 23 different factories in Turin, making a wide range of products. The smallest is the aeronautical plant with 1700 workers while the largest is the Mirafori car plant with 23,000 workers (see Fig. 7.20). There are many other firms supplying the FIAT factories, such as, Pirelli (rubber), Philips and Westinghouse (electrical components), and thousands of smaller businesses. Car manufacture thus dominates the townscapes of Turin with its factories and its new housing. This has brought prosperity (1 car for every 2.6 persons), but also some problems.

Fiat specialises in small economical cars such as the Panda and the Uno. Production has been robotized in Turin. As a result, about one-fifth of the workforce has been made redundant. The effects of this have been far reaching.

Results of robotization

a One in five of the workers have lost their jobs. Many however are still paid 90 per cent of their last wage.

b Many redundant workers and their families have returned to live on their farms in the South.

c Many others now have part-time jobs in other factories, for example, in electronics.

d Unemployment has increased to about one in eight of the workforce. Most affected are the young school leavers.

Turin: 'Fiat City'

. . . in Turin in the 1960s the city's buoyant car plants had drawn hundreds of thousands of migrants from the poor South. In one decade 300 000 people were added to the population. Overcrowding added to the social strain. Advertisements for flats to let often carried the words 'non ai terroni' – southerners need not apply . . . Eventually Fiat and a public housing authority, the Cassa Populari, came to the rescue and built high rise estates in the suburbs, for example, La Villete.

Lopreiato moved north from Calabria as a child, when his father got a job as a Turin garbage collector. His wife, Elizabeth is also a Calabrese. Both left school aged 13. Today he earns £7000 as a laboratory assistant in Fiat. She is pleased to stay at home and cook and clean. They have two children and live in a two bedroom flat in a four storey block.

(*Sunday Times Magazine*, July 1985)

Fig. 7.20 Turin, Northern Italy. The obvious gridiron road pattern, where the CBD is now situated, is a relic of the Roman city

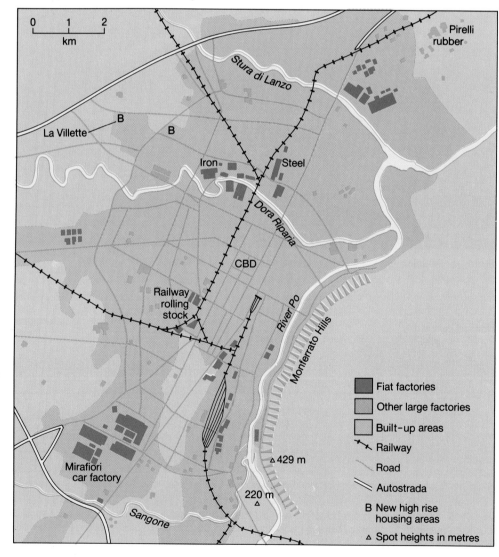

The population of the city has decreased by 200 000 in the last few years. Fortunately, it seems that Turin has a varied enough industrial base to remain relatively prosperous. Nevertheless, Turin remains a company town and a Fiat 'dormitory', very reliant on mechanical engineering.

Assignments

1 (*Atlas work*) From your atlas find the position of Turin and note its position in relation to the Alps and Milan.

2 (*Fig. 7.20*)
   a) Which of these words correctly describe the *site* of Turin: gap town; confluence point; hill top; bridge point? Why is Turin mostly west of the River Po?
   b) What do you notice about the street pattern of the Roman core of the city?
   c) Where are the autostrade in relation to the Roman core and to the factories? Why were the autostrade needed?
   d) Describe the position of the factories in relation to the other features of the city.

3 What proportion of the city's population a) were migrants from the South? b) returned to the South after the mass redundancies?

4 (*Atlas*) Find Calabria in your atlas. How far is it from Turin?

5 (*Atlas*) Trace a map of Italy and on it mark the following vehicle making centres.

Turin	Fiat; Lancia
Milan	Alfa Romeo; Innocenti
Modena	Ferrari
Bolzano	Lancia
Brescia	OM heavy vehicles
Naples	Alfa Romeo (Alfa-Sud)

What do you notice about the distribution?

6 Making motor vehicles is an assembly industry. Draw a diagram to illustrate this using the following figures:

Fiat's consumption of Italian output (Percentage of total)
Rubber: 18.0 per cent; non-ferrous metals: 10.8 per cent; steel: 9.0 per cent; glass: 5.8 per cent; electrical goods: 4.5 per cent; precision instruments: 4.0 per cent; plastic goods: 4.0 per cent.

Making iron and steel: old and new industrial landscapes

Fig. 7.20 shows that there is a Fiat steel works in Turin as part of the system supplying the car assembly lines. Iron and steel making in general represents a different type of industry from the others which have been examined.

> **Characteristics of the steel industry**
>
> Traditionally, steel-making can be described as being *heavy; fixed* (i.e. beside the coal or iron resources); *labour-intensive*, and as belonging to the *smokestack* era.

Fig. 7.21 shows a typical landscape of steel-making in the narrow valley of the River Saar in West Germany. This, on a small scale, is similar to the other steel producing areas of the Ruhr and the Franco-Belgian coalfield (see Chapter 5). There was an eighteenth century iron industry in the Saar, but it was not until the late nineteenth century that steel production began. Now the Saar is faced with the similar problems to the Ruhr of declining production and demand. Steel-making has survived in the Saar at a much reduced level. This is typical of almost all steel-producing areas in Wes-

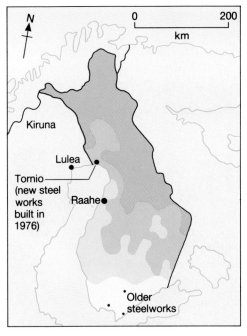

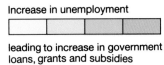

Increase in unemployment

leading to increase in government loans, grants and subsidies

Fig. 7.22 The location of Raahe, Finland

tern Europe (see Chapter 6), and especially of the Ruhr (see below). However, there are others where production is expanding for special reasons. One such centre is Raahe in Northern Finland (see Fig. 7.22).

The steel mill at Raahe was the first in Europe to use the system of continuous casting, that is, the final product is made in

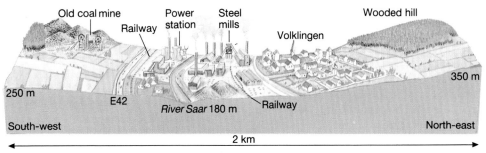

Note Volklingen is 10 km south-east of Saarlouis where Ford have a factory. The coal seams here dip south-west to a depth of 900 metres. Iron ore is brought here from Lorraine and Luxembourg

Fig. 7.21 An old industrial landscape in the Saar

Fig. 7.23 (above) and 7.24 (right) The modern steelworks at Raahe, a very good example of a new industrial landscape in the Taiga in northern Finland

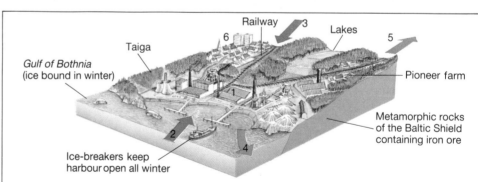

1 Steel works (blast furnaces, coking plant, power station, rolling mills etc). Opened 1964. Annual production: 1.75 million tonnes. Employs 4 400.

2 Imports of concentrated iron and limestone from USSR and NW Europe, and of oil from USSR.

3 Imports by rail of concentrated iron from mines in Northern Finland [half total requirements] and the USSR. Coking coal from USSR.

4 Exports of steel to be used in Finnish shipyards to build ice-breakers.

5 Exports of steel by rail. Used locally to make containers and pipes and in southern Finland, to make sheets and tubes.

6 Town of Raahe. Population has increased from 4000 to 20 000 since 1964.

one operation instead of first making ingots. The reasons for locating the mill here were political (trade agreements with the USSR), and social (the need to stop depopulation by establishing a growth point) rather than economic. Despite this, the mill is profitable, since there is a high demand for its special steels. The Usinor steelworks (see Fig. 7.25) is another example of a new steelworks in a wide-water location.

The Usinor steel-works at Dunkirk: a new industrial landscape

Usinor have older steel-works at Lille (on the Nord coalfield) and Thionville (near iron-ore deposits). The Usinor works at Dunkirk are shown on the map extract (Fig. 7.25). The words 'Aciérie', 'Cokerie', and 'Sidérurgique' show the location of the steel-works.

Assignments

1 From your atlas, locate Dunkirk, Lille and Thionville.

Fig. 7.25 Dunkirk (1:50000), showing the Usinor steel-works

2 Why should Usinor build a steel-works at Dunkirk? Suggest where it might obtain its raw materials.

3 On the map below, identify other industrial areas. Can they be grouped in three or four categories according to type or location?

4 Describe the land on which these industrial areas are located. Mention height, slope and drainage.

5 Study the port area. Can you identify the different stages of port development? (*Note*:The Dover and Ramsgate Ferries use the new West Port 4 km to the west).

6 Find out from a French dictionary the meaning of 'cheminots'. Why does 'Cité des Cheminots' appear on the map?

7 Comment on the relative importance of the different forms of transport shown on the map.

8 Discussion. Is it an advantage or disadvantage to live in such an industrial area?

9 Draw an annotated sketch map to show the main features of Dunkirk.

Rotterdam: Europoort

Royal Dutch Shell and petrochemicals

Shell, like Philips, is a Dutch multinational firm. It is the largest non-American company in the world and has its head offices in London and the Hague. With its operations scattered across the world, only about 10 per cent of its 163 000 strong workforce is found in the Netherlands.

Fig. 7.26 shows the Shell oil refinery and petrochemical plant in the port of Rotterdam-Europoort. Established in 1936, it is the oldest oil refinery in the Netherlands and is one of the largest in the world. Today there are eight areas, 'petroleumhavens', at Rotterdam-Europoort, the world's largest port, given over to the storage and refining of oil (see Fig. 7.28).

Various factors help to explain why Rotterdam-Europoort is such a major oil-refining and petrochemicals centre, which produces a vast range of products from motor fuel, diesel oil and detergents to artificial fibres, plastics and agricultural chemicals.

a In the 1950s and 1960s there was a rapid increase in demand for oil products. Thanks to its central location and excellent transport links by road, rail, barge and pipeline, the port was well placed to serve not only the Netherlands but neighbouring countries as well.

b Thanks to continual investment, by dredging and deepening the channel of the New Waterway the port has been able to accommodate new generations of oil tankers. The eighth petroleum haven can handle oil tankers up to 350 000 tonnes.

c Fig. 7.26 shows the availability of a water supply for cooling purposes, and ample flat land. This older complex has grown up on excavated delta muds but the most recent petroleumhaven is on the massive reclaimed Maasvlakte.

Fig. 7.26 The Shell oil refinery, Rotterdam

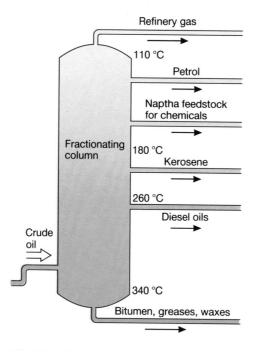

Fig. 7.27 The process of splitting crude oil into its different fractions or products

d Such areas are situated away from the built up districts of Rotterdam.

By taking advantage of such factors, multinationals such as Shell and Esso have created an almost spaceage landscape.

Storage tanks (tall steel towers where the crude oil is split into various fractions) and many kilometres of connecting pipes are the landscape evidence of the many processes which give us oil-based products (see Fig. 7.27).

In producing such a range of products, relatively few people are employed. Refineries are highly automated, making full use of computers. Oil refining, therefore, is a good example of a *capital intensive* industry, i.e. an enormous amount of money has been spent on the complicated equipment but relatively few people are involved.

Since the mid 1970s the Dutch (and the entire Western European) petrochemical industry has suffered setbacks, reducing the level of production. This is the result of: (i) the 1973 energy crisis when oil prices quadrupled; (ii) the economic recession,

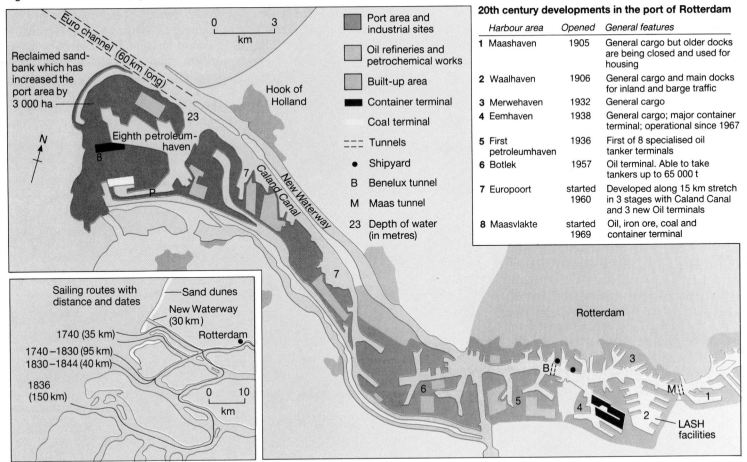

Fig. 7.28 Rotterdam-Europoort

Reclaimed sand-bank which has increased the port area by 3 000 ha

Euro channel (60 km long)

Hook of Holland

Eighth petroleum-haven

New Waterway

Caland Canal

Rotterdam

B

M

LASH facilities

		Port area and industrial sites
		Oil refineries and petrochemical works
		Built-up area
		Container terminal
		Coal terminal
- - -		Tunnels
•		Shipyard
B		Benelux tunnel
M		Maas tunnel
23		Depth of water (in metres)

20th century developments in the port of Rotterdam

	Harbour area	Opened	General features
1	Maashaven	1905	General cargo but older docks are being closed and used for housing
2	Waalhaven	1906	General cargo and main docks for inland and barge traffic
3	Merwehaven	1932	General cargo
4	Eemhaven	1938	General cargo; major container terminal; operational since 1967
5	First petroleumhaven	1936	First of 8 specialised oil tanker terminals
6	Botlek	1957	Oil terminal. Able to take tankers up to 65 000 t
7	Europoort	started 1960	Developed along 15 km stretch in 3 stages with Caland Canal and 3 new Oil terminals
8	Maasvlakte	started 1969	Oil, iron ore, coal and container terminal

Fig. 7.29 Routes through the delta to Rotterdam

Sailing routes with distance and dates

Sand dunes

New Waterway (30 km)

Rotterdam

1740 (35 km)
1740 – 1830 (95 km)
1830 – 1844 (40 km)
1836 (150 km)

and (iii) increased competition from refineries and petrochemical plants in the oil-producing countries of the Middle East.

To ensure that the Rotterdam-Europoort refineries can adapt to changing circumstances, Shell and Esso have invested vast sums in new installations. The new distillation technology allows lighter products to be obtained, for which there is more demand.

Assignments

1 (*Fig. 7.26 and text*) Draw a sketch of the oil refinery. Add labels to show the advantages of its location and site.

2 (*Text and Fig. 7.28*) Are there any disadvantages in locating the refinery west of Rotterdam?

The growth of Rotterdam Europoort

We have seen that the petrochemical industry at Rotterdam-Europoort has had to adapt to new circumstances. Continual change has also marked the growth of this port, especially in the last hundred years. As a result it is not only Western Europe's largest port, but since 1962, when it overtook New York, it has become the largest in the world. The pattern of successful change can be seen in the following ways.

1 Extending the site and deepening access channels

Rotterdam in 1300 was a small cluster of fishing houses at the mouth of the River Rotte, a distributary of the River Rhine. In

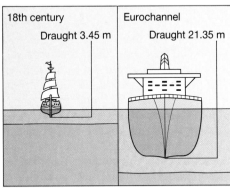

18th century	Eurochannel
Draught 3.45 m	Draught 21.35 m

Fig. 7.30 Shipping and water depth at Rotterdam

theory, with huge quantities of silt being deposited, deltas such as that of the Rhine do not make good sites for ports. Certainly for many hundreds of years, as Rotterdam grew as a result of increased Dutch trade, ships could only reach the port along con-

125

stantly changing routes (see Fig. 7.29). Matters were made a lot easier when the New Waterway was cut through the sand dunes, shortening the route to Rotterdam.

With an increase in trade, new docks have been built involving excavation and dredging. Fig. 7.30 shows the increased depth of water towards the west. This allows the port to handle very large vessels, which approach along the Euro Channel (see Fig. 7.28) from the North Sea.

2 Handling larger and more specialised ships

The western expansion of Rotterdam has allowed it to handle larger and more specialised ships. Fig. 7.28 shows that harbour areas 1 to 4, opened before 1939, handle general cargo; harbour areas 5 to 8 handle more specialised cargoes, especially oil, iron ore, and coal. The ability to cope with enormous quantities of oil has been the key factor in the phenomenal growth of Rotterdam since 1945, seen particularly in the vast Europoort oil-refining and petrochemical complexes and, now, in the artificial Maasvlakte area.

In this way Rotterdam-Europoort can handle all the main types of merchant vessels. These include, for example:

a *VLCC'S (Very Large Crude Oil Carriers):* in spite of their huge size (average 200 000 tonnes), they are relatively simple ships, subdivided into a number of tanks. Cargoes can be loaded or discharged in less than 24 hours.

b *Bulk carriers:* these single deck vessels from 17 000 to 70 000 dwt, transport many of the world's raw materials. Among the commodities handled at Rotterdam are grain, sugar and timber.

c *Ore carriers:* usually larger and stronger versions of the above, bringing iron or coal to Rotterdam. Unlike bulk carriers they have no cargo handling equipment (see Fig. 7.34).

d *General cargo liners:* multi-decked vessels with refrigeration and deep tanks. These are now being replaced by:

e *Container ships:* the holds of such vessels are designed to take standard

containers. These are also carried on road vehicles and trailers on board roll-on/roll-off (Ro-Ro) ships (see Fig. 7.33).

f *Barge carriers:* Up to 90 barges, of a uniform rectangular size, are carried on board a lighter aboard ship (LASH). These are loaded and unloaded at Waalhaven (see Fig. 7.35 and below).

g *Ro-Ro ferries:* these are engaged on short-sea crossings, such as, Harwich to Hook of Holland. Their cargo is mainly private cars and loaded commercial vehicles.

Specialist docks handling specialised ships have reduced the average turnaround

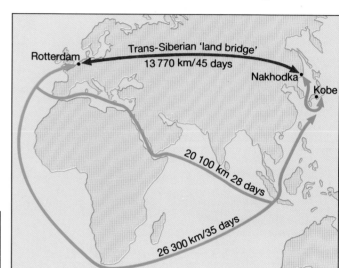

Fig. 7.31 Land and sea-routes to and from Rotterdam

Fig. 7.32 Trade statistics of Rotterdam–Europoort

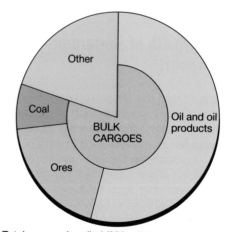

Total cargoes handled (250 million tonnes) in 1985

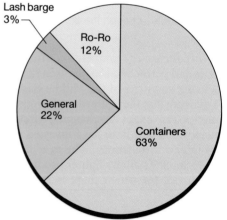

Transport of general cargoes (45 million tonnes) by vessel type (1985)

Turnover of goods (thousand tonnes)

Year	Imports	In transit	Total loaded
1960	36 200	25 351	61 551
1970	118 910	46 273	165 183
1980	144 105	70 803	214 908
1985	113 666	78 915	192 681

Year	Exports	In transit	Total unloaded
1960	14 674	7 180	21 854
1970	47 168	13 439	60 607
1980	44 634	21 569	66 203
1985	33 591	24 297	57 888

Fig. 7.33 (*above*) The container port at Eemhaven. Notice the evidence of landscaping, the power stations (what kind are they?) and the residential area of Rotterdam in the background.

Fig. 7.34 (*right*) Ore carriers unloading at Maasvlakte with a new polder in the background. Notice the barges being loaded. Which industrial areas on the Rhine do you think they will carry ore to?

to well under 24 hours. Fast loading and unloading of cargo has helped Rotterdam-Europoort's success.

3 Containerisation

Increased mechanisation and speed of handling are perhaps best seen in the 'Container Revolution'. Filled with almost any cargo these standardised steel boxes can all be unloaded, using identical dockside cranes, and transferred to the backs of lorries and trains for rapid land based delivery.

The many advantages of containerisation were early recognised by the port authorities. At Eemhaven there is the largest container terminal in the world, handling over one million containers in 1983. But this is to be supplemented by a new terminal at Maasvlakte (see Fig. 7.28), with ample room for future expansion. This move has been encouraged by the lack of room at Eemhaven and the increased size of vessels. Indeed the terminal on the Maasvlakte will function as a trans-shipment point. Containers arriving on a giant ocean going ship will be switched to smaller vessels for forwarding to other European ports and vice-versa.

4 Containers and a wider hinterland

Rotterdam-Europoort is a major industrial area based on imported raw materials. It is cheaper to process raw materials such as oil, sugar and grain at the port itself. But not all the imported goods are for Rotterdam alone or even the Netherlands. Like any other port Rotterdam draws on and serves a wide inland area involving several countries. Such an area is called the *hinterland*.

It is almost impossible to show accurately a port's hinterland on a map. For one thing, the size of a hinterland varies with different commodities; for another, hinterlands expand and contract as ports compete with one another. Rotterdam, for example, competes with Antwerp and Amsterdam. Its success is explained by the fact that Rotterdam Europoort's traditional hinterland extends throughout the Rhine basin

Fig. 7.35 LASH barges stowed on a vessel in Waalhaven

(see page 47 and Fig. 3.59). Rotterdam-Europoort ('poort' means 'gateway') serves over 150 million people in one of the most urbanised and industrialised areas in the world.

Now, thanks to containerisation, Rotterdam's landward links extend even beyond Europe. Freight and shipping companies based at the port and trading, for example, with Japan, now take advantage of the Siberian 'land bridge' route (see Fig. 7.31). Containers landed at Rotterdam can be taken via the Trans-Siberian railway to the port of Nakhodka. From there a container ship will take them to Japan. Containerisation has, therefore, considerably widened Rotterdam-Europoort's hinterland.

Assignments

1 (*Fig. 7.29 and text*) What were the advantages of creating the New Waterway?
2 (*Fig. 7.28*) a) Compare the depth of water at Merwehaven with that at Maasvlakte. b) What is the 'Eurochannel' and why is continual dredging essential?
3 (*Fig. 7.28 and text*) At which parts of Rotterdam-Europoort might the following ships berth? a) a 250 000-tonne oil tanker b) a Ro-Ro ferry from Harwich c) a 40 000-tonne container vessel. d) A 35 000-tonne LASH vessel.
4 (*Fig. 7.28 and text*) a) Draw a simplified

topological map to show the westward growth of Rotterdam-Europoort. b) Write a brief account to explain its growth.
5 (*General*) In what ways does the growth of Rotterdam-Europoort compare with the 'Anyport' model.
6 (*Text*) a) What is meant by a container? b) What are the advantages/ disadvantages of containerisation?
7 (*Text and Figs. 7.31 and 3.59*) a) Explain what is meant by a port's hinterland. b) What countries are included in Rotterdam's traditional hinterland?
8 (*Fig. 7.31*) a) What are the advantages/ disadvantages of the three routes shown on the map? b) How has the Siberian 'land bridge' extended Rotterdam's hinterland?
9 (*General*) a) What are the advantages of a port location for industry? Give examples from Rotterdam-Europoort. b) Land-use conflict and air pollution are two problems facing Rotterdam-Europoort. Suggest reasons for these problems and possible solutions.
10 (*Research/discussion*) a) Find out what is meant by a port's *foreland*. b) As a result of developments such as the Trans-Siberian 'land bridge', is it possible now to separate a port's 'hinterland' and 'foreland'?
11 (*Fig. 7.32*) a) Describe the main types of cargo handled at Rotterdam-Europoort. b) Draw a bar graph of the 1985 turnover of goods. c) Comment on the graph. d) Explain the term 'in transit'.
e) Describe and explain the trends and patterns of imports and exports from 1960 to 1985.

Changing employment

So far in this chapter, the emphasis has been on the landscapes of manufacturing industry. Yet for many people in Europe, even in these industrial areas which have been studied, work is found in the service sector. The relative importance of this employment is shown in Fig. 7.36. The percentage of the workforce involved ranges from less than 35 in Bulgaria (24 per cent) and Albania (14 per cent) to Sweden (61 per cent). In general the so-called 'advanced', wealthier countries have the highest percentage of the workforce in service employment. For a growing number of people, the place of work is the office (Fig. 7.38), bank, shop, laboratory, hotel or restaurant or in the transport system. The workplaces are usually in urban areas, but in rural areas relying on tourism, service employment is vital. The map also shows that in eight countries employment in manufacturing industry has declined.

Fig. 7.37 shows that changes have come about in waves. Service sector employment has increased in Europe as technology has improved, for example through the use of computer-assisted tools and robots. The waves of change have been slower in reaching some European countries. Thus employment in manufacturing was still increasing in Southern and Eastern Europe in the 1980s.

The other result of the waves of change is the growing unemployment rate, especially among the young school leavers.

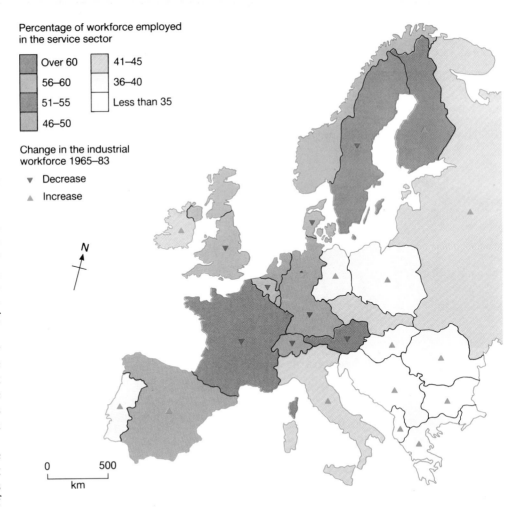

Fig. 7.36 Employment in the service sector in Europe in 1984

Percentage of workforce employed in the service sector

- Over 60
- 56–60
- 51–55
- 46–50
- 41–45
- 36–40
- Less than 35

Change in the industrial workforce 1965–83

- ▼ Decrease
- ▲ Increase

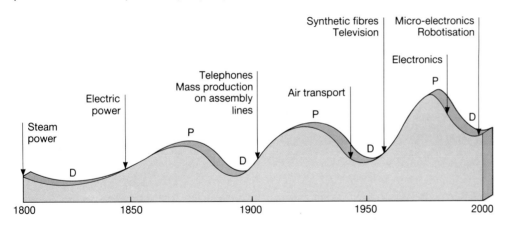

Fig. 7.37 Model of economic development in Western Europe. Various innovations have produced a wave-like pattern of prosperity (P) and depression (D)

Fig. 7.38 Office workers in Paris

129

Chapter 8 Recreation and Tourism

Fig. 8.1 Active recreation: a weekend cycle trip

Fig. 8.2 Passive recreation: a crowded beach

Fig. 8.3 Yatching at Loodsdrechtse Plassen

Recreation and the Dutch countryside

In the Netherlands, as elsewhere in Western Europe, there has been an increase in leisure activities. There are several reasons for this.

a The Dutch enjoy one of the highest standards of living. So they have more money to spend on leisure.
b People in general now have more free time compared with earlier this century. Weekends are usually free and most Dutch workers have at least three weeks paid holiday. But, increasing unemployment has meant enforced leisure.
c Over the past 30 years the Dutch have become more mobile. More people own cars and there is an excellent motorway and road network. There are also many cycle lanes which accompany the main roads. On a fine summer Sunday mopeds and bicycles account for 30 per cent of all transport.

As a result of this 'leisure revolution', about a third of the population travel into the countryside for outdoor recreation (Figs. 8.1, 8.2, and 8.3). The Netherlands is, however, a relatively small and densely-populated country. There is much pressure on land-use between cities and farmland, especially in the west (page 79). Recreation is therefore concentrated in certain areas. These include: (1) the North-Sea and Sand-Dune Belt; and (2) the fertile sandy heath-lands, such as the Hoge Veluwe national park.

Recreation in the North Sea sand-dune belt

From the Friesian islands in the north to the delta area in the south, most of the Dutch coastline is backed by a belt of sand-dunes. In places they are up to five kilometres wide, elsewhere as narrow as 500 m.

For the Dutch, these dunes mark their main line of defence against the sea for the low-lying polders behind (chapter 2). But they also provide a variety of other land-uses (Figs. 8.4 and 8.6). The dunes therefore, serve as a resource for *multiple land-use*, which is particularly important in a country like the Netherlands.

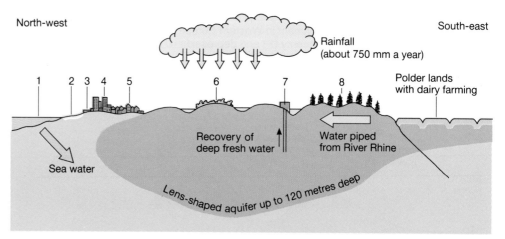

North-west

South-east

Rainfall
(about 750 mm a year)

1 2 3 4 5 6 7 8

Polder lands
with dairy farming

Recovery of
deep fresh water

Water piped
from River Rhine

Sea water

Lens-shaped aquifer up to 120 metres deep

Fig. 8.4 A north-west to south-east transect of land-use in the Zandvoort Area

Assignments

1 (*Atlas and Fig. 8.6*) Locate this stretch of coastline. From which city would you expect most day-trippers to the beach to come?

2 (*Figs. 8.5 and 8.6*) What main land-uses which you can see in the sand-dune area?

3 (*Fig. 8.6*) If you were designing a poster to show the main advantages and features of Zandvoort what information would you include?

4 (*Fig. 8.6*) Name the two conservation areas, describe their environmental features and their advantages for recreation.

5 (*Figs. 8.4 and 8.6, general and research*)
   a) What natural advantages do the sand-dunes have for water storage?
   b) Give two reasons to explain why water from the River Rhine is pumped to the various waterworks in the sand dunes. (Clues: salt infiltration; river pollution.)

6 (*General and Fig. 8.6*) How does the layout of Zandvoort compare with a model of a holiday resort?

7 (*Fig. 8.4*) Make a copy of the diagram and match the numbers with the following list: pine-covered dunes, North Sea, suburbs, hotel and entertainment zone, pumping station, promenade, dunes with buckthorn, beach.

Fig. 8.5 Sand-dune area on the Netherlands coast

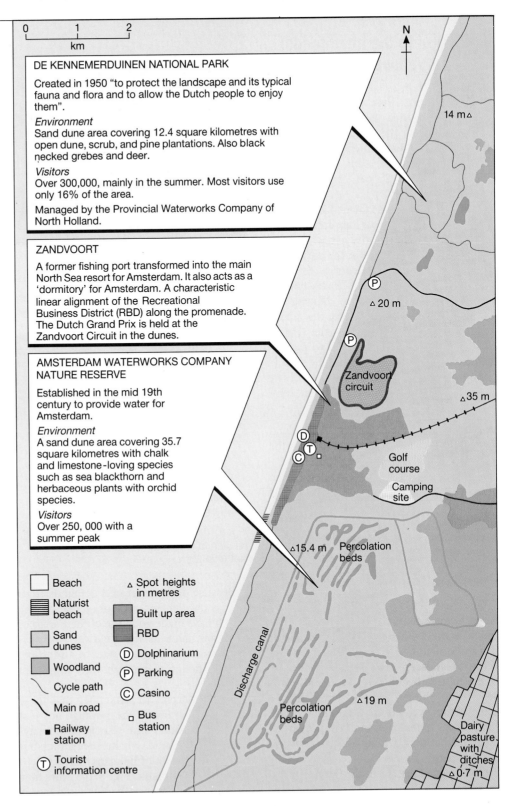

DE KENNEMERDUINEN NATIONAL PARK

Created in 1950 "to protect the landscape and its typical fauna and flora and to allow the Dutch people to enjoy them".

Environment
Sand dune area covering 12.4 square kilometres with open dune, scrub, and pine plantations. Also black necked grebes and deer.

Visitors
Over 300,000, mainly in the summer. Most visitors use only 16% of the area.

Managed by the Provincial Waterworks Company of North Holland.

ZANDVOORT

A former fishing port transformed into the main North Sea resort for Amsterdam. It also acts as a 'dormitory' for Amsterdam. A characteristic linear alignment of the Recreational Business District (RBD) along the promenade. The Dutch Grand Prix is held at the Zandvoort Circuit in the dunes.

AMSTERDAM WATERWORKS COMPANY NATURE RESERVE

Established in the mid 19th century to provide water for Amsterdam.

Environment
A sand dune area covering 35.7 square kilometres with chalk and limestone-loving species such as sea blackthorn and herbaceous plants with orchid species.

Visitors
Over 250, 000 with a summer peak

Legend:
- Beach
- Naturist beach
- Sand dunes
- Woodland
- Cycle path
- Main road
- Railway station
- ⓣ Tourist information centre
- △ Spot heights in metres
- Built up area
- RBD
- Ⓓ Dolphinarium
- Ⓟ Parking
- Ⓒ Casino
- □ Bus station

Fig. 8.6 Land-use along part of the Dutch coastline

Recreation in the heathlands: the Hoge Veluwe National Park

The photographs (Figs. 8.7 and 8.8) show another Dutch area used for country recreation. This is the Veluwe, an area of heathland and forests which covers about 5 per cent of the Netherlands' area but provides as much as 25 per cent of Dutch recreational land.

How the Veluwe was formed is shown in Fig. 8.9. The Veluwe was long considered a 'negative' area. Indeed the name 'Veluwe' means 'barren lands' and in the past it was suitable only for sheep-rearing, forestry, and mills which used the streams flowing from the undulating ridges. During the nineteenth century, when there was a need for more agricultural land, the Dutch Heathland Society was formed to reclaim the infertile sandy soils.

Today, however, attitudes to the Veluwe have changed. Now various land-uses compete for it. These include:

a *Agriculture*: the Dutch Heathland Society pays farmers grants to keep the heath instead of ploughing it up.
b *Military training*: in the crowded Dutch countryside this is one of the few areas suitable for using large armoured-vehicles.
c *Recreation*: by Dutch standards this is one of the few remaining 'wilderness' areas of any size, with up to 250 000 visitors per week in the summer months.

One particularly popular attraction is the Hoge Veluwe national park. Covering an area of some 5 400 hectares it is similar in size and function to a British country park. With its landscape of wet and dry heathland, mixed deciduous woodland, and Scots Pine, the park is popular with cyclists. Many cycle from Arnhem. Others come by car to the park and then use one of the free bikes to ride along a 40 km network of cycle paths (Fig. 8.7).

One unusual feature in the middle of the park is the Kröller-Muller Museum which houses a collection of sculpture (Fig. 8.8), and nineteenth and twentieth century paintings, especially those by Van Gogh.

Fig. 8.7 Cyclists in the Hoge Veluwe

Fig. 8.8 Sculptures in the grounds of the Kröller-Muller Museum, Hoge Veluwe

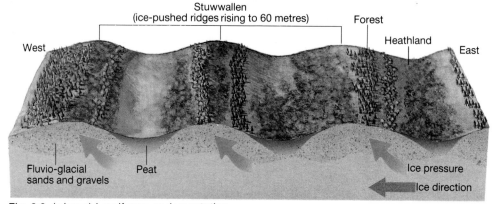

Fig. 8.9 (*above*) Landforms and vegetation in the Veluwe

Fig. 8.10 (*right*) Major population centres in relation to recreation areas in the Netherlands

Because of the increased demands from the city dwellers for outdoor recreation, the Dutch have made good use of their areas of poor soil, such as the Veluwe. Also, recreation has been made part of a multiple land-use policy, along with water supply, in the dunes.

It is important to remember that these varied environments are popular not just with day visitors but also with holiday-makers. Most holidaymakers are Dutch but there are also a lot of Belgians and, particularly, West Germans. Fig. 8.10 shows how accessible the dunes or the Veluwe are; only a few hours' drive from major population centres, like the Ruhr, thanks to major Euroroutes such as the E35 and E36.

Tourists to the Netherlands

The Netherlands is popular with tourists from abroad although its tourist industry does not compare with those of countries such as Switzerland or Spain. Fig. 8.11 shows that West Germany, Britain and Belgium are the main sources of tourists for the Netherlands.

Assignments

1 (*Fig. 8.11*) Use the pie graph to find the total percentage of visitors to the Netherlands from West Germany, the United Kingdom and Belgium.

2 (*Figs. 8.11 and 8.12*) Copy these paragraphs selecting the correct 'lefts' and 'rights'.

Tourists from various countries are attacted to different parts of the Netherlands. The largest/smallest group of tourists, West Germans, are mainly attracted to the large cities/North Sea coast. Italian tourists, rather like Americans, are drawn to the large cities/North Sea coast. They account for as many as 75 per cent. British tourists, however, fall between these two patterns, and tend to be more widespread/concentrated, and visit both the coast and cities.

Overall, it seems that tourists from distant/neighbouring countries are more interested in the cultural and historical features of cities such as Amsterdam. On the other hand, those from distant/neighbouring countries have interests more like the Dutch themselves, and are attracted by beaches, heaths, and lakes which are close in terms of time and cost distance.

3 (*Fig. 8.12*) Look at the photograph of one of the older parts of Amsterdam.
   a) Write a description of what you see. Make use of a sketch.
   b) If you were writing a tourist brochure for the Netherlands would you include this photograph? Briefly explain your answer.

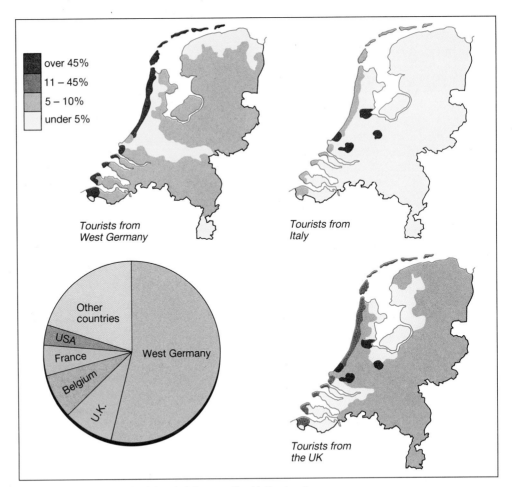

over 45%
11 – 45%
5 – 10%
under 5%

Tourists from West Germany

Tourists from Italy

Tourists from the UK

Other countries
USA
France
Belgium
U.K.
West Germany

Fig. 8.11 Countries of origin of visitors to the Netherlands

Fig. 8.12 The old architecture and canals of Amsterdam attract many tourists to the city

Tourism and change in the Austrian Alps

Austria is the most popular destination for winter tourists from the Netherlands. West Germany provides the largest group of foreign visitors to Austria, the Dutch ranking fourth. But the main tourist magnet for all, is the Austrian Alps. By the mid 1980s Tyrol, Salzburg and Vorarlberg had 15 million visitors a year.

Yet the Alps were not always seen as a place to visit and enjoy. It is only really in the past two hundred years that we have come to appreciate the scenery of such mountains. Before that, visitors travelling from Northern Europe to Italy saw the Alps only as an evil necessity that had to be crossed, as this excerpt suggests.

> The next morning we mounted again through strange, horrid, and fearful crags and tracts, abounding in pine trees, and only inhabited by bears, wolves and wild goats; nor could we see above a pistol-shot before us, the horizon being terminated with rocks and mountains, whose tops, covered in snow, seemed to touch the skies ... Some of these vast mountains were but one entire stone, betwixt whose clefts now and then precipitated great cataracts of melted snow, and other waters which made a terrible roaring, echoing from the rocks and cavities.
>
> (John Evelyn, 1646)

Attitudes to the Alps, and other mountains, have changed for various reasons.

a After the 'Age of Enlightenment', artists, poets, writers, and musicians paid attention to remote mountain areas and so helped to popularize them.

b By the mid-nineteenth century mountaineering was emerging as a sport. In 1865 the British mountaineer, Edward Whymper, scaled the Matterhorn for the first time. He was assisted by Swiss guides from the then small village of Zermatt. Soon mountain inns became

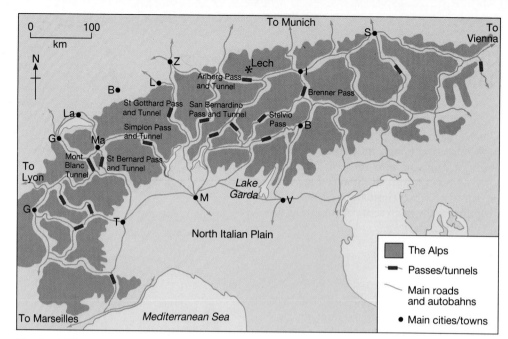

Fig. 8.13 The Alpine road, pass and tunnel network

hotels, and small villages, such as Davos, St Moritz, and Zermatt, became major winter sports resorts (see atlas).

c In the twentieth century improved transport and the development of hydropower has boosted the Alpine tourist industry. New roads, trans-Alpine tunnels, rack and pinion railways, ski-lifts, chair-lifts, and aerial cableways have transformed the Alpine landscape.

Assignments

1 (Text) Read the excerpt by John Evelyn. Pick out words and phrases which show that he was not impressed by the Alps.

2 (Text) Explain why attitudes to the Alps began to change.

Crossing the Alps; shrinking distances

Perhaps the most important factor in the development of tourism has been improved accessibility. Whatever scenic or skiing attractions the Lech area has, they would be

Fig. 8.14 The St Gotthard Pass, Italy

of little use unless people could travel quickly and easily to the area. Lech benefits from its location close to the Arlberg Pass and Tunnel (Figs. 8.13 and 8.14). The Arlberg Rail Tunnel (10.25 kilometres long, completed in 1884) and the road tunnel (14 kilometres long, completed in 1978) provide west-east links between Switzerland and Austria all the year round.

Travel is quicker, faster, and more comfortable now. Thanks to civil engineering, the Alps are easily crossed. The post-1945 construction of road tunnels such as Mt Blanc, San Bernardino or St Gotthard (Fig. 8.14) have: (1) reduced road distance; (2) helped to shrink time-distance and (3) made trans-Alpine journeys almost independent of the weather.

Assignments

1 (*Fig. 8.13*) **a)** Name the main towns and cities shown on the map. **b)** If you were travelling by road between the following cities which pass/tunnel would you use? Zurich to Milan? Zurich to Innsbruck? Geneva to Turin?

2 (*Fig. 8.14*) What difficulties face the civil engineer in building such a road? How are they overcome?

A case study: Lech

The Alpine community of Lech has changed as a result of tourism. Located in Western Austria, almost all its 1200 inhabitants live in three settlements (Fig. 8.15). The largest of these is Lech itself (Fig. 8.16) which caters for summer and winter tourists; the small hamlet of Zug is more dependent on agriculture; Zürs, the highest of the three, is entirely dependent on winter tourism.

Yet until 1900 the whole of the Lech community could be completely cut off for months during the winter, while in summer it could only be reached by cart and mule tracks across avalanche-prone slopes. Farming was the main livelihood, and the valley slopes, such as those around Zürs,

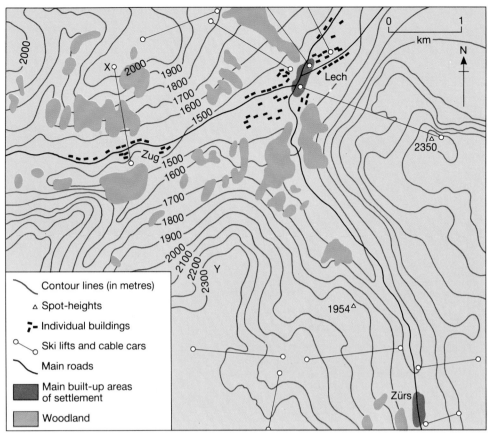

Fig. 8.15 The area around Lech, Austria

Fig. 8.16 Children gather at a ski school at Lech

were used as summer pasture for sheep and goats.

When a road over the Flexen Pass (south of Zürs) was built in 1910, the development of Lech as an alpine ski-resort could begin. Thanks to its altitude and inland location there is a guaranteed snow cover from the end of November until the end of April, with an average snow depth from 1.5 metres to 2.5 metres. In addition, even in January, there are up to seven hours of sunshine a day.

In spite of its natural advantages, the growth of Lech's tourist industry has taken place mainly in the past 30 years. Like the rest of the Austrian Alps, development was slower than in Switzerland. It is only since the end of the Second World War and the re-unification of Austria in 1955, that the full potential of the Austrian Alps has been realized.

Today the valley sides of Lech are covered with a network of lifts and ski-runs. Lech and Zürs have an up-market reputation; they cater for the wealthy and

famous, and have plenty of après-ski activities. Both settlements have modern hotels, guesthouses and apartments, most of which have been constructed in the traditional styles of the area. There is also a wide range of summer activities, with tennis courts, heated open-air swimming pools, riding, and hiking. Walking holidays are increasingly popular in this area, following tracks used by sheep and cattle climbing to the summer pastures. In this part of the Alps, despite the influence of tourism on landscape and life, pastoral farming still exists (Figs. 8.17 and 8.18). So far the eastern Alps have been spared the development of high-altitude, large-scale ski-resorts, such as La Plagne in the French Alps.

Assignments

1 (*Figs. 8.15 and 8.16*)

   a) There are three settlements shown on the map: Lech, Zug and Zürs. Name the highest and lowest settlements and give their heights.

   b) Draw a cross-section between points X and Y on the map. Add on labels to show: Zug; the ski-lift; woodland; the road; the cross-section shape of the valley.

2 (*Fig. 8.17*)

   a) Match the numbers on the top diagram with the following: coniferous wood for shelter, fuel, timber, and avalanche control; narrow road blocked in winter; pyramid peaks over 2500; winding mountain tracks; small village in valley bottom; mountain pastures for summer grazing; snowline in summer; glacier; small strip fields.

   b) Match the numbers on the bottom diagram with the following: large village with hotels, guesthouses, discos, gift shops; ski-lifts, aerial cableways etc; ski-runs; new all-weather road bypassing village centre; glacier used for summer ski-ing; mountain-tracks used for hiking; mountain pasture; chalets used as second homes on former mountain pasture; winding mountain roads; enlarged fields.

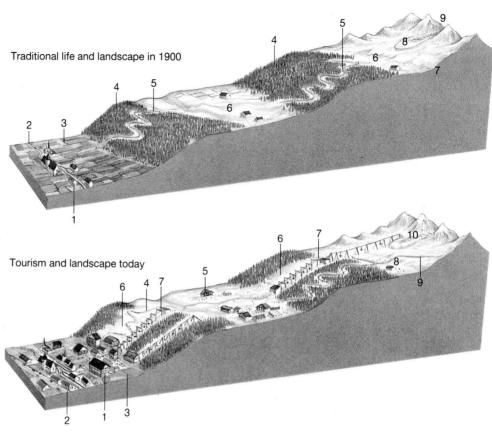

Traditional life and landscape in 1900

Tourism and landscape today

Fig. 8.17 The impact of tourism on an area in the Eastern Alps

Fig. 8.18 A conversation in the Alps

Tourism in Spain and Portugal

Tourism is of major importance to Spain and Portugal. Many British holidaymakers travel there each year, mostly by air or by car. If, for example, you booked a villa in Puerto de la Selva in Spain you could use either method of transport. The actual distance is less important than the *cost distance* or the *time distance*.

Assignments

1 (*Fig. 8.19 and atlas*) Name the ferry routes 1–5. The English ports are Portsmouth, Newhaven, Dover, Weymouth, Folkestone (but not in that order).

2 (*Fig. 8.19*) Airport 1 is Gerona. Name the other airports, choosing from Alicante; Gibralta; Palma; Malaga; Barcelona; Oporto; Lisbon.

3 (*Fig. 8.19*) Name the towns in France marked: To; B; L, and T.

4 (*Fig. 8.19*) The distance from the Channel ports 1–5 to Puerto de la Selva is about 1200 km. It would take two or three days. Which route would you take and why?

5 The cost of the land journey would involve charges for the ferry, petrol, tolls, and hotel bills. The air journey to Gerona from Gatwick would only take two hours, but would be more expensive. Discuss which method you would use.

Puerto de la Selva

The village is some distance from the airport at Gerona, and from the Euroroute (E4). This isolation is one reason why it has not been affected much by tourism. It has the attraction of sunshine and summer drought without being too hot. It is an attractive village with good services (Fig. 8.21). The village has a restricted site because of the steep ridge to the east (Fig. 8.20). This has spared it from the high-rise developments typical of more popular re-sorts on the Costa Brava, such as Lloret de Mar.

The village is linear in shape, little more than 100 m and four streets wide, and some 800 m from north to south. Its permanent population is about 750, but in the height of summer, the population is more than doubled. There are several small hotels and many villas and flats for rent. One firm, Catalan Villas, has 200 bed spaces available in the village itself, and more in the newer villas on the west side of the bay (Fig. 8.21).

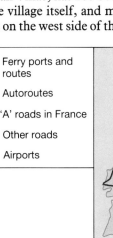

Fig. 8.19 Major travel routes between England and the Iberian Peninsula

Legend:
- ○···● Ferry ports and routes
- Autoroutes
- 'A' roads in France
- Other roads
- ✳ Airports

Fig. 8.20 The village of Puerto de la Selva, from the ridge

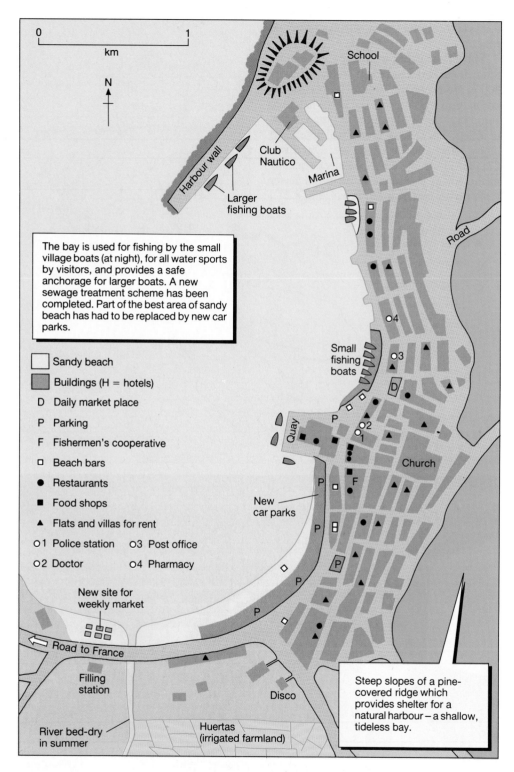

The bay is used for fishing by the small village boats (at night), for all water sports by visitors, and provides a safe anchorage for larger boats. A new sewage treatment scheme has been completed. Part of the best area of sandy beach has had to be replaced by new car parks.

	Sandy beach
	Buildings (H = hotels)
D	Daily market place
P	Parking
F	Fishermen's cooperative
□	Beach bars
●	Restaurants
■	Food shops
▲	Flats and villas for rent
○1	Police station
○3	Post office
○2	Doctor
○4	Pharmacy

New site for weekly market

Road to France

Filling station

River bed-dry in summer

Huertas (irrigated farmland)

Disco

Steep slopes of a pine-covered ridge which provides shelter for a natural harbour – a shallow, tideless bay.

School

Club Nautico

Harbour wall

Larger fishing boats

Marina

Road

Small fishing boats

Quay

New car parks

Church

Fig. 8.21 Puerto de la Selva: village plan and services

Fig. 8.22 The new promenade and car park

Fig. 8.23 Fishing boats moored in front of renovated houses at the north end of Puerto de la Selva

Fig. 8.24 New villas on the west of the bay

Fig. 8.25 The grape harvest for local wine making

Benefits of tourism The village has a range of services far greater than could be supported by its population. Most old houses have been renovated, giving work to local builders and carpenters. There is an electricity supply and a new mains water supply. The school has been rebuilt, and the people have money to buy TV sets and electrical household goods.

Problems caused by tourism The influx of visitors has caused problems. The new car parks (Fig. 8.22) and sewage-treatment system have attempted to solve two of these problems. In the late 1960s and 70s, the villagers neglected their fishing and farming, and many terraced vineyards and olive groves were abandoned. Now there is a renewed interest in fishing, growing vegetables and fruit on the huertas, and making wine. It is still a working village, with a boatbuilder and a blacksmith fully employed.

Assignments

1 (*Text*) in what ways does Puerto de la Selva differ from the Greek village, Ambeli? (Page 12)

2 (*Figs. 8.21–8.24 and text*) Has Puerto de la Selva lost more than it has gained from tourism? Use evidence from the photographs, diagrams and text to back up your view.

Tourism on the Costa Del Sol

Refer back to Fig. 8.19 and find the Costa del Sol, the most southerly of the tourist coasts in Spain. Because it is further south, it is even hotter and drier than the Costa Brava, as the graph shows (Fig. 8.26).

This type of climate is a major attraction to the people of Northern Europe, and the increased prosperity and leisure time of the 1970s brought millions of tourists (page 141). This demand for accommodation resulted in ribbon development of villas and multi-storied flats and hotels all along the

The strain in Spain

Eight kilometres from Marbella in the hills behind the town, is the whitewashed village of Ojen. It is like a set from Carmen, with not a tourist in sight. Inside the newly-completed day centre, old men are playing bridge and drinking coffee. Down the road, plasterers are skimming the final coat onto a new medical centre. In among the traditional Moorish architecture are 80 new houses. Ojen has grown more fragrant since the villagers gave up burying their rubbish. A truck comes weekly from Marbella now to take it away.

All of this is paid for by the socialist provincial government of Malaga. 'They have done more for us in the last three years than the others did in 20', says a 79 year-old man. What did he think of events in Marbella? 'I never go there. It is not Spain.

(*Sunday Times*, 5 May 1985)

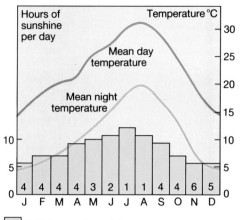

Daily hours of sunshine

4 Number of days with rain (the mean annual rainfall is only 500 mm)

Fig. 8.26 Climate data for the Costa de Sol

Costa del Sol. Some resorts are more popular and cheaper, for example Torremelinos, while others are more exclusive, such as Marbella. Even interior villages have been affected, such as Mijas (Fig. 8.28) which has many daily visitors, and Ojen (see extract on the left).

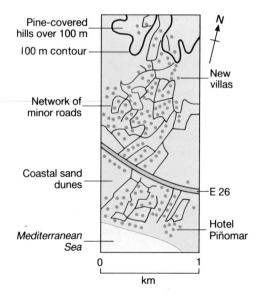

Fig. 8.27 Unplanned development east of Marbella

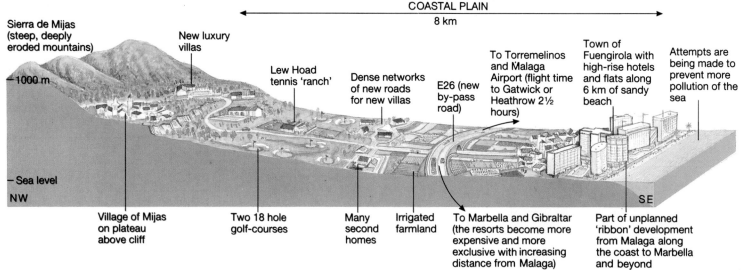

Fig. 8.28 A landscape of tourism and recreation in the Costa del Sol

Results of tourism

On the Costa del Sol, even more than in other coastal areas, tourism has transformed both the landscape and the lives of the people. Do you think that the developments have been worthwhile?

Spain, like other countries in Southern Europe, has come to depend on income from tourists. So the decrease in numbers of tourists in recent years, because of the recession and the rising crime rate in Spanish resorts, has been a major blow.

Assignments

1 a Draw a diagram to show the following figures.

Visitors to Spain 1984 (millions)

France	10.0	Portugal	8.4
UK	6.0	West Germany	5.3
Morocco	2.5	Netherlands	1.4
Belgium	1.0	Switzerland	0.8
Italy	0.8	Sweden	0.6
Denmark	0.4	Norway	0.4
Others	5.3	Total	42.9

b Use the text to comment on the origin of these visitors.

2 (*Fig. 8.29*) From your atlas, name the places marked by initial letter. (Sa is Santiago de Compostela).

3 (*Fig. 8.29*) Suggest reasons why tourists might visit Madrid.

4 (*Fig. 8.29*) Is there any apparent connection between income in Spain and tourism?

5 (*Fig. 8.32 and Table below*) Comment on the following figures.

Tourism in Portugal

	1970	1982
Visitors (millions)	3.3	7.3
Tourist income (£m)	27.7	303.4

7 (*Fig. 8.32 and text*) On balance, are tourist developments worth all the money invested in them? Refer to the examples given in this chapter. Consider the views of local people.

Tourism in Spain has also been affected by changes in the exchange rate, and increases in prices. It provides employment which is usually seasonal. In 1981, the unemployment rate in Andalusia was the highest in Spain at 20.3 per cent. The diagram tries to sum up the effects of 'El Boom' in tourism (Fig. 8.32).

The results of tourism in Portugal has included an increase in population. For

Majorca, 1985

Night and day, packages of people fly into and out of Palma airport, buying their few days of sunshine; at all hours coaches call at the resort hotels . . . Second only to tourism on this island is building for yet more tourism. 'Paradise for the Happy Few' declares a modest signboard outside yet another architect-designed jigsaw . . . Yet there is also an environment for the 'happy many' in the resorts like Santa Posa and Magaluf, the latter a tourist fantasy gone mad in which people are stacked 25 high in repulsive tower blocks, while at street level 'English pubs' and Mexican fast-food joints and no-waiting snooker clubs argue with one another in a conflagration of flickering neon.

(A Troon *The Scotsman Magazine*, 10 January 1986)

example, the Algarve, the most popular tourist area (Fig. 8.31), which has all the advantage of sunshine and high temperatures, had almost a 20 per cent increase in population between 1970 and 1980. The development of new tourist resorts and of intensive irrigated agriculture have also increased water consumption.

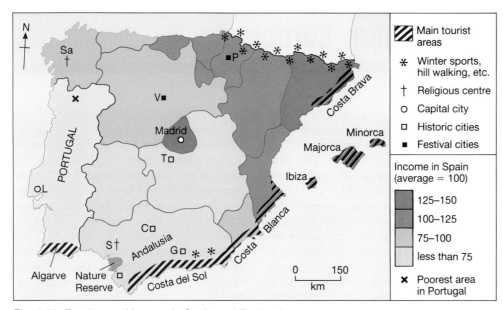

Fig. 8.29 Tourism and income in Spain and Portugal

Main tourist areas

* Winter sports, hill walking, etc.

† Religious centre

○ Capital city

□ Historic cities

■ Festival cities

Income in Spain (average = 100)

125–150
100–125
75–100
less than 75

✕ Poorest area in Portugal

Fig. 8.30 Ribbon hotel development in Fuengirola

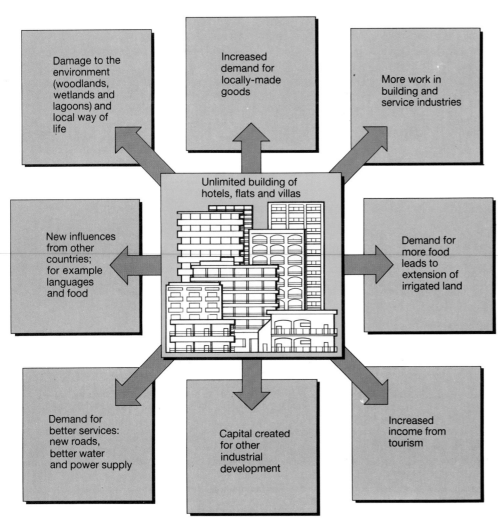

Damage to the environment (woodlands, wetlands and lagoons) and local way of life

Increased demand for locally-made goods

More work in building and service industries

Unlimited building of hotels, flats and villas

New influences from other countries; for example languages and food

Demand for more food leads to extension of irrigated land

Demand for better services: new roads, better water and power supply

Capital created for other industrial development

Increased income from tourism

Fig. 8.31 An aerial view of part of the Algarve

Fig. 8.32 (left) Effects of tourism in Spain and Portugal

141

Chapter 9 Problems in Western Europe

Core and periphery in Western Europe

Although Europe can now be divided into three major economic groups, there is still inequality within each. This is sometimes expressed in terms of a simple model with a prosperous *core*; from which prosperity decreases as distance from the core increases (Fig. 9.1). The core in the case of Europe is centred on Brussels, and distance is shown by concentric circles at 250 km intervals.

There is some truth in the theory. The core does include some of the most prosperous areas of Western Europe (such as, the Brussels area, Greater Paris, Randstad, and the Cologne-Dusseldorf area). The most distant parts (for example, Portugal, Greece, Southern Italy) are among the poorest parts of Europe. These distant, least developed areas in the model are usually referred to as the *periphery*.

However, to some, the core and periphery model is too simple. There is a more complex model shown in Fig. 9.2. While this is more useful, because it suggests that there are regions at several different stages of development, it is also misleading because: (i) it suggests a concentric pattern; in reality the distribution of prosperous areas is random rather than centralized (ii) it suggests that the areas of different economic development are always found in the sequence shown in the diagram; (iii) it suggests that each European state must be considered as a whole. Each country within Europe has regions that are better developed or less developed than others.

In some countries the most advanced and prosperous area is centrally located. In Spain, much of the wealth is concentrated in the capital, Madrid, but there are also peripheral areas of prosperity (such as, Valencia). In many countries, the most developed area is found round one large city which is not centrally placed, for example Norway (Oslo) and Greece (Athens). Fig. 9.3 shows how much more prosperous Athens is than the rest of Greece.

Greece is dominated by Athens. It is a country of small, unproductive farms, and of small family businesses. There is much disguised unemployment with many unpaid family workers. The towns in general, and Athens in particular, attract people because of: (i) the better services; (ii) the greater job opportunities; (iii) the higher standards of living.

However, this concentration of people, work, and wealth in Athens, has resulted in unplanned urban sprawl; and a large number of motor vehicles, causing much pollution and traffic congestion (see Fig. 9.5).

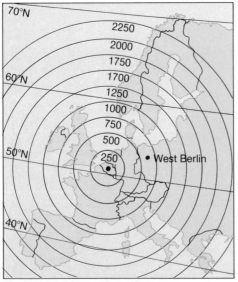

The 'core' is taken as Brussels
Circles are at 250 km intervals centred on Brussels

Fig. 9.1 In theory, economic prosperity decreases with increased distance from the 'core' of Western Europe, Brussels

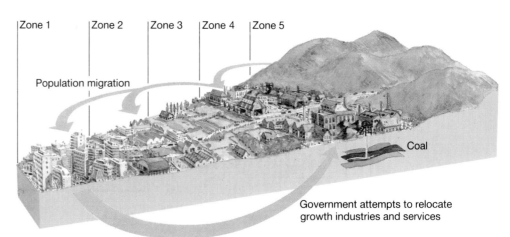

Zone 1: Over-developed. An area of rapid economic growth often at the expense of the other zones. Concentration of service sector employment and jobs in 'sunrise' industries. Rapid population growth. Housing and traffic problems

Zone 2: Neutral. Levels of employment and income almost as high but without the problems of Zone 1

Zone 3: Intermediate

Zone 4: Depressed. Areas of declining 'smokestack' industries and below-average levels of development and investment

Zone 5: Under-developed. Rural areas which lack large-scale investment in industry

Fig. 9.2 A model of economic development in Western Europe

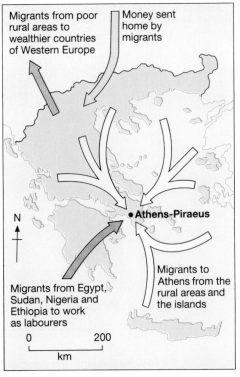

Migrants from poor rural areas to wealthier countries of Western Europe

Money sent home by migrants

N

Athens-Piraeus

Migrants from Egypt, Sudan, Nigeria and Ethiopia to work as labourers

Migrants to Athens from the rural areas and the islands

0   200
km

Fig. 9.3 The location of Athens, a primate city

Population of Athens 3.1 millions i.e. approximately one third of the total population of Greece

Income The average income in Athens is more than 2× that of the poorest part of Greece

People per doctor
Athens 2150   Rest of Greece 14 000

Concentration of industry

Rest of Greece | Athens area

Industrial units

Rest of Greece | Athens area

Industrial workers

Rest of Greece | Athens area

Private investment

Fig. 9.3 also illustrates a common feature in Europe today, the importance of money sent home by migrant workers. For Greece, this money is as important as the earnings from exports, and is used to renovate old houses, build new houses, or buy electrical goods, and so also provides more work in Greece itself.

All European countries have problem areas, although they vary in the severity of the problems. A problem area in Denmark or West Germany for instance, will not be as poor as one in the south of Europe. The best known example of such a problem area is Southern Italy. Before moving on to the Mezzogiorno, look at Fig. 9.4 which attempts to summarize core and periphery.

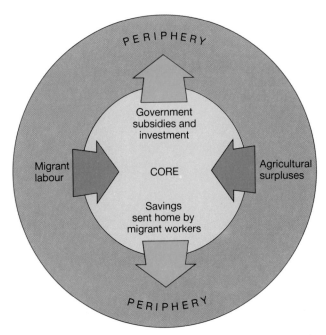

PERIPHERY

Government subsidies and investment

Migrant labour

CORE

Agricultural surpluses

Savings sent home by migrant workers

PERIPHERY

Fig. 9.4 A model of core and periphery in Western Europe

Core

Focus of rapid economic growth

Concentrations of skill and expertise

High population density

High index of accessibility through an efficient network of communications

Focus of change, decision making, and capital

Periphery

Very much slower economic growth rate

Fewer job opportunities; lower wage rates

Lower standard of living

Remote because of distance and poorly developed communications

Fig. 9.5 Athens: a city facing pollution problems. Early morning smog

143

The Mezzogiorno (The land of the midday sun)

There are several different types of problem areas in Europe which may overlap with each other:

a peripheral areas
b mountain areas
c old industrial areas
d inner city areas
e political problem areas
f environmental problem areas
g affluent areas

The main reason for the South of Italy being a problem area is that it is peripheral (Fig. 9.4). It is, however, a largely mountainous area and also has political and social problems. Fig. 9.6 shows how the South of Italy, known as the Mezzogiorno, differs from the rest of the country.

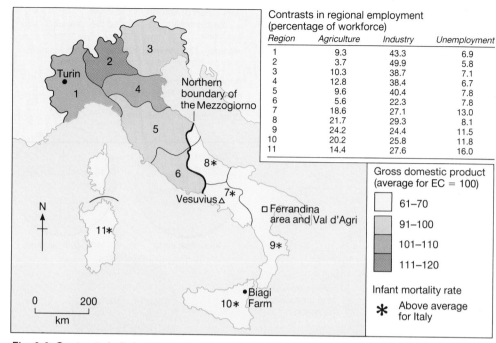

Contrasts in regional employment (percentage of workforce)

Region	Agriculture	Industry	Unemployment
1	9.3	43.3	6.9
2	3.7	49.9	5.8
3	10.3	38.7	7.1
4	12.8	38.4	6.7
5	9.6	40.4	7.8
6	5.6	22.3	7.8
7	18.6	27.1	13.0
8	21.7	29.3	8.1
9	24.2	24.4	11.5
10	20.2	25.8	11.8
11	14.4	27.6	16.0

Gross domestic product (average for EC = 100)

- 61–70
- 91–100
- 101–110
- 111–120

Infant mortality rate
∗ Above average for Italy

Fig. 9.6 Contrasts in Italy

Fig. 9.7 The Basilicata landscape: notice the water pipeline, the limestone quarry, the contrast between the dry scrub and the irrigated land, and the agro-town on the far hilltop

Assignments

1 (*Fig. 9.6*) How many regions in Italy have:
 a) a higher GNP than the average for the European Community?
 b) a lower GNP than the average for the European Community?

2 (*Fig. 9.6 and atlas*) Identify the large cities which form the most prosperous part of the following: **a)** region 2 (Lombardia); **b)** region 6 (Lazio); **c)** region 7 (Campania).

3 (*Fig. 9.6*)
 a) From the information on the map and in the table give *five* facts about region 1 (North-West) in which Turin is located, and region 2 (Sicily) in which the Biagi farm is found.
 b) What have regions 7–11 in common (at least two facts from the map)?
 c) Which of the regions 7–11 seems to be the one with the most problems? Give reasons for your choice.

4 (*Fig. 9.8*)
 a) Describe the main physical features of the river and its valley.
 b) The three main *agro-towns* are shown. How far apart are they? Why are there no settlements on the valley floor?
 c) Give the heights of the highest and lowest points on the map.
 d) Calculate the gradients between A and B, and between C and D.
 e) Give two pieces of evidence from the map which indicate: how road and rail have overcome the problems of slope; how water shortage is tackled; any recent improvements in the area.

5 (*Fig. 9.8*) If you had to travel from the railway station to the northern end of Ferrandina, you could follow a mule track directly uphill, or follow road X. Using the formula given, calculate the *detour index* for the road journey, if the actual road distance is 8.5 km.

$$DI = \frac{\text{actual road distance}}{\text{straight line distance}} \times 100^{\bullet}$$

6 (*Fig. 9.8*) Draw an annotated sketch cross-section from Ferrandina to Pomarico to show the physical and human features.

Fig. 9.8 The Ferrandina area

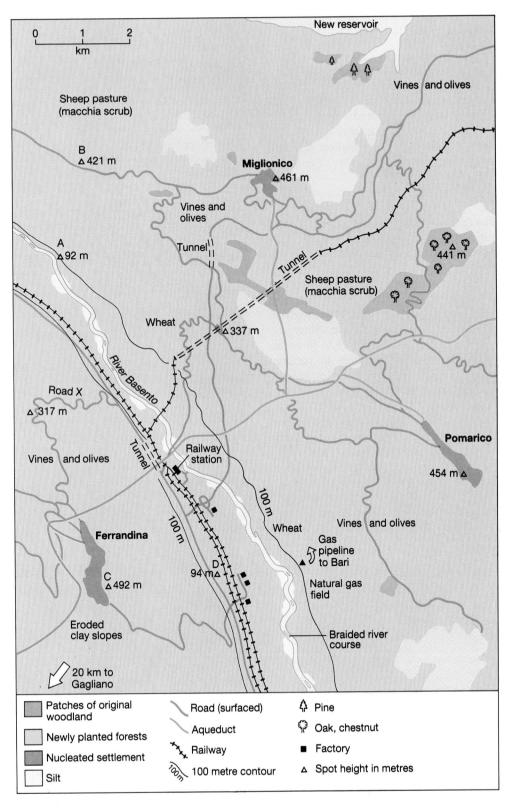

Problems of the Mezzogiorno

Peripheral

Although it is close to the capital Rome, the Mezzogiorno is remote from the wealthy industrial centres of Milan and Turin. Most of the land was in latifundia until the programme of land reform was carried out. Because of its economic isolation, it lacked investment in industry.

Physical

The map of the Ferrandina area gives some indication of the physical problems, in particular the relief (Fig. 9.8). The mountains and hills are of limestone or granite. Earthquakes and landslides are common and the plains are often waterlogged. The soils (usually clay) are either baked hard (in summer), or wet and sticky (in winter).

The new reservoir (Fig. 9.8) is an attempt to solve the problem of summer drought. Although all of the Mezzogiorno has this drought, rainfall totals vary from over 2000 mm in the western Apennines (there may be up to four months snowfall in the mountains), to less than 500 mm in the eastern rain shadow area. The rainfall which does occur is often of limited value because of rapid run-off (which increases the erosion of the hillsides) and high evaporation rates in the summer. Floods are common in the mountain valleys (Fig.

Fig. 9.10 Climate data for Palermo, Sicily

	Jan	Feb	Mar	Apr	May	Jun	Jul	Aug	Sep	Oct	Nov	Dec
Average max temp °C	29	22	25	28	31	33	40	39	33	29	29	24
Precipitation (mm)	41	101	53	34	7	5	7	0	63	94	49	29
No. of days with rain	10	14	10	5	3	2	1	0	9	6	9	8

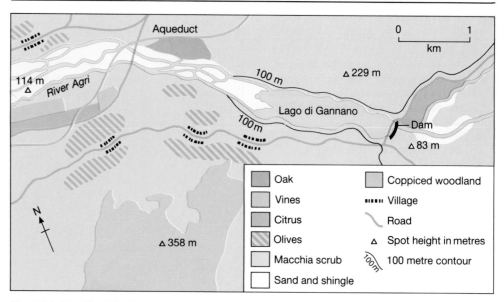

Fig. 9.11 The Val d'Agri area

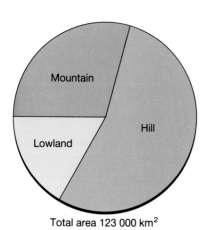

Total area 123 000 km²

Fig. 9.9 Types of land in the Mezzogiorno

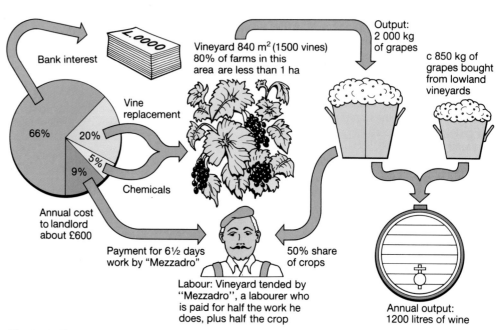

Fig. 9.12 Economic inputs and outputs for a small vineyard in the Val d'Agri

9.11) and coastal plains. This is a problem even as far south as Basilicata, where there can be heavy snowfalls on the mountains. Fortunately, however, the summer heat and sunshine do some good – they now attract vast numbers of tourists.

Economic and social

Until recently, the south of Italy has lacked power resources (Calabria excepted). Summer drought and permeable rocks limited HEP development. There is little coal, and although there is gas and oil, there is not as much gas as in the Po Valley, and the oil yields are very low.

Industries in the Mezzogiorno have always suffered from competition with industries in Turin and Milan. The problems

Basilicata in 1936

Gagliano has twelve hundred inhabitants, and there are two thousand men from Gagliano in America . . . During the day when the peasants are far away in the fields, the village is left to the women, queen bees reigning over a teeming mass of children . . . Many of the babies die; others age prematurely, turn yellow and melancholy with malaria . . . In this region, malaria is a scourge of truly alarming proportions; it spares no one . . . the result is a poverty so dismal and abject that it amounts to slavery. Malaria arises from the impoverishment of deforested clayey land, from neglected water and inefficient tilling of the soil . . .

(from *Christ Stopped at Eboli*, by C. Levi)

have increased by lack of investment and the small scale of operations. The attitudes of the people (page 73) have always been a problem, both in industry and farming.

Farming has been limited by the physical problems, but also by the system of land-holding. Fig. 9.11 shows the characteristics of minifundia in the Val d'Agri. Soil erosion resulted from the mismanagement of hill and mountain land.

The extract on the left describes how other problems arose from careless land-use. Fig. 9.11 shows how valley floors became choked with eroded material from the steep clay slopes. Gagliano is a small 'agro-town', about 20 kilometres southwest of Ferrandina, and on a ridge above the Val d'Agri. Overpopulation, as a result of the high birthrate, is another problem.

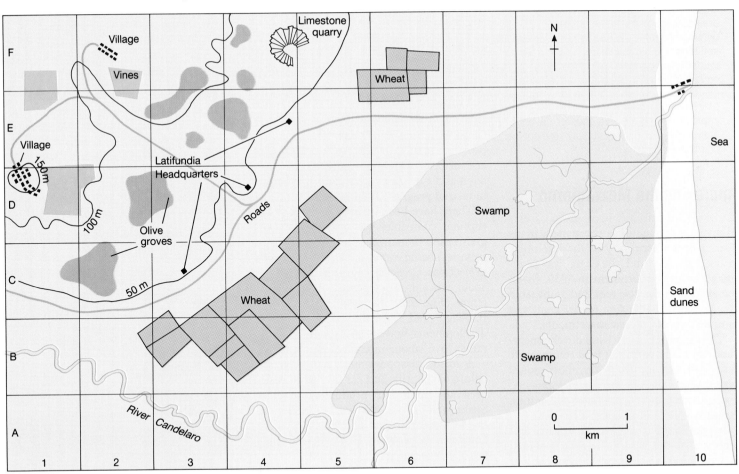

Fig. 9.13 Section of the coastal plain of Apulia, 50 years ago

147

Assignments

1 (*Fig. 9.13 and 9.14*) Part of the eastern coast of Mezzogiorno is shown as it was 50 years ago. **a**) Describe the area as it was then, by completing the following paragraph.

The area is mostly a flat plain about _____km wide. It was of little value because the river was liable to _____ and there was much _____ land. The coastline is very _____ and consists of _____-_____. The dry hills in the north-west are made of _____. The area was thinly-populated, with settlement mostly in the form of _____ villages. Land was _____ cultivated, with _____ and _____ on the hillsides, and _____ on the drier part of the plain. Many people suffered from _____ because of the poor drainage on the plain.

2 (*Fig. 9.13*) Decide how this area could be improved. Consider the following: *i*) drainage schemes; *ii*) improved communications; *iii*) changes in settlement; *iv*) innovations in land use; *v*) tourist developments; *vi*) industrial developments. Not all of these have to take place. The area has a climate similar to that of Palermo. Draw a map to show the improvements you have chosen. Give the map a title, and full key. Justify your choice of improvements.

Improving the Mezzogiorno

Many improvements have been made in the Mezzogiorno, especially in the last thirty years. A special fund, the Cassa, was established by the Government in 1950. State-owned firms were also required to invest in the Mezzogiorno, at first 60 per cent, and later 80 per cent of new investments.

The Cassa began as a rural development-fund, and its attempts at land reform were discussed on page 73. Later, most money was invested in industrial developments, especially at growth points such as Taranto, Brindisi, Palermo, and Naples (Fig. 9.14). Now the Cassa is involved in special projects such as the cleaning up of the polluted Bay of Naples; the overall development of interior areas; urban renewal schemes in Naples and Palermo.

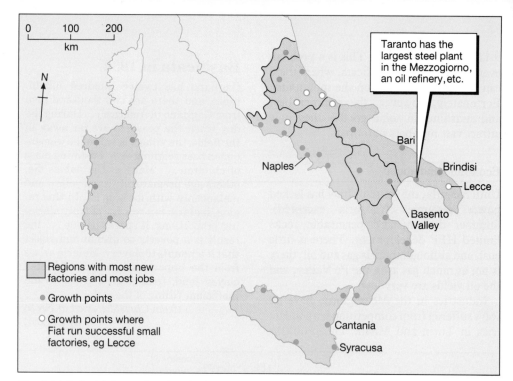

Fig. 9.14 Industrial growth points in the Mezzogiorno

Taranto has the largest steel plant in the Mezzogiorno, an oil refinery, etc.

Regions with most new factories and most jobs

● Growth points

○ Growth points where Fiat run successful small factories, eg Lecce

The Cassa: success or failure?

Like all regional development schemes, the Cassa has been criticized. It had many problems to solve in addition to the physical and historical ones. Lack of technical education and a distrust of industry have made industrial progress difficult.

There have been complaints about corruption; companies scrambling to obtain grants, and industrial estates (without any factories) being established to obtain votes in elections. Criticisms have also been made about concentrating investment in growth points (Fig. 9.14) while ignoring most of Basilicata and Calabria. Most industrial developments have been capital-intensive rather than labour-intensive (Fig. 9.15).

A major disappointment has been the failure of the Alfa-Sud car factory to reach even its minimum production targets. Strikes among its 15 000 workers, drawn to the factory built east of Naples in 1968, have been the problem. However, the Cassa has achieved much:

a an improved infrastructure: better communications, water supply and housing

b better land drainage and irrigation

c an extensive land reform programme

d the development of more commercial, intensive farming

e the expansion of the tourist trade

Yet there are still areas of great poverty, both rural and urban.

Fig. 9.15 Industrial jobs created by foreign investment in the Mezzogiorno

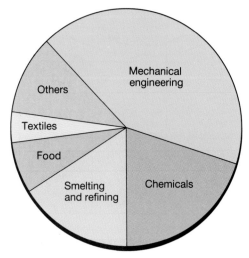

Poor and rich cities: Naples and Oslo

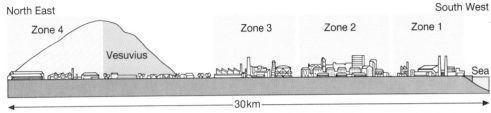

One of the urban areas of poverty is the Naples metropolitan area. It is the largest city in the Mezzogiorno (1.2 million people) and is a place of contrasts. The extract comes from an account which calls Naples more 'oriental than European'.

Not all of the city is like the description. Fig. 9.16 suggests that there are contrasting industrial zones. Despite all the new industrial development, there is still much unemployment and poverty, especially in the *inner city* area. Although Naples has its own special problems (crime, for example) most large cities in Europe have inner city problems. Some cities which are affluent, such as Oslo (Fig. 9.17), have other problems.

Oslo is an area of low density housing, with a high level of services and amenities. People have high incomes and there are high standards of cleanliness and excellent

Zone 1 South-western coastal fringe: Early 20th century steelworks at Bagnoli, kept open for social and economic reasons. New Olivetti factory at Pozzuoli

Zone 2 Inner city area (round C.B.D): Area of slum housing ('bassi') i.e. one-room over-crowded flats without water or windows, and small workshops making furniture, shoes and gloves (see description)

Zone 3 New industrial zone on outskirts of original urban area: chemicals; FIAT-IRI aircraft; metal industries. Problem of lack of space

Zone 4 New industrial area in satellite town of Pomigliano. Industries include the Alfa-Sud car factory

Problems of Naples: Limited infrastructure; poverty; organized crime (the Camarro); smuggling; poor health; contamination of the Bay of Naples

Fig. 9.16 Contrasts in the poor metropolitan area of Naples (see Fig. 2.25)

Naples: 'Oriental rather than European'

'Our submerged economy' was Valenzi's description of the child labour existing in Naples to an extent found nowhere else in the western world. There is no way of calculating the number of children from the age of eight upwards employed in cafés, bars, or in the unnumerable sweat shops tucked away in the narrow streets, but there are certainly tens of thousands of them. . . Naples has the highest birth-rate in Italy and it is an everyday accomplishment for a woman to have 10 children by the age of 35. . . When up to 5 or 6 children contribute small regular sums to the budget, a family is not only more affluent but securer than a less numerous one in the trap of a chronic unemployment. . . The little courtyards in Naples are full of small boys aged upwards of eight years who work for 10 or 12 hours a day, stitching and glueing shoes.

(*Sunday Times*, 6 April 1980)

health care. Yet people often prefer to live out of the city, or have a second home (see Fig. 9.17) in the distant countryside. There are several reasons for this, such as the decline in the family unit, lack of privacy, a high degree of stress, repetitive work and high levels of vandalism and crime.

Assignments

1 (*Fig. 9.16 and extract*) Make a table of the main features of Naples which you think are characteristics of Europe and of the Orient.

2 (*Fig. 9.16 and extract*) What do you think should be done to solve the problems of Naples?

3 (*Fig. 9.16 and Fig. 9.17*) Oslo is about half the size (in population) of Naples, and the people, on average, are much wealthier. Would you rather live in Oslo or Naples? Give reasons for your choice.

4 (*Fig. 9.17 and text*) Suggest reasons why many people in Oslo have second homes in the countryside.

5 (*Text*) Many tourists visit both Naples and Oslo. Suggest reasons for this, and comment on the importance of this.

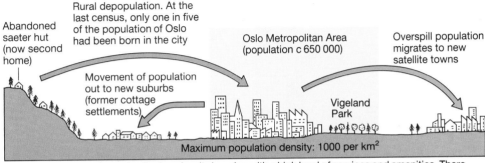

Oslo: The urban area is marked by low density housing with a high level of services and amenities. There are high standards of cleanliness; excellent health care and high income

Fig. 9.17 Contrasts in the affluent metropolitan area of Oslo

Cities in West Germany and the Netherlands

West Germany (the Federal German Republic) is one of the wealthiest countries in Western Europe. It is also one of the most urbanized. The map (Fig. 9.19) shows the distribution of the largest cities in the German Federal Republic. The inner cities are problem areas which are usually also the sites of old industries. They therefore provide examples of different types of problem areas that overlap.

A major factor in the problems of the German inner cities is the age of the townscapes concerned, and in particular, how they have been affected over the last fifty years by political, economic, and social changes.

Assignments

1 (*Atlas and Fig. 9.19*) Identify from the list in the key, the cities numbered 1–13.

2 (*Atlas and Fig. 9.19*) Identify the area in which the cities numbered 5–8 are located.

3 (*Atlas and Fig. 9.19*) Along which river and its tributaries are over half of the cities located?

Fig. 9.18 The Aldstadt of Frankfurt

Characteristics of the inner city

The map (Fig. 9.20) shows the inner city area of Cologne, which, like many other West German cities, surrounds the historic core, the Altstadt. The Altstadt contains the cathedral, the town house, and the market square, as well as the modern commercial functions, such as the central business district (CBD), and housing (Fig. 9.18).

The inner city is a typical mixed zone or *zone of transition* and is the result of the nineteenth century Industrial Revolution. As elsewhere in Western Europe, cheap housing was needed quickly. In most cities, blocks of flats were built in limited spaces. Although they were poorly-built (without bathrooms and toilets), some areas survived the bombing raids during World War II and are still occupied (Fig. 9.21).

Since 1945, the inner city areas of West German cities have been affected by many changes, but not all of the problems have been solved.

Fig. 9.19 Cities in West Germany (Federal German Republic)

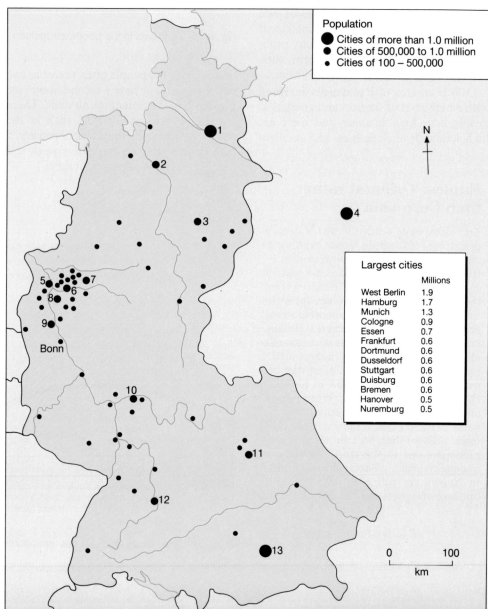

Population
- Cities of more than 1.0 million
- Cities of 500,000 to 1.0 million
- Cities of 100 – 500,000

Largest cities	Millions
West Berlin	1.9
Hamburg	1.7
Munich	1.3
Cologne	0.9
Essen	0.7
Frankfurt	0.6
Dortmund	0.6
Dusseldorf	0.6
Stuttgart	0.6
Duisburg	0.6
Bremen	0.6
Hanover	0.5
Nuremburg	0.5

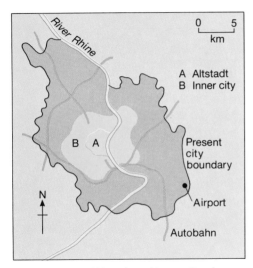

Fig. 9.20 The Aldstadt and inner city of Cologne

Changes in the inner city

First phase: 1945–65

a Reconstruction and renovation of apartments, workshops, and factories.

b No co-ordinated plan.

c Building of new apartment blocks, many of which were to provide subsidized social housing for rent.

Second phase: 1965–75

a Building of urban motorways.

b Replacement of housing by office blocks and large stores.

c Building of high rise flats.

Third phase: 1975–85

a Integrated plans.

b Conservation schemes.

Fig. 9.23 West German townscapes in 1985

During this time, there have been changes in the population of the inner city areas. In all cases, the population has declined but there is a high concentration of guest-workers and their families. In general, the population of the inner city areas is ageing. People have moved out to areas of low density housing, in the outer city, or in new satellite towns. Some of the main features of West German urban areas are shown on the summary diagram (Fig. 9.23).

Housing in Germany

West Germany has had a serious housing problem since 1945. Some housing was damaged during the war, and others were badly built. On top of all this, over 11 million refugees and over 4 million guest-workers and their families have come to West Germany, all of whom have had to be housed.

As a result, two out of every three houses in West Germany have been built since 1945. Many of them have been blocks of apartments even on the urban fringes. Apartments are more economic; they are cheaper to construct and can share domestic heating systems. They can also house more people, which has also meant that population density in satellite towns is high.

Fig. 9.21 Inner city townscape of about 1900

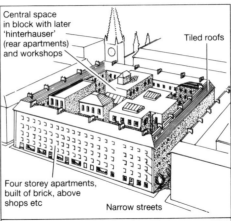

Central space in block with later 'hinterhauser' (rear apartments) and workshops

Tiled roofs

Four storey apartments, built of brick, above shops etc

Narrow streets

General features. High density of houses e.g. 230 per hectare with problems of overcrowding, poor ventilation, sanitation, and lighting, with a high fire risk. Limited open space; high population density

Fig. 9.22 New flats in West Berlin

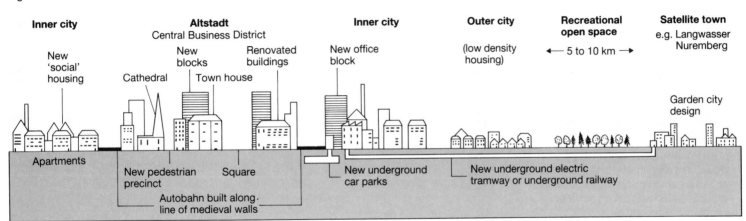

Inner city

New 'social' housing

Apartments

Altstadt
Central Business District

Cathedral

New blocks

Town house

Renovated buildings

New pedestrian precinct

Square

Autobahn built along line of medieval walls

Inner city

New office block

New underground car parks

Outer city

(low density housing)

New underground electric tramway or underground railway

Recreational open space

← 5 to 10 km →

Satellite town
e.g. Langwasser Nuremberg

Garden city design

Problems of Berlin: West Berlin

a *Position* Berlin is located within the German Democratic Republic, less than 50 km from the Polish frontier. (Berlin was the capital of a much larger Germany before 1945, and was at one time more centrally placed.)

b *Isolation* from West Germany as a result of this position.

c *Division* into West and East Berlin, with token protection for West Berlin from a small military force from France, the UK and the USA.

d *Dependence* on the Federal German Republic for large subsidies (more than half the annual budget), raw materials for industry, fuel supplies, etc.

e *Changing population structure* with an ageing population and a large *guestworker* minority (20 per cent of the work force; 10 per cent of the population). Kreuzberg has become a Turkish ghetto.

f *Housing shortage* Despite the building of satellite towns within the city boundary, there is still a shortage of houses of good quality. Many substandard houses are still used.

g *Growing unemployment* especially among immigrant youths.

Assignments

1 (*Fig. 9.19*) Find Cologne and West Berlin. How far apart are they? How far is West Berlin from the Federal German Republic? Is Bonn more centrally placed as capital of the Federal German Republic?

2 (*Text*) Write a paragraph giving possible reasons to explain why in Cologne today only one person in three lives in the inner city, compared with seven out of ten people 50 years ago.

Fig. 9.24 The Berlin Wall

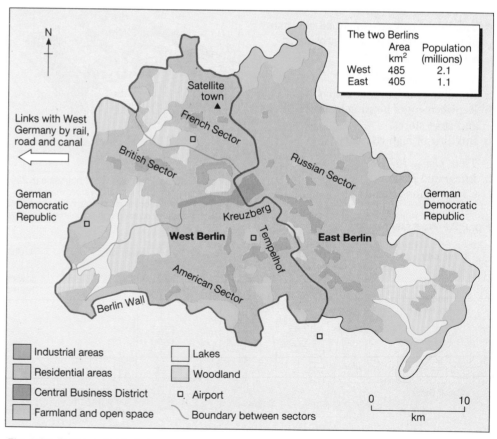

The two Berlins	Area km²	Population (millions)
West	485	2.1
East	405	1.1

Links with West Germany by rail, road and canal

German Democratic Republic

German Democratic Republic

Satellite town

French Sector

British Sector

Russian Sector

Kreuzberg

West Berlin

Tempelhof

East Berlin

American Sector

Berlin Wall

Industrial areas

Residential areas

Central Business District

Farmland and open space

Lakes

Woodland

Airport

Boundary between sectors

0   10   km

Fig. 9.25 Berlin, a divided city

Fig. 9.26 A Koran school in West Berlin

3 Draw accurate graphs/diagrams to illustrate the data below. Make sure that each diagram has a scale, a title and a key. Add a brief comment on each.

Inner city housing conditions, Wuppertal 1971	%
Rented	89
Built of wood	24
'Hinterhauser'	20
Less than 3 rooms	31
Without bath	27
Without toilet	29

(Total number of houses 9 300)

Major land use in Langwasser (satellite town of Nuremburg)	%
Housing (mostly apartments)	43
Open space, roads, car parks	35
Shops, schools, recreation	22

Immigrants in the city

It is not just German cities that have high concentrations of immigrant workers and their families.

Initially such guestworkers lived in large hostels before sending for their families. Since the recession, unemployment rates among immigrants and their children have risen sharply. Despite this many have chosen to stay, although over 300 000 Turkish immigrants accepted money from the Federal German government to return home. The presence of immigrants in West European cities can cause much tension as in Marseilles, for example. One city determined to integrate immigrants is Amsterdam, part of the Randstad the Netherlands (Fig. 9.27). Apart from the mosques for Turkish and Moroccan immigrants, the immigrant neighbourhoods in Amsterdam are difficult to distinguish from the rest of the city. In addition to the guestworkers, there are many Dutch citizens who have come from the former colonies of Surinam and the East Indies.

A positive policy of dealing instantly with grievances, insults, and discrimination, and of making immigrants eligible for welfare benefits, and housing allowances, has resulted in much greater racial harmony.

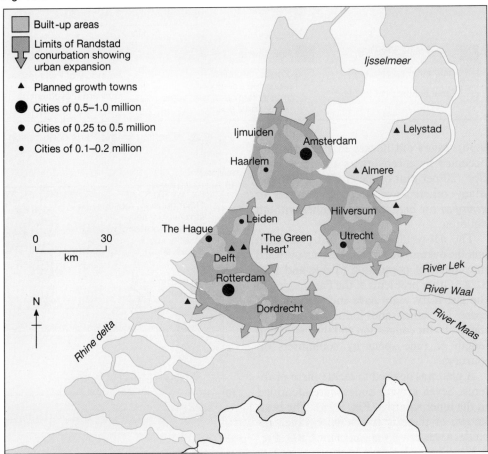

Key

- Built-up areas
- Limits of Randstad conurbation showing urban expansion
- ▲ Planned growth towns
- ● Cities of 0.5–1.0 million
- ● Cities of 0.25 to 0.5 million
- • Cities of 0.1–0.2 million

Fig. 9.27 The Randstad or 'Ring city' of the Netherlands

Planning urban growth: Paris

Fig. 9.27 has shown that the Dutch planners have made provision for urban growth by selecting towns on the edge of Randstad. These growth points, which include Lelystad, are similar to the satellite towns in West Germany or the new towns created round Paris (Fig. 9.28).

Paris has grown from its nucleus on the Ile de la Cité to its present extent. The map shows that the actual city of Paris is quite small (105 km²), but is the centre of a large densely-populated area.

Population change in the Paris region

	millions 1982	% change 1975–82
City of Paris	2.17	−5.7
Inner suburbs	3.90	−1.9
Outer suburbs	4.00	+10.7
Paris region	10.07	+1.8

The highest population densities are in the city, and particularly the inner city. Before redevelopment, densities were up to 80 000 per square kilometre. In these areas (as in the cities of West Germany and in Naples) housing consisted of small, overcrowded, sub-standard apartments.

Most of the expansion of Paris has been unplanned, for example, the building of small, individual poorly-built houses with tiny gardens (lotissements) along the main routes out of Paris. This happened between 1920 and 1939; thirty years later many large housing-estates (grands ensembles) were constructed in the same areas of the inner suburbs. These blocks were built to a uniform pattern of four or five storeys, sometimes 300 metres long, with occasional twelve to fifteen-storey tower-blocks. As in many similar areas in European cities, these estates have been criticized for their architecture and their lack of services.

Much demolition and rebuilding has taken place in the city of Paris itself (Fig.

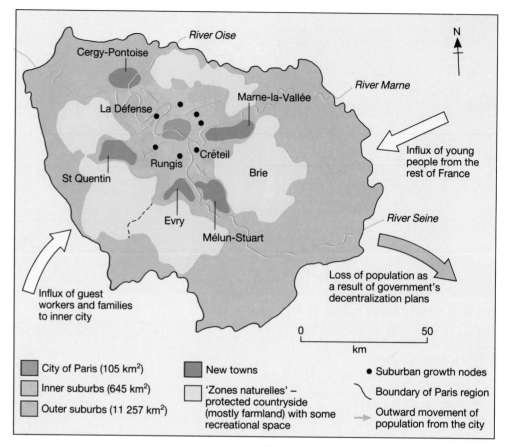

Fig. 9.28 Planning for the Paris conurbation

9.30). Many old houses in Paris are now occupied by guestworkers and their families. (20 per cent of the city's population). Many others have been modernized or gentrified for high income families without children.

The net-result of the housing problem and the overcrowding, has been an outward movement of population (Table and Fig. 9.28). Other problems of the Paris region in the last forty years have included lack of space for office and industrial developments; traffic congestion and the increasing length of time spent by commuters on journeys.

A plan was devised to tackle these problems. Seven growth nodes were identified in the inner suburbs (Fig. 9.28). The best-known of these is La Défense which includes a western extension of the CBD (Fig. 9.32). The nodes have been developed as centres of higher order services and tertiary

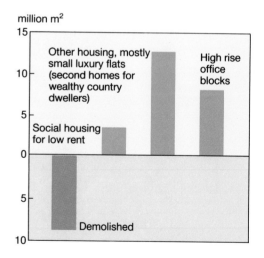

Fig. 9.29 Changes in floor space in the city of Paris, 1954–1974

Figs. 9.30 and 9.31 Paris contrasts: the inner city (*above*) and the Seine (*below*) flowing through the ancient heart of Paris with tower blocks looming on the horizon

employment. This has been done to reduce commuting traffic and reduce pressures on the CBD.

Paris contrasts

The centres of most French cities exhibit sharp contrasts over relatively short distances. Blocks of decaying properties stand close to the cleaned and restored facades of seventeenth century hotels; the overcrowded dwellings of immigrant families are within a stone's throw of the gentrified apartments of young professionals; smart new office blocks look down on abandoned factory sites; whilst the antique and souvenir shops of a newly cobbled pedestrian precinct have little in common with the back street café-bar.

(from *Urban France:* I. Scargill

Originally eight new towns were planned but only five were actually implemented between 1969–73. It was thought that each new town would eventually have a population between 0.5 and 1.0 million. However, the target populations have now been substantially reduced to 0.1–0.2 million. Two of the towns have been affected by the withdrawal of member communes (Evry and St Quentin) (Fig. 9.33). Although the new towns have not been as successful as was hoped, the population of the outer suburbs as a whole has been increasing. The construction of a new suburban fast rail network has given these growing settlements excellent links with Paris.

Fig. 9.28 also shows that large areas of the outer suburbs have been designated as *zones naturelles* to protect them from development, so that they form almost a green belt round the inner suburbs.

Paris is therefore an example of a large metropolitan area (and a primate city) where careful plans had to be made to: (1) prevent it from becoming even more dominant; and (2) help solve the problems caused by its vast size.

In the city of Paris itself, the early efforts at urban-renewal resulted in demolition of houses, workshops, and warehouses in the city centre. They were replaced by concrete blocks which did not blend well with the townscape. The result of unplanned improvement is described in the passage.

In the last twenty years, new laws and government funds have increased conservation of the city centre. More thought is being given to careful planning in order to improve the quality of life. Attempts are being made to attract people back to the city centre. This policy is not confined to Paris alone; it is a common feature of urban planning in most West European countries, such as West Germany and Spain.

The description of part of Paris also illustrates the point that it is difficult if not impossible to construct a model which accurately shows the structure of a West European city. We have studied many European cities. They have similarities, but there is no urban model that fits them all.

Fig. 9.32 La Défense, one of the growth nodes showing some of its interesting architecture

Fig. 9.33 Evry, a new town near Paris

Assignments

1 (*Fig. 9.27*) Most conurbations have a green belt surrounding the densely built-up area. How is Randstad similar to this and how does it differ?

2 (*Fig. 9.28 and table*) a) Using the population figures and areas given, calculate the population densities for: the city of Paris; the inner suburbs; and the outer suburbs. b) What is the correlation between population density and population change?

3 (*Fig. 9.30–9.33 and text*) Write brief descriptions of the contrasting townscapes of the inner city, the growth nodes, and the new towns of Paris.

4 (*Text and Fig. 9.28*) Is Paris too large? Discuss the advantages and disadvantages of its size.

Belgium: an old industrial area

We have seen centrally-placed Belgium is in Western Europe (Fig. 9.1). Today Brussels is the centre of Europe's most densely-populated, prosperous areas. However, not all of Belgium is equally prosperous or equally densely populated. Fig. 9.34 shows that there is a thinly-populated upland-area in the south-east, the Ardennes.

Belgium was the second country in Europe to be affected by the Industrial Revolution. It was fortunate in that it possessed extensive coal deposits in the Sambre-Meuse Valley (a continuation of the coalfield in the north of France). Later, the coalfield in Kempenland was developed. Heavy industries (iron and steel, chemicals and engineering) were established in the area between Mons and Liège. The textile industry of Flanders developed later in the nineteenth century. Other industries which were established during this first Industrial Revolution were glass-making, cement, and ship-building at Antwerp.

Problems of Belgian industry

a Old factories and equipment.
b Increasing costs.
c Falling demand.
d Over-production.
e Increasing competition from other countries and new technologies.

The coal-mining and iron and steel industries have been most affected by these problems, and by the subsequent closures and mergers. At the same time, there were other problems to be faced:

a Inner city problems in Brussels, the capital, and the major industrial cities, such as Liège and Namur
b Political problems because of the language division between Flanders and Wallonia.

Fig. 9.35 Old and new in a Belgian mining landscape

Fig. 9.34 The industrial area of Belgium

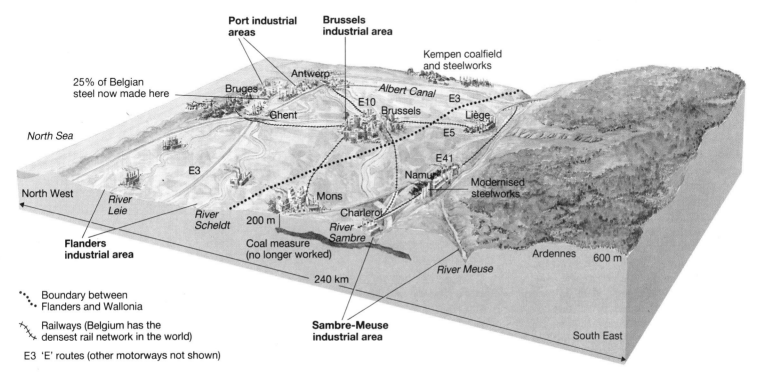

Solutions to the problems

The last problem was tackled in 1981 when devolution gave Flanders and Wallonia their own regional assemblies. Both regions then had the authority to tackle the problems of the industrial areas. The national government however retained responsibility for the five most troubled industries; steel, coal, textiles, ship-building, and glass-making.

In addition to the state subsidies given to the steel and coal industries, both also qualify for grants and loans from the European Community. These are provided to re-train redundant miners and steel-workers. (The Ruhr, the Saar, the Limburg coal-field, and the Nord industrial area in France all benefit in the same way.)

Two regions have both been relatively successful in attracting new industries. Belgium has now reached a third stage of industrialization. The first stage was the Industrial Revolution, and the second was the period of reconstruction after 1945.

Belgium's industrial growth

Belgium has now made the most of the advantages it has for the development of modern industries (Fig. 9.36).

In Wallonia, much of the investment had to be put towards saving the traditional steel industry which faced extinction. Now that it has survived, investment is being directed into using new materials and new technology, such as robotics, as well as introducing biotechnology. All of this has to be supported by research on a large scale.

In Flanders, foreign investors were more easily attracted by lower wages, and new industries were established much earlier than in Wallonia. It is a major centre of the micro-electronics industry; the European headquarters of the American Bell Telephone Company are located in Antwerp, for example. The University of Louven is a world famous centre for research into computers, semi-conductors, micro-chips, and lasers. Many industrial estates have been

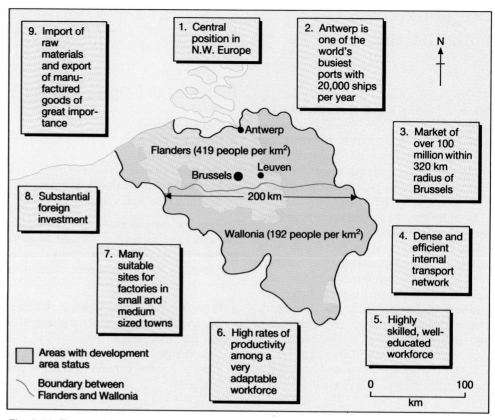

Fig. 9.36 Factors that promote industrial development

built for the new industries. (However, four out of every ten jobs in industry in the Leie Valley are still in textiles.)

While precision engineering, chemicals, and motor-vehicle manufacturing are of major importance, it is probably in micro-electronics and software manufacture that the future of industry lies, for Flanders in particular, and for Belgium in general.

Assignments

1 (*Text*) Suggest what problems have arisen as a result of Belgium's first phase of industrialization.

2 (*Text and Fig. 9.36*) In Belgium, is it the site or the situation of a factory which is more important?

3 Use the data below to draw a pie-chart or divided bar-graph to show employment in Belgium. Comment on the figures.

Employment in Belgium (per cent)

Primary	2.4
Secondary	25.9
Tertiary	58.5
Unemployed	13.1

4 (*Fig. 9.34*) Draw a diagram or map to show the following figures. Comment on them in relation to the location of the steel works in Belgium.

Sources of iron ore for the Belgian steel industry, 1984 (millions of tonnes)

France	4.4
Sweden	3.7
Brazil	3.9
Others	7.6

Mediterranean France

The lower part of the Rhône valley and the coastal areas on either side of the Rhône Delta form the last problem area to be examined. The pressures on the wildscape of the delta have already been described (page 42). Although a large area (950 km²) of the delta in the Camargue district (Fig. 9.39) has been designated a Regional Park to protect it from development (especially agricultural, and tourist-related) there are land-use conflicts elsewhere. Urban and industrial growth cause problems east of the delta. Marseille, an ancient port which had been extended, was expanded again into the Etang de Berre to provide berths for large oil-tankers and ore-carriers. As Fig. 9.37 shows, extensive port and industrial areas were constructed. Not all the available land has yet been used, and although Marseille-Fos is a major seaport, it is not yet the 'Europoort of the South' hoped for.

Although 10 000 jobs were created at Fos, many local people were against the development. Their objections were largely because the results of this expansion included: (i) an increase in urban population, with a new town between Fos and Istres; (ii) rural depopulation; (iii) an influx of foreign workers, especially to Marseille; (iv) an increase in the pollution of the atmosphere and of the water areas; (v) a reduction in the area of farmscape and of wildscape.

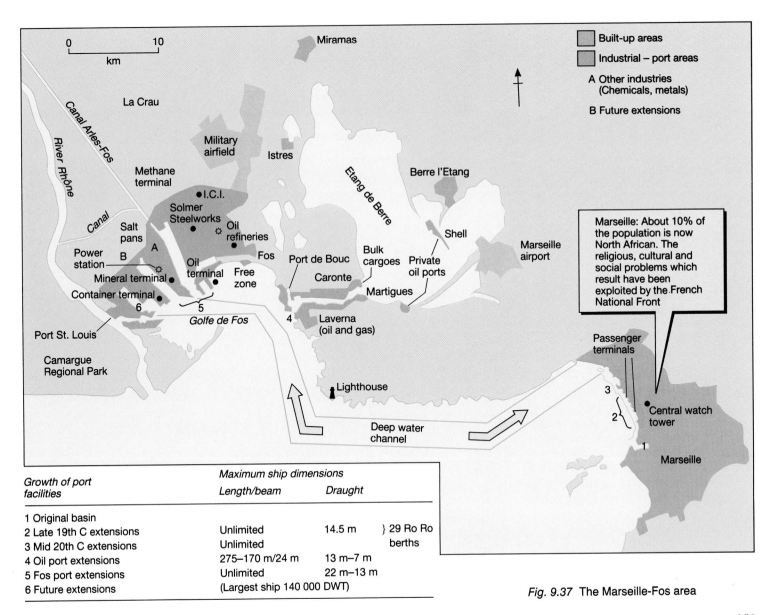

Growth of port facilities	Maximum ship dimensions		
	Length/beam	Draught	
1 Original basin			
2 Late 19th C extensions	Unlimited	14.5 m	} 29 Ro Ro
3 Mid 20th C extensions	Unlimited		berths
4 Oil port extensions	275–170 m/24 m	13 m–7 m	
5 Fos port extensions	Unlimited	22 m–13 m	
6 Future extensions	(Largest ship 140 000 DWT)		

Fig. 9.37 The Marseille-Fos area

Rural change

The rural areas in the South of France have seen great change. Upland areas in particular have suffered from rural depopulation. The villages of the Cévennes have been affected by several factors:

Pre-1914: Isolation meant a subsistence economy with vines, olives, silkworms

1914–18: Many men died in the war. Silkworm rearing ended

Post 1920s: Vines destroyed by disease. Men began to migrate in search of work

Post 1945: Outmigration increased

Post 1960: Second homes boom

Post 1970: Influx of new settlers, often retired city workers

A small village, Goudorgues, which had a population of over 100 in 1914, now has only 26 permanent residents. However, the population is trebled in summer although the village has no shops or services. The table below shows how housing has changed.

Changing housing patterns in Goudorges

	Number of houses	
	1968	*1978*
Inhabited by local people	11	7
Inhabited by incomers	1	4
Second homes	4	8
Holiday homes	0	4
Empty houses	10	3

The village, on a hill, consists of an irregular cluster of houses built in the sixteenth century. To the south is the plain of Languedoc which has experienced even greater changes than the Cevennes in the last 20 years. These changes have been carried out in an attempt to solve some of the problems of the area, and to capitalize on the Mediteranean climate.

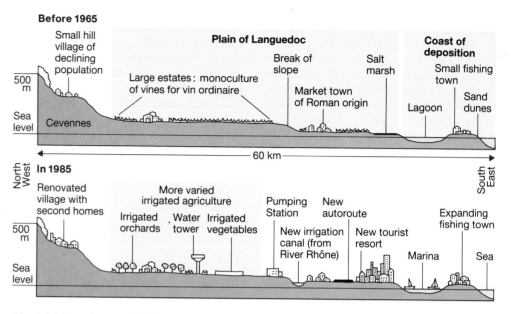

Fig. 9.38 Development in the Languedoc area

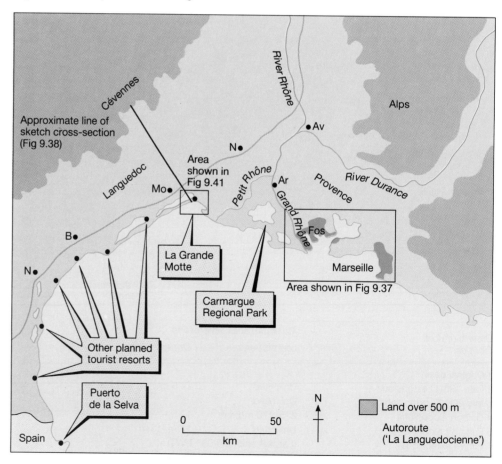

Fig. 9.39 Developments in Southern France

Fig. 9.40 The walled town of Aigues-Mortes from the north-west. Identify the main features of this landscape

The changes in Languedoc were part of an ambitious development plan which included the following:

a improving the infrastructure;
b expanding agriculture;
c eradicating malaria;
d conserving the ancient towns;
e introducing tourism on a large scale.

The developments were promoted by the French Government in an attempt to improve the standard of living of the local people. The environment has been changed, especially near the coast, sometimes for the better, but other times perhaps for the worse.

The south of France therefore is an example of an area where there were both social and economic problems. The large-scale investments have solved these to some extent, but in so doing have created other problems to do with the environment.

161

Assignments

1 (*Fig. 9.37, Fig. 9.39 and text*) Why did the original port of Marseille not develop near the mouth of the Rhône? Why was it necessary to expand the port into the Etang de Berre? How does this expansion compare with the usual model of port development?

2 (*Fig. 9.37 and text*) 80 per cent of the trade of Fos is in oil and gas. How does the trade of Fos and its industrial growth compare with that of Europoort (page 125).

3 (*Text, Fig. 9.39*) The Camargue Regional Park is one of the major wetland areas of Europe. What developments are threatening the Park? Do you think that the developments have gone: too far; or not far enough (that is, is the Camargue worth protecting?)

4 (*Text*) Simulation:
a) Imagine you are a resident in one of the small villages in the Cévennes which had many empty houses **b**) Imagine you are one of the incomers who has bought a second home in the village. Discuss the changes which have taken place and the attractions of living there.

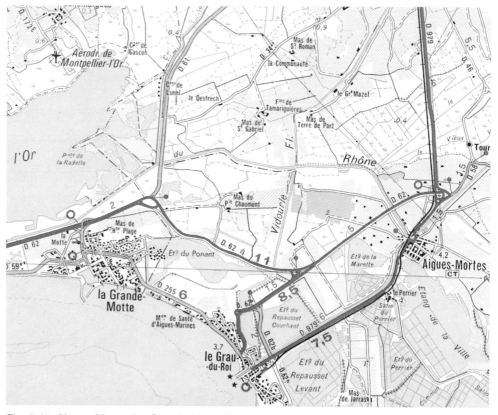

Fig. 9.41 Aigues-Mortes/La Grande Motte (1:100 000)

Fig. 9.42 Beehive/pyramid flats and a marina at La Grande Motte

5 (*Fig. 9.38*) Study the two transect diagrams. Describe the environment and the way of life: before 1965; and in 1985.

6 (*Fig. 9.39 and atlas*) Identify the towns marked by initial letters. Comment on the route followed by the autoroute in relation to the towns west of the Rhône.

7 (*Fig. 9.39, Fig. 9.41 and atlas*) Supposing you were going on holiday to La Grande Motte. Work out your best route there from Britain.

8 (*Fig. 9.40 and Fig. 9.42*) What are the attractions of the area to the tourist? Why is Aigues-Mortes an attraction?

9 (*Fig. 9.42 and research*) The flats were designed to catch as much sun as possible. Do you like them? From tourist brochures, find out all you can about La Grande Motte.

Climate statistics

Reykjavik (Altitude 18 m) Mean annual rainfall: 799 mm

	Jan	Feb	Mar	Apr	May	Jun	Jul	Aug	Sep	Oct	Nov	Dec
°C	0.0	0.5	1.5	3.5	7.0	9.5	11.5	11.0	8.5	5.0	2.0	0.0
mm	89	64	62	56	42	42	50	56	67	94	78	79

Narvik (Altitude 40 m) Mean annual rainfall: 728 mm

	Jan	Feb	Mar	Apr	May	Jun	Jul	Aug	Sep	Oct	Nov	Dec
°C	−4.5	−4.5	−2.0	−1.5	3.0	10.5	14.5	13.0	9.0	4.0	0.5	−3.0
mm	55	47	61	45	44	65	58	84	97	86	59	27

Amsterdam (Altitude 2 m) Mean annual rainfall: 650 mm

	Jan	Feb	Mar	Apr	May	Jun	Jul	Aug	Sep	Oct	Nov	Dec
°C	2.5	3.0	5.0	8.5	12.5	15.5	17.5	17.0	15.5	11.0	6.5	3.5
mm	51	36	33	41	46	46	66	69	71	71	66	56

Paris (Altitude 75 m) Mean annual rainfall: 585 mm

	Jan	Feb	Mar	Apr	May	Jun	Jul	Aug	Sep	Oct	Nov	Dec
°C	3.0	3.5	7.0	10.5	14.0	17.0	19.0	18.5	16.0	11.0	7.0	4.0
mm	54	43	32	38	52	50	55	62	51	49	50	49

Madrid (Altitude 667 m) (The highest capital in Europe) Mean annual rainfall: 436 mm

	Jan	Feb	Mar	Apr	May	Jun	Jul	Aug	Sep	Oct	Nov	Dec
°C	5.0	6.5	10.0	13.0	15.5	20.5	24.0	23.5	19.5	14.0	9.0	5.5
mm	38	34	45	44	44	27	11	14	31	53	47	48

Barcelona (Altitude 95 m) Mean annual rainfall: 598 mm

	Jan	Feb	Mar	Apr	May	Jun	Jul	Aug	Sep	Oct	Nov	Dec
°C	9.5	10.0	12.5	14.5	17.5	21.5	24.5	24.0	21.5	17.5	13.5	10.0
mm	30	40	53	45	54	40	30	47	79	77	54	49

Rome (Altitude 115 m) Mean annual rainfall: 650 mm

	Jan	Feb	Mar	Apr	May	Jun	Jul	Aug	Sep	Oct	Nov	Dec
°C	8.0	8.5	11.0	14.0	18.0	21.5	24.5	24.5	22.5	17.5	12.5	9.0
mm	68	58	38	43	51	25	15	23	68	94	96	71

Athens (Altitude 107 m) Mean annual rainfall: 402 mm

	Jan	Feb	Mar	Apr	May	Jun	Jul	Aug	Sep	Oct	Nov	Dec
°C	9.5	10.0	11.5	15.0	20.0	24.5	27.5	27.0	23.5	19.0	14.5	11.0
mm	62	36	38	23	23	14	6	7	15	51	56	71

Milan (Altitude 106 m) Mean annual rainfall: 802 mm

	Jan	Feb	Mar	Apr	May	Jun	Jul	Aug	Sep	Oct	Nov	Dec
°C	1.5	4.5	8.5	13.5	17.0	21.5	23.5	22.5	19.5	13.5	7.0	3.0
mm	56	51	53	61	86	86	58	56	71	99	84	61

Santis (Altitude 2500 m) Mean annual rainfall: 2486 mm

	Jan	Feb	Mar	Apr	May	Jun	Jul	Aug	Sep	Oct	Nov	Dec
°C	−9.0	−9.0	−6.5	−4.0	0.5	3.5	5.5	5.5	3.5	−0.5	−0.5	−8.0
mm	202	180	164	166	197	249	302	275	209	183	190	169

Berlin (Altitude 57 m) Mean annual rainfall: 556 mm

	Jan	Feb	Mar	Apr	May	Jun	Jul	Aug	Sep	Oct	Nov	Dec
°C	−0.5	0.0	4.0	9.0	14.5	17.5	19.5	19.0	15.0	9.5	4.5	1.0
mm	41	37	30	39	44	60	67	65	45	45	44	30

Stockholm (Altitude 45 m) Mean annual rainfall: 555 mm

	Jan	Feb	Mar	Apr	May	Jun	Jul	Aug	Sep	Oct	Nov	Dec
°C	−3.0	−3.0	−0.5	4.5	10.0	15.0	18.0	16.5	12.0	7.0	3.0	0.0
mm	43	30	26	31	34	45	61	76	60	48	53	48

Helsinki (Altitude 9 m) Mean annual rainfall: 641 mm

	Jan	Feb	Mar	Apr	May	Jun	Jul	Aug	Sep	Oct	Nov	Dec
°C	−7.0	−7.5	−4.0	2.0	9.0	14.5	17.0	15.5	10.5	5.0	0.5	−3.0
mm	49	34	32	41	38	47	68	71	70	72	61	58

Pitea (Altitude 6 m) Mean annual rainfall: 517 mm

	Jan	Feb	Mar	Apr	May	Jun	Jul	Aug	Sep	Oct	Nov	Dec
°C	−9.5	−10.0	−6.0	0.5	6.5	12.5	16.5	14.5	9.0	3.0	−3.0	−3.5
mm	37	25	23	28	30	47	50	68	69	48	48	44

Western Europe: population and urban population

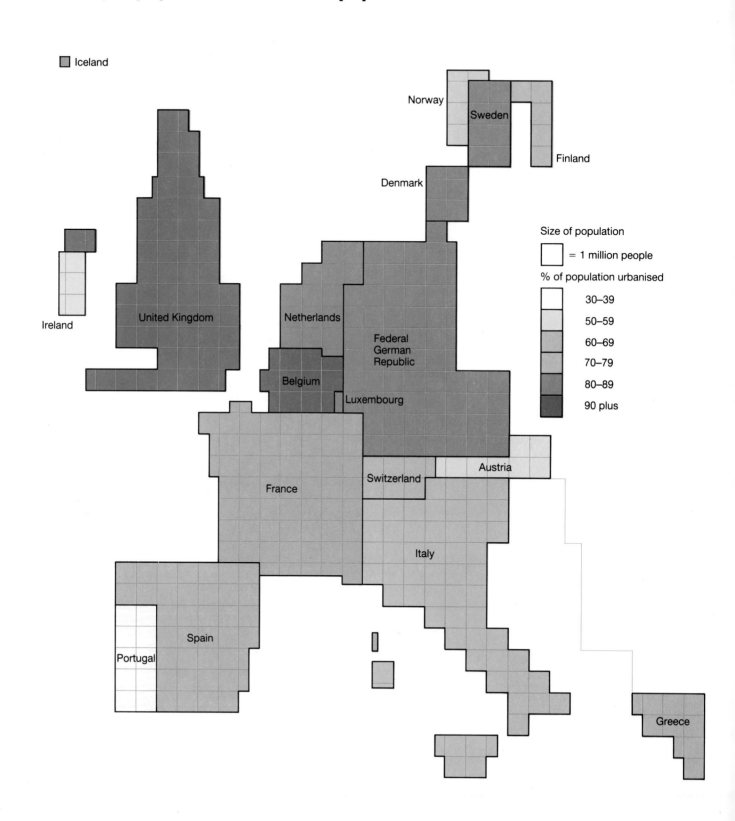

Iceland

Norway

Sweden

Finland

Denmark

Ireland

United Kingdom

Netherlands

Federal
German
Republic

Belgium

Luxembourg

Switzerland

Austria

France

Italy

Portugal

Spain

Greece

Size of population

= 1 million people

% of population urbanised

30–39

50–59

60–69

70–79

80–89

90 plus

The diagram opposite (it is not a map) shows the countries of Western Europe in an unusual way. They are in their correct position in relation to one another. Their shapes should also be recognisable. However, their sizes are not what we would expect, since each country's area is calculated on the basis of its population. Therefore Norway and Sweden appear much smaller than the Netherlands.

The colour shading adds information about the urban population of each country i.e. the percent age of the total population which lives in towns.

The table below provides much basic information about West European countries.

Data table for Western Europe
(all figures are for 1985 unless otherwise stated)

Country	Gross National Product ($ per person)	Total population (millions)	Population growth rate (per cent) 1980–85	Population density (persons per km²)	Life expectancy (years)	Infant mortality (per cent)	Persons per doctor (1981)	Percentage of population aged 15–64	Percentage of workforce in agriculture 1965	Percentage of workforce in agriculture 1980	Percentage of workforce in manufacturing 1965	Percentage of workforce in manufacturing 1980	Percentage of population living in towns	Daily calorie intake per person	Passenger vehicles in use (per thousand people, 1984)	TV sets*/licences (per thousand people, 1983)	Tourist arrivals (millions), 1983	Energy consumption per person (kg of coal equivalent), 1984
Austria	9120	7.6	0.0	90	74	11	440	67	19	9	45	41	56	3514	327	311	14.5	4007
Belgium	8280	9.9	0.1	323	75	11	370	68	6	3	46	36	96	3679	331	303	6.6	4939
Denmark	11200	5.1	0.1	119	75	7	420	66	14	7	37	32	86	3547	283	369	3.8	4521
Finland	10890	4.9	0.5	14	76	6	460	67	24	12	35	35	60	3026	308	357	0.5	5002
France	9540	55.2	0.6	100	75	8	460	66	18	9	39	35	73	3359	355	375*	33.6	3923
West Germany	10940	61.0	−0.2	247	75	10	420	70	11	6	48	44	86	3474	416	360	11.3	5564
Greece	3550	9.9	0.6	75	68	16	480	65	47	31	24	29	65	3721	118	178	4.8	2243
Iceland	10710	0.2	1.2	2	77	6	467			16		32	89		468	293	0.1	5105
Ireland	4850	3.6	0.9	50	74	10	780	60	31	19	28	34	57	3831	208	249*	2.3	3248
Italy	6520	57.1	0.3	188	77	12	750	67	25	12	42	41	67	3538	360	243	22.1	3105
Luxembourg	14260	0.4	−0.1	140	72	12	735			5		26	81		399	256*		11190
Netherlands	9290	14.5	0.4	352	77	8	480	69	9	6	41	32	88	3343	362	310	3.0	5854
Norway	14370	4.2	0.3	13	77	8	460	64	16	8	37	29	73	3239	349	319	1.3	6570
Portugal	1970	10.2	0.7	110	74	19	500	64	39	26	30	37	31	3161	154	153	3.7	1307
Spain	4290	38.6	0.7	76	77	10	360	65	34	17	35	37	77	3358	235	258*	25.6	2180
Sweden	11890	8.4	0.1	19	77	6	410	65	11	6	43	33	86	3091	370	390	3.4	4703
Switzerland	16370	6.5	0.2	158	77	8	390	67	9	6	49	39	60	3432	400	378*	9.2	3733
United Kingdom	8460	56.5	0.1	228	75	9	680	65	3	3	47	38	92	3131	283	479*	12.5	4760

Index

General Index